Bemisia tabaci (Gennadius)
Crop Pest and Principal
Whitefly Vector of Plant Viruses

Bemisia tabaci (Gennadius)
Crop Pest and Principal Whitefly Vector of Plant Viruses

A.N. BASU

Professor and Principal Scientist (Retd.)
Advance Centre for Plant Virology
Division of Mycology and Plant Pathology,
Indian Agricultural Research Institute,
New Delhi

Routledge
Taylor & Francis Group

LONDON AND NEW YORK

First published 1995 by Westview Press

Published 2018 by Routledge
52 Vanderbilt Avenue, New York, NY 10017
2 Park Square, Milton Park, Abingdon, Oxon OX14 4RN

Routledge is an imprint of the Taylor & Francis Group, an informa business

Library of Congress Cataloging in Publishing Data available upon request.

ISBN 13: 978-0-367-01693-7 (hbk)
ISBN 13: 978-0-367-16680-9 (pbk)

Preface

The whitefly, *Bemisia tabaci* (Gennadius), stands out as one of the most formidable enemies of tropical agriculture. The aleyroid has few rivals in the insect world as a prolific vector of plant viruses. In fact, with the exception of cotton and a few other crops, the menacing role of the whitefly as a virus vector tends to obscure the magnitude of direct damage due to heavy colonisation and the associated problem of sooty moulds. Most of the diseases transmitted by *B. tabaci* are caused by gemini viruses, a fascinating group of plant viruses that cause colossal crop losses, especially of cassava, grain legumes and vegetables in various parts of the world. Interestingly enough, the transmission of geminiviruses is almost a monopoly of *B. tabaci*, leaving aside a few leafhopper-borne ones.

During the last decade, unprecedented population explosions of *B. tabaci* in various parts of the world created a sensation. The whitefly seemed to be out on a global conquest, extending its prevalence in new geographical areas, attacking previously uninfested plant species, transmitting more diseases and showing resistance to more and more insecticides. All these strengthened the earlier indications regarding the possible development of biotypes of the highly opportunistic and adaptable whitefly. Due to the alarmingly growing notoriety, *B. tabaci* became an object of intensive study on an international scale that exposed the lack of organised information on many important aspects of the whitefly and associated problems. Concerted efforts in recent years have endeavoured to compensate this deficiency but a consolidated account, providing a bird's-eye view of the panoramic information, is still lacking. This monograph is intended to rectify this lack for the benefit of students, researchers and plant protection workers involved in whitefly-related problems. Up-to-date information on the basic and applied research on the morphology, taxonomy, biology, ecology, behaviour, natural enemies and various methods of control is provided. The disease aspect, so vital to agricultural production, has received due emphasis with presentation of the information available on etiology, areas of prevalence, nature of damage etc. In view of the economic importance of geminiviruses, pertinent information on their fascinating molecular biology has been furnished. The last chapter is devoted to the epidemiology of the diseases transmitted by the whitefly and the approaches to control.

On the whole, the intent has been to extract the essentials from the vast pool of multidisciplinary literature to enable the reader to be conversant with the various facets of research and the current state of knowledge about different aspects. I shall consider my efforts to be fruitful and gratifying if the monograph is found to provide a comprehensive overview of *B. tabaci*-related information.

I am indebted to the Department of Science & Technology, Government of India, for financial grants and I greatly appreciate the gesture of co-operation extended by Dr. I. Ahmad and Dr. A. Sinha. I am thankful to the Indian Phytopathological Society (IPS), New Delhi for facilities. Special thanks are due to Dr. A. Varma, Head of the Division of Mycology & Plant Pathology, Indian Agricultural Research Institute, and the former Secretary of the IPS, for his keen interest and active co-operation in initiating the project.

I acknowledge with great pleasure the response of my former students, Drs. M. Konai, D. Lakshman, A.K. Mohanty, Sally K. Thomas, T.V.K. Singh and A.K. Dhar who helped me in sundry ways. I am grateful to Drs. N.V. Rao, S.N. Puri, S.K. Ghose, M.R. Ghosh, S.S. Ghatak, B.D. Sharma and B.K. Giri for providing literature and unpublished information. Thanks are due to Mrs. S. Jana for assisting me in the library work.

I wish to place on record my thanks to Dr. Dan Gerling, Tel Aviv University, Israel, and Messrs Elsevier Science Publishers B.V., Amsterdam, for permitting me to reproduce some illustrations. Last but not least, I express gratitude to my wife, Meena, who took meticulous care in correcting and editing the manuscript.

New Delhi,   A.N. BASU
October, 1994

Contents

monocotyledonous plants   Leafhopper-transmitted
geminiviruses infecting dicotyledonous plants
Molecular biology of geminiviruses   Genome
organisation   Replication   **Geminivirus diseases
of economic importance**   African cassava mosaic
Bean golden mosaic   Bhendi (okra) yellow vein
mosaic   Chino del tomate   Cotton leaf crumple
Mung bean yellow mosaic   Squash leaf curl
Tobacco leaf curl   Chilli leaf curl   Papaya leaf curl
Tomato leaf curl   Tomato yellow leaf curl   **Diseases
caused by other viruses**   Cowpea mild mottle
Cucumber vein yellowing   Lettuce infectious yellows
Sweet potato mild mottle   Tomato necrotic dwarf
Virus-vector relationships   Effect of virus-infacted
host plant on *B. tabaci*   References

1

Introduction

Bemisia tabaci (Gennadius) stands out as the most important member of the family Aleyrodidae for its grave impact on tropical and subtropical agriculture. The whitefly causes direct damage by feeding, soils the plant and the produce with honeydew and, more alarmingly, inflicts severe crop losses by transmitting a fairly large number of viral diseases.

Eggs of *B. tabaci* are usually laid on the lower surface of leaves. After hatching, the minute first-instar nymphs crawl actively in search of suitable sites for settling down. In fact, mobility during the entire period of immature development is limited to exploratory crawling during the early part of the first nymphal stage. The second-, third- and fourth-instar nymphs look like scale insects with atrophied legs and antennae. The fourth-instar nymphs stop feeding after some time. Since the adult develops inside the fourth-instar nymph, the same is referred to as the pupa.

The number of eggs laid by a single female in captivity is usually over 50 and the maximum recorded number exceeds 300. The species is capable of laying unfertilised eggs which develop into males only. The minimum period of development from egg to adult during the warmer parts of the year has been recorded as 11–14 days while the same period during the winter months may range from about 6–12 weeks. The number of generations in a year depends on local conditions and generally ranges between 11 and 15.

Since its first description as *Aleurodes tabaci* from Greece in 1889, the species has been described in various names over the years. Like most whitefly species, *B. tabaci* is identified on the basis of pupal morphology, which shows a wide range of host-correlated variations. Even the host-correlated variations in pupal characters in one season may be quite different in another. The wide range of intraspecific variations has led to a long list of synonyms, of which *Bemisia gossypiperda* Misra and Lamba is most frequently encountered in the economic literature.

Although *B. tabaci* is recognised as an important pest, quantitative data on the damage or economic thresholds are strikingly scant. Sucking of plant sap by large populations of nymphs and adults can greatly reduce plant vigour. Chlorotic spots appear at feeding sites on leaf surface, followed by wilting and leaf shedding. Such damage to foliage at the early stages of growth, affects development of the reproductive structures and consequently the yield may be greatly reduced. Mound (1965) experimentally demonstrated that general weakening of the plants due to whitefly infestation could cause serious reduction of cotton yield, due in part to a decreased number of bolls and in part to a decline in weight of seed and lint per boll. Byrne et al. (1990) cited an estimated population of 80 million adults per hectare on defoliated cotton regrowth in the Imperial Valley of California (pers. comm.). The impact of such population levels on plant vigour is readily imaginable. However, direct damage due to feeding would not appear to have been a matter of much concern, as reflected by the general lack of attention to this aspect in the literature.

Heavy colonisation of *B. tabaci* can cause serious indirect damage to some crops due to honeydew excreted by all insect stages, particularly the late nymphal instars. Accumulation of honeydew on leaf or fruit surfaces encourages growth of sooty moulds, which affect yield both in quantitative and qualitative terms. Deposition of the sticky exudate on cotton lint can cause serious problems during the ginning and spinning processes. In fact, the latter is the most serious economic damage caused to cotton by *B. tabaci* (Horowitz et al., 1984).

Bemisia tabaci is highly polyphagous and has been recorded on more than 500 species of plants including numerous field crops, ornamentals and weeds. Oddly enough, there is far more information on *B. tabaci* with respect to cotton than any other crop. The apparent reasons for this lopsided attention in favour of cotton are its commercial value, large-scale cultivation and the formidable pest complex affecting the crop. The transition of *B. tabaci* from a minor or locally important pest to a 'superpest' of cotton in various parts of the world today, merits discussion.

Bemisia tabaci first proved to be a serious pest of cotton in northern India, parts of which are now in Pakistan, in the late 1920s and early 1930s (Misra and Lamba, 1929; Husain and Trehan, 1933). Subsequently, severe whitefly infestation of cotton was recorded in the Sudan and Iran (1950s), El Salvador (1961), Mexico (1962), Brazil (1968), Turkey (1974), Israel (1976), Thailand (1978), Arizona and California (1981), and Ethiopia (1984). In all these areas *B. tabaci* had initially been a sporadic pest before reaching epidemic proportions (Horowitz, 1986). In the Sudan, for instance, the major concern of growers was the transmission of cotton leaf curl disease by the whitefly (Eveleens, 1983). With the advent of synthetic organic pesticides, the severity and frequency of infestations of *B. tabaci* became such that it rose from a secondary to a primary pest of Sudanese cotton in the late 1970s. Again, the whitefly was present on desert cotton in California for 14 years before it became a major pest in 1981, following an unprecedented population explosion (Dowell, 1990).

Such abrupt changes in pest stature of *B. tabaci* in various parts of the world are difficult to explain. The plausible explanations point to human involvement as the main factor due to increased production and protection of the same at any cost. The production thrust has necessitated wiping out natural vegetation to bring more and more land under cultivation and intensive cultivation of crops in order to achieve maximum return from that land. This enabled the whitefly to flourish with consequent pressure on plant-protection measures. The urgency to protect the crops led to overreliance and overuse of organic insecticides with limited effect on the whitefly, but drastic effect on the non-target beneficial natural enemies of the target species. Studies have shown that indiscriminate use of insecticides may not only induce resistance problems, but sublethal exposure to certain insecticides, such as DDT, may also stimulate the reproductive potential of *B. tabaci*. This is just an overview of the situation and different sets of factors may be responsible for unmanageable outbreaks in different agroecosystems. The sudden violent population explosions of *B. tabaci* in various parts of the world in the recent past and gross differences in susceptibility of the same plant species to the whitefly in different locations, suggest the existence of different biotypes of the whitefly. Recent studies on the biochemical characteristics provide evidence of such a possibility and a clear picture is expected to emerge in the near future.

Another disturbing factor is that *B. tabaci* has expanded its range of distribution to new parts of the world, apparently due to human-assisted introduction. The species has already been reported as a glasshouse pest in Canada, some North American areas and several countries in Europe where it was previously unknown. With the notorious greenhouse whitefly, *Trialeurodes vaporariorum*, already problematical, *B. tabaci* is likely to add new dimensions to the problem, especially as a potent virus vector. The appearance of *B. tabaci* on greenhouse plants such as poinsettia, may be a matter of considerable concern to growers but data on the magnitude of infestation and damage is not yet adequate to allow detailed discussion of this matter at the moment.

Incidentally, *Bemisia tabaci* is the first whitefly species to be implicated as a vector, the disease being cotton leaf curl in the Sudan and Nigeria (Kirkpatrick, 1930; Golding, 1930). Besides leaf curl of cotton, the whitefly-borne diseases that caused considerable concern during the early period, include tobacco leaf curl and African cassava mosaic. The notoriety of the species as a vector has risen so steadily over the years that this has obscured the direct injury due to dense insect colonisation.

Understandably, much lower levels of whitefly populations can cause much more damage by transmitting diseases. In fact, with the exception of cotton and a few other crops, agriculturalists are much more concerned about the role of the whitefly as a vector than as a pest, due to colossal losses caused to various economic crops such as cassava, tobacco, grain legumes, tomato, chillies, squash, melons and various cucurbits, lettuce and papaya. A few loss estimates in recent years provide some idea of the impact of whitefly-borne diseases on crop production. Sastry and Singh (1973) estimated 20–95% loss in tomato yield due to tomato leaf curl disease in India. Bock (1982) reported yield losses due to bean golden mosaic virus to vary from 40–100%, depending on age, variety and possibly also on strain of the virus. Lettuce infectious yellows virus occurred pandemically in 1981 in the south-western United States (Duffus et al., 1986), virtually affecting every major crop grown in the desert region. Yield reduction in lettuce ranged from 50 to 70% and in sugar beet from 20 to 30%. Yield losses in cassava, the most important food crop grown in the African continent, due to the African cassava mosaic virus are staggering. On the basis of available data, Fauquet and Fargette (1990) estimated that the total reduction of cassava yield in Africa in plants raised from diseased cuttings, is at least 50% or 50 million metric tons and may be equivalent to $2 billion (U.S.). Mung bean yellow mosaic virus (MYMV) is a major constraint to the cultivation of grain legumes in India, especially mung bean (*Phaseolus aureus*) and black gram (*P. mungo*). According to Varma et al. (1991), in epidemic years losses due to MYMV have exceeded $300 million in three major crops, namely, black gram, mung bean and soybean. Brown and Bird (1992) have pointed out the increased prevalence as well as expanded distribution of whitefly-borne viruses during the last decade and the devastating impact. Yield losses range from 20 to 100%, depending on the crop, season, vector prevalence and other factors.

Most whitefly-borne diseases are now known to be caused by gemini-viruses, a group established as a taxon in 1978. This fascinating group of plant viruses with geminate particles and circular, single-stranded DNA genome, eluded detection for many decades, the reasons for which are not difficult to understand. Many geminiviruses are not mechanically trans-missible, thus requiring manipulation exclusively through the whitefly vec-tor. The phloem-limited or phloem-restricted nature of geminiviruses adds to the difficulty; purification attempts have yielded only small quantities of virions. Moreover, the virus particles are generally fragile. Whitefly-transmitted geminiviruses cause an array of diseases in various parts of the world, sometimes exhibiting similar symptoms but often revealing dis-tinct host ranges, which is quite confusing. Most of the viruses have not been adequately characterised as to host range, transmission characteristic

2

Morphology and Taxonomy

Bemisia tabaci (Gennadius) belongs to the subfamily Aleyrodinae, family Aleyrodidae, superfamily Aleyrodoidea and is placed either in the sub order Homoptera of the order Hemiptera (Richards and Davies, 1977; Woodward, Evans and Eastop, 1970) or in the suborder Sternorrhyncha, order Homoptera (Borror and De Long, 1964). The family is rather small, comprising 1156 species in 126 genera (Mound and Halsey, 1978). The other families under Sternorrhyncha include such important groups as aphids, coccids and psyllids.

Morphology of Immature Stages and Adults

The aleyrodids differ from other members of Strenorrhyncha in the position of anus and associated structures. The anus opens on the dorsal surface of the abdomen, ventrally to a tongue-shaped projection called the *lingula*. Both lie in a shallow depression called the *vasiform orifice*, partially covered by the *operculum*. The dorsal position of the anus permits effective removal of the honeydew excreted by these phloem feeders in copious amounts. An accumulation of this viscous fluid, which promotes the growth of sooty moulds, would understandably be detrimental to the sessile nymphs. The lingula takes care of this by bending backwards into the honeydew filling the vasiform orifice and on straightening catapults the honeydew away. The aforesaid structures as well as the number of elongated dorsal setae are of considerable taxonomic importance (Fig. 2.1). As with other whitefly species, the specific identification of *B. tabaci* is based on the morphological features of the so-called pupae (fourth-instar nymphs) or, to be more precise, the pupal cases.

Various workers have recognised four immature stages of *B. tabaci* between the egg and emergence of the adult. The first three stages are generally referred to as larval instars and the fourth as the pupal stage. Since the metamorphosis undergone by the whitefly is incomplete, the term *nymph* seems to be more appropriate than *larva*. Similarly, the use

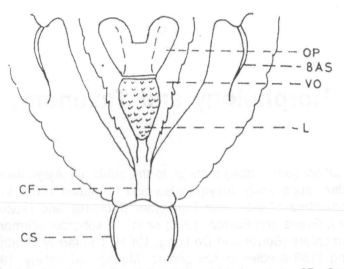

Fig. 2.1 Magnified view of the vasiform orifice and associated structures. CF = Caudal furrow; CS = Caudal (anal) seta; L = Lingula; OP = Operculum; VO = Vasiform orifice

of the term *pupa* for the fourth nymphal instar is not strictly applicable since what takes place during this stage in whiteflies is, in fact, distinct from what occurs in holometabolous insect groups (Byrne and Bellows, 1991). However, the term has been used universally for so many years that its replacement now would create utter confusion. Rather, the stage between the third instar nymphs and adult emergence may rationally be divided into the fourth nymphal instar (earlier phase of the last stadium) and the later fourth instar termed the pupa on the basis of morphology and the differences in behaviour of parasitoids towards these stages. Following Lopez-Avila (1986), separate descriptions are provided here to show the pattern of changes in the earlier and later stages of the last stadium. Byrne and Bellows (1991) have also labelled the earlier part of the last stadium as the fourth nymphal instar and reserved the term pupa for the last non-feeding part of the final stadium following apolysis.

Before going through the morphology of *B. tabaci*, it may be pointed out that the measurements given for different morphs are after Lopez-Avila (1986) to give an idea of the relative differences in size. His figures, however, do not cover the range of variations with regard to size reported by various workers studying under different climatic conditions and working with different host plants. The intraspecific variations in pupal morphology, discussed later in this chapter, reveal the extent of these differences.

and serology. However, with the emergence of new technologies, exciting progress in our knowledge of the biological, biochemical and molecular nature of some whitefly-borne viruses has been achieved in recent years. Enhanced knowledge of the composition, genomic organisation and virus-encoded polypeptides has certainly improved diagnostic techniques and removed earlier confusion regarding the previously unrecognised white-fly-borne geminiviruses. The efforts so far have managed to bring order out of chaos but much remains to be done to isolate and characterise the viruses involved in whitefly-transmitted diseases.

The high reproductive potential, mobility, polyphagy and growing prevalence of the whitefly and the diseases borne by it in more and more areas, account for the intense attention that *B. tabaci* has been receiving in recent years. The proceedings of a symposium on various aspects of *B. tabaci* appeared as a special volume of *Agriculture, Ecosystems and Environment*, Vol. 17, 152 pp. (1986). In the same year a Literature Survey of *B. tabaci* edited by Cock (1986) was brought out by the C.A.B. International Institute of Biological Control with an annotated bibliography. In view of the growing notoriety of the whitefly, a newsletter titled BEMISIA was launched by the working group on *B. tabaci*, led by Professor Dan Gerling of the Tel Aviv University, Israel and six issues of the same have already appeared. *Bemisia tabaci* has also figured prominently in the recent multiauthored book on whiteflies edited by Gerling (1990), dealing with broad aspects of the systematics, diversity, ecology, behaviour, management and control of whiteflies in general. Besides the above, research papers on diverse aspects of *B. tabaci* and related topics have been steadily accumulating, which are multidisciplinary in nature. The present venture is the result of a long-felt need for a monograph presenting the essence of diverse and scattered information for the benefit of students, researchers and others involved in whitefly-related problems. An attempt has been made to provide an up-to-date projection of the development in the fundamental and applied directions of studies on *B. tabaci* as a pest and vector of plant diseases.

REFERENCES

Bock, K.R. (1982). Geminivirus diseases in tropical crops. *Plant Disease* 66: 266–270.
Brown, J.K. and Bird, J. (1992). Whitefly-transmitted geminiviruses and associated disorders in the Americas and the Caribbean Basin. *Plant Disease* 76 (3): 220–225.

Byrne, D.N., Bellows, T.S. and Parrella, M.P. (1990). Whiteflies in agricultural systems. In: *Whiteflies: Their Bionomics, Pest Status and Management* (D. Gerling, ed.). Intercept, Wimborne, England, pp. 227–261.

Dowell, R.V. (1990). Integrating biological control of whiteflies into crop management systems. In: *Whiteflies: Their Bionomics, Pest Status and Management* (D. Gerling, ed.). Intercept, Wimborne, England, pp. 315–335.

Duffus, J.E., Larsen, R.C. and Liu, H.Y. (1986). Lettuce infectious yellows virus—a new type of whitefly transmitted virus. *Phytopathology* **76**: 97–100.

Eveleens, K.G. (1983). Cotton-insect control in the Sudan Gezira: analysis of a crisis. *Crop Protection* **2**: 273–287.

Fauquet, C. and Fargette, D. (1990). African cassava mosaic virus: etiology, epidemiology, and control. *Plant Disease* **74** (6): 404–411.

Gerling, D. (ed.) (1990). *Whiteflies: Their Bionomics, Pest Status and Management.* Intercept, Wimborne, England, 348 pp.

Golding, F.D. (1930). A vector of leaf curl of cotton in southern Nigeria. *Empire Cotton Growing Review* **7**: 120–126.

Horowitz, A.R. (1986). Population dynamics of *Bemisia tabaci* (Gennadius) with special emphasis on cotton fields. *Agriculture, Ecosystems and Environment* **17**: 37–47.

Horowitz, A.R., Podoler, H. and Gerling, D. (1984). Life-table analysis of the tobacco whitefly *Bemisia tabaci* (Gennadius) in cotton fields in Israel. *Acta Oecol., Oecol. Applic.* **5**: 221–233.

Husain, M.A. and Trehan, K.N. (1933). Observations on the life history, bionomics and control of the whitefly of cotton (*Bemisia gossypiperda* M. & L.). *Indian J. Agric. Sci.* **3**: 701–753.

Kirkpatrick, T.W. (1930). Leaf curl in cotton. *Nature* **125**: 85–97.

Misra, C.S. and Lamba, K.S. (1929). The cotton whitefly (*Bemisia gossypiperda*, n. sp.) *Bull. Agric. Res. Inst., Pusa* **196**, 7 pp.

Mound, L.A. (1965). Effect of whitefly (*Bemisia tabaci*) on cotton in the Sudan Gezira. *Empire Cotton Growing Review* **42**: 290–294.

Sastry, K.S.M. and Singh, S.J. (1973). Assessment of losses in tomato by tomato leaf curl virus. *Indian J. Mycol. & Plant Pathol.* **3** (1): 50–54.

Varma, A., Dhar, A.K. and Mandal, B. (1991). MYMV—the virus, its vector and their control in India. In: Consultative group meeting for MYMV, July, 2–6 AVRDC, Taiwan.

Egg: The egg is subelliptical in shape, the basal portion being considerably broader than the tapering distal end. The base is provided with a stalk or pedicel, a peg-like extension of the chorion which attaches the egg to the leaf. Gameel (1974) found a gluey substance enveloping the egg pedicel similar to that reported much earlier for the eggs of *Trialeurodes vaporariorum*. Several workers have suggested that the pedicel in whiteflies serves as a means of absorbing water into the egg. Avidov (1956) found eggs to be unaffected by air humidity when attached to healthy leaves. It has also been reported that the eggs collapse even on the verge of hatching when the leaf harbouring them withers. Byrne et al. (1990) demonstrated that water extracted from plant tissue through the pedicel accounted for approximately 50% of the mass of the mature egg of *T. vaporariorum*.

Eggs are laid indiscriminately almost always on the undersurface of the leaves, sometimes in small circular or semi-circular groups due to rotation of the female, anchored by the labium which remains closely apposed to the leaf surface. The females usually lay a few eggs on the very leaf upon which they emerge as adults before moving to newer growths. The egg dimensions (mean ± SE) as given by Lopez-Avila (1986) are: length 0.211 ± 0.005 mm; width at the broadest part 0.096 ± 0.002 mm; length of pedicel 0.024 ± 0.003 mm. Freshly laid eggs are translucent, creamy white and covered with mealy powder from the wings of the female. They turn pale brown before hatching, the distal tip being distinctly darker, with two small reddish spots denoting the oncoming eyes of the nymph. Near the base of the egg two yellowish spots, representing the mycetomes of the nymph, are distinctly visible through the chorion.

The incubation period of the egg depends on various factors, discussed in Chapter 5.

At the time of hatching, the egg cracks at the apical end along a longitudinal line of dehiscence (Byrne and Bellows, 1991). The emerging nymph bends towards the leaf surface until its front legs can clasp it. The eggshell is pushed away by the other four legs, assisted by alternate contraction and expansion of the abdomen (Azab et al., 1971). The nymph then walks away from the empty eggshell, which retains its shape and upright position.

First-instar Nymph: After emergence, the minute first-instar nymphs crawl actively in search of suitable sites on which to settle down. In fact, mobility during the entire period of development of the immature stages is limited to the exploratory crawling during the initial activity of the first-instar nymph. That is why this nymphal stage is often called the *crawler.*

The first-instar nymphs are pale, translucent white, oval, with a convex dorsum and flat ventral side. They measure 0.267 ± 0.007 mm in length and 0.144 ± 0.010 in width (Lopez-Avila, 1986).

There are 16 pairs of marginal setae, of which 3 pairs occur in the cephalic region, 5 pairs in the thoracic and the remaining 8 pairs in the abdominal region. The anal pair is conspicuously longer than the others. The dorsum bears 3 pairs of microsetae, one pair each in the cephalic region and on abdominal segments I and VIII. The eyes are represented by two small, inconspicuous crimson spots on each side of the cephalic region. The three-segmented antennae have an apical spine.

The crawlers have functional walking legs which are four-segmented but the trochanter is inconspicuous. The coxa is short and thick, bearing one spine on the inner side. The femur is almost as long but much thicker than the tibia, which is slender. The tibia bears a large curved spine at mid-length of its outer side. The unisegmented tarsus has two small claws.

The vasiform orifice is subtrapezoidal. The semi-circular operculum covers about half of the digitiform lingula which bears two setae.

Second-instar Nymph: These are quite distinct from the first instar and, apart from size, show a number of marked morphological changes. The margin of the oval body is crenulated, with three pairs of marginal setae according to Lopez-Avila (1986) but only two pairs according to Azab et al. (1969a).

According to Lopez-Avila (1986), there are three pairs of dorsal microsetae, the first pair being cephalic while the second and third pairs occur on abdominal segments I and VIII, respectively. El-Helaly et al. (1971) mentioned another pair on the mesothorax and two pairs of ventral microsetae, one cephalic, near the base of the mouthparts, and the other pair located on abdominal segment VIII. There are three pairs of spiracles, two pairs on the thorax and the pair on abdominal segment VIII.

The eyes are still inconspicuous but no longer divided as in the first instar. The antennae are atrophied. The legs are two segmented but lack setae and end in a disc-like sucker.

The vasiform orifice is triangular with a semi-circular operculum and a long thick lingula. The mycetomes, visible through the integument, appear to be orange-yellow. The second instar nymphs are 0.365 ± 0.026 mm long and 0.218 ± 0.012 mm at the broadest part in the thoracic region.

Third-instar Nymph: The body is more elongated than of the earlier instar, measuring 0.489 ± 0.022 mm in length and 0.295 ± 0.018 mm in width.

As in previous instars, the mouthparts are located between the forelegs and consist of four long stylets; however, compared to the two earlier instars, the basal trapezoidal structure is more elongated. The legs are unsegmented and end in a disc-like sucker.

The setae of this stage are identical in number and location as in the second instar.

Fourth-instar Nymph: For the reasons stated earlier, the description furnished here corresponds to those given by various workers for the early, or freshly formed, pupa.

Body elliptical, 0.662 ± 0.023 mm long and 0.440 ± 0.003 mm broad. Cephalic region semi-circular, thin and flat, with the margin crenulated and sometimes deeply indented due to leaf hairs. The marginal setae are as in the second and third instars. Dorsal hairs long, spine-like, originating from distinct tubercles that are conspicuously long and thick, but highly variable in number, from none to the full set of seven. Various dorsal and bilateral structures, such as tubercles, pores, porettes and ridges are discernible, but become better defined at the later stage described here as the pupa.

The eyes are still small but now appear as two conspicuous red spots.

The vasiform orifice has the shape of an elongated triangle and the lingula, with a pair of hairs, extends beyond the operculum towards the caudal margin.

Pupa: Two very distinctive characters of the pupa are the eyes and the caudal furrow. For the first time the eyes are truly distinguishable, resembling two red spots constricted in the middle. Likewise, the caudal furrow (the median longitudinal depression along the posterior abdominal dorsum between the distal portion of the vasiform orifice and the tip of the abdomen) appears only in the pupa (see Fig. 2.1).

The dorsal surface of the elliptical body is convex and the thoracic and abdominal segments are apparent.

The marginal and dorsal setae are as in the fourth instar, but the marginal ones are inconspicuous with the exception of the quite prominent caudal pair.

Mound (1963) showed host-correlated variations with regard to the number of elongated dorsal hairs in the pupal stage of *B. tabaci* and later Azab et al. (1969b), Harakly (1973) and David and Ananthakrishnan (1976) reported similar phenomena. Elaborate studies by Mohanty and Basu (1986) revealed spectacular variations due to seasonal effect besides host-correlated ones, which will be detailed later in this chapter. The number of elongated dorsal setae is known to vary from the full set of seven pairs to none at all. When the full set of seven pairs is present, their arrangement is as follows: two pairs in the cephalic region (one pair in front of the eyes, and the other pair behind them), two sublateral pairs in the thoracic region and three pairs in the abdominal

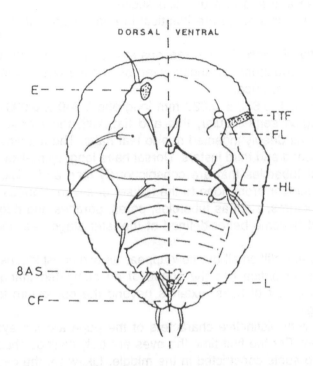

Fig. 2.2. *Pupa of B. tabaci.* 8AS = 8th abdominal seta; CF = caudal furrow; E = eye; FL = foreleg; HL = Hindleg; L = Lingula; TTF = Thoracic tracheal fold.

region (one sublateral pair each on segments II and IV and one pair on either side of the vasiform orifice near its base) (Fig. 2.2). The ventral side of abdominal segment VIII bears a pair of microsetae.

There are four pairs of spiracles, of which two pairs are thoracic and two pairs abdominal. Thoracic tracheal folds extend between the first pair of spiracles and the body margin. These shallow breathing folds in the ventral body wall possibly assist in conduction of air by forming a passage to the spiracles.

Contrary to the observations of Pruthi and Samuel (1941) and Mound (1963) that the pupae from which females emerge are larger than those producing males, Azab et al. (1969a) found no such sexual dimorphism, declaring pupae of male and female to be similar in size.

The Adult: The external morphology of the adult male and female of *B. tabaci* was studied by Misra and Lamba (1929), Azab et al. (1969a) and Gupta (1972). The newly emerged adult is soft and pale yellow, changing to white within a few hours due to deposition of wax on the body and wings. The males are generally more slender and smaller than the females (Fig. 2.3), measuring 0.82 mm in length (from vertex to the tip of genitalia) and 1.15 mm (from vertex to the tip of wings) while the corresponding measurements for females are 0.96 mm and 1.30 mm respectively. The head is more or less conical, being broadest at the level of the antennae. The antennae are filiform and seven-segmented. The mouth parts are typically homopteran, with fine mandibular and maxillary stylets for piercing and sucking.

Wings hyaline, covered with a thin white meal. The forewings show the radial sector as an inconspicuous flexture and the cubits as a hyaline streak. The legs are slender.

The females can be distinguished from the males by a bigger and broader abdomen which does not taper distally as in the males. The vasiform orifice is situated near the tip of the abdominal dorsum. The male genitalia, permanently extended, consist of an aedeagus and a pair of claspers. The ovipositor in females consists of two pairs of sharply pointed lobes. At rest, it is bent dorsally towards the vasiform orifice.

Intraspecific Morphological Variations Due to Host Factors

Since the majority of whitefly species cannot be identified by morphological characters of the adults, genera and species are defined on the structure of the fourth instar nymph or the so-called 'pupal case' (Mound and Halsey, 1978). Unfortunately, *Trialeurodes vaporariorum* and *B. tabaci* show great variations depending on host-plant cuticle on which they develop. Husain and Trehan (1933) reported variation in the distribution of dorsal spines in *Bemisia gossypiperda* M. & L. (which is now known as *B. tabaci*). They pointed out the significance of intraspecific variability in this important taxonomic character. The progeny of the same parent showed a wide range of variation in the number and arrangement of dorsal setae. They came across specimens with the full complement of seven pairs of setae to some with none.

Russell (1948) reported the effect of the physical nature of leaves on the morphology of *T. vaporariorum*. Such evidence led Russell (1957) to synonymise several described species of *Bemisia* with *B. tabaci*.

Host-correlated variation in the morphology of pupal cases of *B. tabaci* was demonstrated by Mound (1963). He raised a culture of whitefly from a single progeny line on six hosts and obtained a larger number of pupal cases from tobacco and cassava, which he then subjected to statistical analysis. The pupal cases raised on tobacco differed significantly from those on cassava not only in size but also in shape. The forms from tobacco were relatively longer and narrower than those from cassava, the vasiform orifice considerably broader, the lingula tip much narrower and longer, and the caudal furrow relatively shorter. In the same work (Mound, 1963), results were also furnished regarding the number of dorsal setae in pupal cases collected from six hosts including cotton near Nairobi, Kenya. Pupal cases on densely hairy leaves showed more dorsal setae than those on glabrous leaves. Mound considered these variants to be induced phenotypically by morphological characters of the host-plant leaves such as cuticle irregularity and hairiness. He further opined that whatever the reason might be, the fact remained that several nominal species of *Bemisia* were synonyms of *B. tabaci*.

Studies by Azab et al. (1969b) revealed an apparent correlation between the degree of pubescence of leaves of the host plant on the outline of the pupal case and also the number and distribution of dorsal spines in *B. tabaci*. Pupal cases on glabrous leaves of cabbage, *Ipomoea batatas* and sometimes from cotton, had a regular outline contrary to those from pubescent leaves of *Euphorbia pulcherima* and *Lantana camara*. Pupae reared on glabrous leaves were found invariably to possess fewer than seven pairs of dorsal spines, if not completely devoid of the same. In sharp contrast, most of the pupae reared on pubescent leaves had seven pairs of dorsal spines.

Variations in pupal morphology in *B. tabaci* reared on different hosts were shown by Harakly (1973) to correlate largely with the nature of the leaf surface.

David and Ananthakrishnan (1976) reported striking variation in pupal morphology of *B. tabaci* on several host plants.

Combined Effect of Host and Seasonal Factors on Morphology

Mohanty and Basu (1986) provided evidence that host-correlated variation in pupal morphology in one season may not necessarily be the same in another. Studies until then were restricted to morphological variation due to hosts without consideration of the seasonal factors operating during different times of the year. Inclusion of the seasonal factor added a new dimension, providing a glimpse into the respective roles played by hosts as well as seasons. The pronounced seasonal effect on the number of elongated dorsal setae and also on the length and width of pupal cases is evident from Tables 2.1 to 2.3 (Mohanty and Basu, 1986).

Fig. 2.3. Adults and immature stages of *B. tabaci*. Note the two adults in the middle which are in the process of courtship, the smaller of the two being male.

Fig. 2.4. Heavy infestation of *B. tabaci* on a cucurbitaceous host.

Table 2.1   Host and season-correlated variation in number of elongated dorsal setae of *B. tabaci*

Host	No. of elongated dorsal setae	
	Feb–March	Aug–Sept
Brinjal	7	7
Cotton	7	0
Lantana camara	7	4
Tobacco	7	0

Table 2.2   Host and season-correlated variation in pupal length of *B. tabaci*

Host	Mean length during Feb–March (mm)	Mean length during Aug–Sept (mm)
Brinjal	0.679	0.578
Cotton	0.738	0.655
L. camara	0.676	0.490
Tobacco	0.751	0.695
C.D. at 5%	0.0308	0.0457
C.D. at 5% for host × season	0.0317	

Table 2.3   Host and season-correlated variation in pupal width of *B. tabaci*

Host	Mean width during Feb–March (mm)	Mean width during Aug–Sept (mm)
Brinjal	0.488	0.416
Cotton	0.545	0.472
L. camara	0.484	0.323
Tobacco	0.540	0.488
C.D. at 5%	0.250	0.0413
C.D. at 5% for host × season	0.0314	

Taxonomy

Bemisia tabaci was first described as *Aleurodes tabaci* from tobacco in Greece (Gennadius, 1889). The genus *Bemisia* was erected by Quaintance and Baker in 1914, with the type species *Aleurodes inconspicua* Quaintance, a synonym of *B. tabaci* (Genn.). Due to the well-established host-correlated morphological variation of this highly polyphagous species, a large number of synonyms has accumulated over the years. Takahashi (1936) and Russell (1957) synonymised a number of described species of *Bemisia* as *B. tabaci*. Mound and Halsey (1978) listed these synonyms (see Table 2.4).

Table 2.4   Synonyms of *Bemisia tabaci* (Genn.)

Species	Type locality
Bemisia achyranthes Singh, 1931	India
B. bahiana Bondar, 1928	Brazil
B. costa-limai Bonder, 1928	Brazil
B. emiliae Corbett, 1926	Sri Lanka
B. goldingi Corbett, 1935	Nigeria
B. gossypiperda Misra & Lamba, 1929	India, Pakistan
B. gossypiperda var. *mosaicivectura* Ghesquiere, 1934	Zaire
B. hibisci Takahashi, 1933	Taiwan
Aleurodes inconspicua Quaintance, 1900	Florida
B. longispina Priesner & Hosny, 1934	Egypt
B. lonicerae Takahashi, 1957	Japan
B. manihotis Frappa, 1938	Madagascar
B. minima Danzig, 1964	USSR
B. miniscula Danzig, 1964	USSR
B. nigeriensis Corbett, 1935	Nigeria
B. rhodesiaensis Corbett, 1935	Nigeria
B. signata Bondar, 1928	Brazil
B. vayssierei Frappa, 1939	Madagascar

Of the various synonyms of *B. tabaci, B. gossypiperda* is most frequently encountered in economic literature.

Biotype Issue

A great degree of genetic plasticity in adult host selection behaviour and
host suitability for nymphal development of *B. tabaci*, has resulted in apparent race formation. Thus *B. tabaci* does not feed on cassava in the
New World but does so in Africa, India and Malaysia. The most abundant
strain of *B. tabaci* in Puerto Rico is distinguished by its inability to breed
on Euphorbiaceae or on Cucurbitaceae, the highly preferred hosts in other
parts of the world (Fig. 2.4). Mound (1984) pointed out that when a
species is introduced to a new area, only part of the total potential genetic
variability of the species will be transported. He felt that this might be
the explanation of some reports of local biotypes. The concept of the
possible existence of biotypes has been encouraged following unprecedented outbreaks of *B. tabaci* in recent years in various parts of the world.
Studies on this aspect were initiated in the 1980s. Work mostly comprised
running of electrophoretic profiles of the specimens, using esterases.
It gained considerable momentum following unusually severe outbreaks
of *B. tabaci* in Florida from 1986 onward, resulting in unfamiliar plant

disorders. The investigations revealed that at least two biotypes (designated as 'A' and 'B') of the whitefly presently occur in the USA.

Adults of six species of whiteflies from Israel and Colombia (South America) were studied electrophoretically by Wool et al. (1989). Besides *B. tabaci* and *Trialeurodes vaporariorum* two other species of *Bemisia* and two species of *Dialeurodes* were studied. The patterns of esterase and glycerophosphate dehydrogenase isoenzymes were found to be species-specific and useful for identifying species that are difficult or impossible to distinguish on the basis of morphological characters.

More recently, considerable work has been done in Israel, Colombia and the USA on various aspects of the problem of biotype or strain. *Bemisia tabaci* populations in Israel appeared to be electrophoretically very similar apart from variations related to insecticide application. No host races or geographic races were detected in large samples from many crop localities. On the other hand, samples from Colombia revealed at least four electrophoretically distinct 'biotypes', which were geographically separated, apparently regardless of host plant (Wool and Greenberg, 1990; Wool et al., 1991).

Recent studies have shown the existence of at least four distinct biotypes of *B. tabaci* in North America and the Caribbean basin. The criteria of differentiation include suitability of different host plants for feeding and reproduction, differential isozyme patterns, and the ability or inability to induce silver leaf symptoms by bioassay into the *Cucurbita* indicator host (Costa and Brown, 1991). Whether there is an absolute correlation between these parameters remains to be determined (Brown and Bird, 1992).

Intensive surveys of *B. tabaci* populations in south-western USA and north-western Mexico by esterase typing were conducted from 1989–1992. In the south-western USA in 1989, the 'A' type was found exclusively in the field while the 'B' biotype was found on greenhouse-grown ornamentals. In 1990, the 'A' biotype still predominated in the field but the 'B' type was detected on melons in the field in addition to greenhouse crops. During the next two years, the situation changed drastically. In 1991, the 'B' type predominated in all urban and rural agroecosystems while the 'A' type could be found only in several scattered but remote areas of Arizona. In 1992, the 'B' biotype was exclusively identified from all sites sampled. The results suggest that the 'B' biotype, believed to have been introduced into the USA and elsewhere by infested plant materials, has nearly or completely displaced the indigenous populations (Brown, 1992). However, Byrne (1992) has pointed out that there is some controversy as to whether or not this is the result of competitive displacement. He cited the unpublished findings of N.J. Gawel and A.C. Bartless of the USDA-Phoenix, who have had remarkable success using the RAPD-PCR technique to compare current field populations ('B' strain) with insects collected several years ago ('A' strain), eliminating thereby problems associated with laboratory colonies that are subject to 'genetic drift'. Differences in DNA structure between the two strains were demonstrated by the RAPD-PCR technique. All twenty of the RAPD primers tested, readily identified 'A' and 'B' types. DNA extracted from individual eggs and nymphs showed similar differences. According to Byrne (1992), differences found in DNA composition and those noted by other researchers in host range, honeydew production, fecundity, disease transmission characteristics and esterase patterns suggest no clear reason to include these insects under the same specific designation.

Limited analysis of field-collected whiteflies from the California desert region indicated an almost complete shift in the population from the previously occurring 'A' biotype to the newly introduced 'B' biotype (Li et al., 1992), which been known earlier to differ in suitability of various hosts for nymphal development. In order to determine how the shift in population took place, equal numbers of males and females of both biotypes were enclosed in large muslin-covered cages. An esterase isozyme analysis on polyacrylamide gels at approximately monthly intervals of the caged mixed population, showed a substantial number of hybrids or segregates. This indicated the possibility of a breakdown of apparent reproductive barriers during the prolonged mixing experiments.

Li et al. (1992) further reported the findings of an isozyme analysis of the whitefly from California ('A' and 'B'), Florida, Texas, Nigeria and Israel. All these populations except the last were found to have the range of isozymes representative of the variations or segregates of the 'A' and 'B' types. The Israeli population had additional bands not present in populations from the other regions. Recent analyses of desert populations indicate a mixture of 'A's, 'B's and hybrids. Thus populations of these two types do not remain distinct under laboratory and field conditions.

More recently, Perring et al. (1993) concluded that the 'A' and 'B' types are distinct species, proposing that the 'B' type be named the silver-leaf whitefly for the disorder in squash, known as silver leaf, caused by the same. Their studies included mating behaviour, crossing experiments, allozymic frequency analyses, and the use of polymerase chain reaction-based DNA differentiation tests.

A video camera revealed the behaviour of mixed pairs. Although the males courted the females, such pairs did not mate. Isoelectric focussing was used to identify enzymes, representing 18 loci. Allelic frequencies were used to calculate genetic distances and comparison of allele frequencies of type 'A' and type 'B' whiteflies showed a genetic distance

(D) value of 0.24, which is indicative of a species. Genomic DNA of laboratory-reared, type 'A' and type 'B' whiteflies was analysed by the use of polymerase chain reactions (PCR) to assess variation in segments of DNA. While populations of the same type shared 80 to 100% similarity, less than 10% similarity was observed between types.

It is evident from the foregoing discussion that characterisation and identification of the biotypes of *B. tabaci* are presently under intensive study and in spite of the present differences in opinion, a clear picture is likely to emerge in the near future. In any case, future taxonomic work on the whitefly must be field oriented with studies on the living morphs, in addition to utilisation of morphological and biochemical characteristics (Bink-Moenen and Mound, 1990).

REFERENCES

Avidov, Z. (1956). Bionomics of the tobacco whitefly (*Bemisia tabaci* Gennad.) in Israel. *Ktavim* (English edition) 7: 25–41.

Azab, A.K., Megahed, M.M. and El-Mirsawi, H.D. (1969a). Studies on *Bemisia tabaci* (Genn.) (Hemiptera-Homoptera: Aleyrodidae). *Bull. Soc. Entomol. d'Egypte* 53: 339–352.

Azab, A.K., Meghahed, M.M. and El-Mirsawi, H.D. (1969b). Effect of degree of pubescence of host-plant on the number and distribution of dorsal spines in pupa of *Bemisia tabaci* (Genn.) (Hemiptera-Homoptera: Aleyrodidae). *Bull. Soc. Entomol. d'Egypte* 53: 353–357.

Azab, A.K., Megahed, M.M. and El-Mirsawi, H.D. (1971). On the etiology of *Bemisia tabaci* (Genn.) (Hemiptera-Homoptera: Aleyrodiae). *Bull. Soc. Entomol. d'Egypte* 55: 305–315.

Bink-Moenen, R. and Mound, L.A. (1990). Whiteflies: Diversity, biosystematics and evolutionary patterns. In: *Whiteflies: Their Bionomics, Pest Status and Management* (D. Gerling, ed.) Intercept, Wimborne, England, pp. 1–11.

Borror, D.J. and De Long, D.M. (1964). *An Introduction to the Study of Insects*. Holt, Rhinehart & Winston, New York, 819 pp.

Brown, J.K. (1992). Update on the status of whitefly biotypes in the Americas and Caribbean Basin. *Bemisia Newsletter* No. 6: 2–3.

Brown, J.K. and Bird, J. (1992). Whitefly-transmitted geminiviruses and associated disorders in the Americas and the Caribbean Basin. *Plant Disease* 76 (3): 220–225.

Byrne, D. (1992). Status of *Bemisia tabaci* biotype research in Arizona. *Bemisia Newsletter* No. 6: 4.

Byrne, D.N. and Bellows, T.S. (1991). Whitefly Biology. *Ann. Rev. Ent.* 36: 431–451.

Byrne, D.N., Bellows, T.S. and Perrella, M.P. (1990). Whiteflies in agricultural systems. In: *Whiteflies: Their Bionomics, Pest Status and Management* (D. Gerling, ed.) Intercept, Wimborne, England, pp. 227–261.

Costa, H.S. and Brown, J.K. (1991). Variation in biological characteristics and esterase patterns among populations of *Bemisia tabaci*, and the association of one population with silver leaf symptom induction. *Entomol. Exp. Appl.* 61: 211–219.

David, B.V. and Ananthakrishnan, T.N. (1976). Host correlated variation in *Trialeurodes rara* Singh and *Bemisia tabaci* (Gennadius) (Aleyrodidae: Homoptera: Insecta). *Curr. Sci.* **45**: 223–225.

El-Helaly, M.S., El-Shazli, A.Y. and El-Gayar, F.H. (1971). Biological studies on immature stage of *Bemisia tabaci* Genn. (Homopt., Aleyrodidae) in Egypt. *Zeitschrift für Angewandte Entomologie* **69**: 48–55.

Gameel, O.I. (1974). Some aspects of the mating and oviposition behaviour· of the cotton whitefly *Bemisia tabaci* (Genn.). *Rev. Zool. Africaine* **88**: 784–788.

Gennadius, P. (1889). Diseases of tobacco plantations in the *Trikonia*, the aleurodid of tobacco. *Ellenike Georgia* **5**: 1–3 (in Greek).

Gupta, P.C. (1972). External morphology of *Bemisia gossypiperda* (M. & L.), a vector of plant virus diseases (Homoptera: Aleurodidae). *Zool. Beiträge* **18**: 1–23.

Harakly, F.A. (1973). Variation in pupae of *Bemisia tabaci* (Gennadius) bred on different hosts (Homoptera-Aleyrodidae). *Bull. Soc. Entomol. d'Egypte* **57**: 407–412.

Husain, M.A, and Trehan, K.N. (1933). Observations on the life-history, bionomics and control of the whitefly of cotton (*Bemisia gossypiperda* M. & L.). *Indian J. Agric. Sci.* **3**: 701–753.

Li, H.Y., Duffus, E.J. and Cohen, S. (1992). *Bemisia* biotype alterations by hosts and intra-biotype mating. *Bemisia Newsletter* No. 6: 5–6.

Lopez-Avila, A. (1986). Taxonomy and Biology. In: *Bemisia tabaci—a Literature Survey* (M.J.W. Cock, ed.). C.A.B. International Institute of Biological Control, pp. 3–11

Misra, C.S. and Lamba, K.S. (1929). The cotton whitefly (*Bemisia gossypiperda* n. sp.). *Bull. Agric. Res. Inst., Pusa* **196**, 7 pp.

Mohanty, A.K. and Basu, A.N. (1986). Effect of host plants and seasonal factors on intraspecific variations in pupal morphology of the whitefly vector, *Bemisia tabaci* (Genn.), (Homoptera: Aleyrodidae). *J. Ent. Res.* **10**: 19–26.

Mound, L.A. (1963). Host-correlated variation in *Bemisia tabaci* (Gennadius) (Homoptera: Aleyrodidae). *Proc. Royal Entomological Society London (A)* **38**: 171–180.

Mound, L.A. (1984). Zoogeographical distribution of whiteflies. *Current Topics in Vector Research* **2**: 185–197.

Mound, L.A. and Halsey, S.H. (1978). *Whitefly of the World. Systematic Catalogue of Aleyrodidae (Homoptera) with Host Plant and Natural Enemy Data*. British Museum (Natural History). John Wiley & Sons, London, 340 pp.

Perring, T. (1992). A study of the relatedness of the *B. tabaci* types. *Bemisia Newsletter* No. 6: 5. ,

Perring, T.M., Cooper, A.D., Rodriquez, R.J., Farrar, C.A. and Bellows, T.S. (1993). Identification of a whitefly species by genomic and behavioural studies. *Science* **259**: 74–77.

Pruthi, H.S. and Samuel, C.K. (1941). Entomological investigation on the leaf-curl disease of tobacco in northern India. IV. Transmission of the disease by whitefly (*Bemisia gossypiperda*) from some new alternate hosts. *Indian J. Agric. Sci.* **11**: 387–409.

Richards, O.W. and Davies, R.G. (1977). *Imm's General Textbook of Entomology*. Chapman and Hall, London-New York, 10th ed., 1354 pp.

Russell, L.M. (1948). The North American Species of Whiteflies of the Genus *Trialeurodes*. Miscellaneous Publications, USDA **635**: 1–85.

Russell, L.M. (1957). Synonyms of *Bemisia tabaci* (Gennadius) (Homoptera, Aleyrodidae). *Bull. Brooklyn Entomol. Soc.* **52** (5): 122–123.

Takahashi, R. (1936). Some Aleyrodidae, Aphididae, Coccidae (Homoptera), and Thysanoptera from Micronesia. *Tenthredo* **1** (2): 109–120.

Woodward, T.E., Evans, J.W. and Eastop, V.F. (1970). Hemiptera. In: *The Insects of Australia*. Commonwealth Scientific and Industrial Research Organization (CSIRO), Melbourne University Press, pp. 387–457.

Wool, D. and Greenberg, S. (1990). Esterase activity in whiteflies (*Bemisia tabaci*) in Israel in relation to insecticidal resistance. *Entomol. Exp. Appl.* **57**: 251–258.

Wool, D., Gerling, D., Bellotti, A.C., Morales, F.J. and Nolt, B.L. (1991). Spatial and temporal genetic variation in populations of the whitefly *Bemisia tabaci* (Genn.) in Israel and Colombia: an interim report. *Insect Sci. Appl.* **12**: 225–230.

Wool, D., Gerling, D., Nolt, B.L., Constantion, L.M., Bellotti, A.C. and Morales, F.J. (1989). The use of electrophoresis for identification of adult whiteflies (Homoptera, Aleyrodidae) in Israel and Colombia. *J. Appl. Ent.* **107** (4): 344–350.

3

Distribution

Bemisia tabaci is widespread in the tropics and subtropics and seems to be on the move, having been recorded in recent years from many areas outside the previously known range of distribution. The whitefly has been reported as a greenhouse pest in several temperate countries in Europe, e.g. Denmark, Finland, France, Norway, Sweden and Switzerland. Besides in greenhouses, the species has been reported on outdoor plants in France and (one report) in Canada.

The information furnished by the C.A.B. International Institute of Entomology, London, (Cock, 1986) is updated below. For the sake of brevity, references are provided only for new entries.

EUROPE
  Cyprus
  Denmark   Sonne et al. (1989)
  Finland   Markkula (1988)
  France   Giustina et al. (1989), Bink-Moenen and Mound (1990)
  Greece
  Italy
  Norway   Stenseth (1990)
  Portugal
  Sicily
  Spain
  Sweden   Petterson and Råmert (1987)
  Switzerland   Anon (1989)
  Turkey
  United Kingdom   The record of Mound & Halsey (1978) has been omitted from the
                     distribution list prepared by the C.A.B. International Institute of
                     Entomology in 1986, as it was based on an accidental introduction
                     into Kent and no permanent colony has been established there.

USSR (Former)
  Azerbaijan SSR
  Georgian SSR
AFRICA
  Angola
  Pagalu
  Cameroon
  Cape Verde Is.

Central African
  Republic
Chad
Congo
Egypt
Ethiopia
Gambia
Ghana
Ivory Coast
Kenya
Libya
Madagascar
Malawi
Mauritius
Morocco
Mozambique
Nigeria
Reunion
Rwanda
Senegal
Sierra Leone
Somalia
South Africa
Sudan
Tanzania
Togo
Tunisia
Uganda
Zaire
Zimbabwe
ASIA
Afghanistan
Burma
China
  Chekiang
  Fukien
  Kwangtung
  Shensi
  Szechwan
India   Throughout the subcontinent except in the hills at high altitudes.
          Reported for the first time from the Kashmir Valley (Khan, 1987).
Indonesia
  Java
  Sulawesi
  Sumatra
Iran
Iraq
Israel
Japan
Jordan
Kuwait

Lebanon
Malaysia
Oman
Pakistan   Quite widespread in the country.
Philippines
Saudi Arabia
South Yemen
Sri Lanka
Syria
Taiwan
Thailand
AUSTRALASIA AND PACIFIC ISLANDS
  Australia
    New South Wales
    Queensland
    Western Australia
  Caroline Is.
  Fiji
  Hawaii
  Mariana Is.
  New Zealand   Martin (1989)
  Papua New Guinea
  Solomon Is.
  Tuvalu
  Western Samoa
NORTH-WEST ATLANTIC
  Bermuda   Monkman (1989)
AMERICA, NORTHERN USA
  Arizona
  California
  Dist. of Columbia
  Florida
  Georgia
  Maryland
  Texas
  Mexico
  Pennsylvania   Brown and Stanghellini (1988)
CANADA
  Alberta   Broadbent et al. (1989)
  British Columbia   Recorded on poinsettia and *Hibiscus* spp., in greenhouse and identified once on an outdoor crop for the first time in Canada.
  New Brunswick
  Nova Scotia
  Ontario
  Quebec
AMERICA, CENTRAL & CARIBBEAN
  Barbados
  Costa Rica
  Cuba
  Dominican Republic
  El Salvador

Guatemala
Honduras
Jamaica
Nicaragua
Panama
Puerto Rico
AMERICA, SOUTH
Agrentina
Brazil
Colombia
Venezuela

REFERENCES

Anonymous (1989). [*Bemisia tabaci*—a new whitefly in greenhouse crops] *Bomisia tabaci*—eine neue weisse Fliege in Gewächshauskulturen. *Gärtnermeister* 13: 242—243.

Bink-Moenen, R.M. and Mound, L.A. (1990). Whiteflies: Diversity, biosystematics and evolutionary patterns. In: '*Whiteflies; Their Bionomics, Pest Status and Management*' (D. Gerling, ed.). Intercept, Wimborne, England, pp. 1–11.

Broadbent, A.B., Foottit, R.G. and Murphy, G.D. (1989). Sweet-potato whitefly *Bemisia tabaci* (Gennadius) (Homoptera: Aleyrodidae), a potential insect pest in Canada. *Canad. Ent.* **121** (11): 1027–1028.

Brown, J.K. and Stanghellini, M.E. (1988). Lettuce infectious yellows virus in hydroponically grown lettuce in Pennsylvania. *Plant Disease* **72** (5): 453.

Cock, M.J.W. (ed.) (1986). '*Bemisia tabaci*—a Literature Survey. C.A.B. International Institute of Biological Control, U.K., 121 pp.

Giustina, W. Della, Martinez, M. and Bertaux, F. (1989). [*Bemisia tabaci* : the new enemy of glasshouse crops in Europe]. *Bemisia tabaci* : le nouvel enemi des cultures sous serres en Europe. *Phytoma* **406**: 48–52.

Khan, M.A. (1987). Occurrence of whiteflies—an important virus vector in Kashmir Valley. *Res. Devel. Reporter* **4** (1): 102.

Markkula, M. (1988). Pests of cultivated plants in Finland during 1987. *Ann. Agric. Finniae* **27** (4): 323–327.

Martin, N.A. (1989). Greenhouse tomatoes. A Survey of Pest and Disease Control. DSIR Plant Protection Report No. 1, 42 pp.

Monkman, K.D. (1989). A new insect pest in Bermuda. *Monthly Bull. Bermuda Dept. Agric. Fish.* **60** (1): 2.

Mound, L.A. and Halsey, S.H. (1978). *Whitefly of the World. A Systematic Catalogue of the Aleyrodidae (Homoptera) with Host Plant and Natural Enemy Data*. British Museum (Natural History). John Willey Sons, London, 340 pp.

Petterson, M.K. and Råmert, B. (1987). [Plant protection-1987-horticulture]. Växtskyddsåret 1987—trädgård. *Växtskyddsnotiser* **52** (3): 66–70.

Sonne, H., Aagesen, J. and Amsem, M. (1989). [The cotton whitefly, *Bemisia tabaci*.]. Bomuldsmellusen *Bemisia tabaci*. *Gartner Tidende* **105** (17): 399–401.

Stenseth, C. (1990). [Whiteflies on ornamental plants in the greenhouse]. Mellus pa prydplanter i veksthus. *Gartneryket* **80** (3): 16–18.

4

Host Plants

Bemisia tabaci is highly polyphagous and has been recorded on a very wide range of cultivated and wild plants. However, the magnitude of infestation and the nature and extent of injury vary with plant species, seasons and localities. Besides, many records do not provide information on the status of the plants as breeding hosts. The host range of the whitefly often has regional characteristics and the same plant species subjected to severe infestations in one area, may be relatively free from the whitefly in another. For example, *B. tabaci* is a serious threat to the cotton crop in the Sudan but hardly a problem for the same crop in Egypt. While such differences may be largely due to different agroecosystems, there are indications of the existence of physiological races of *B. tabaci*. For instance, *B. tabaci* does not attack cucumber in Puerto Rico but the same plant is infested elsewhere. Similarly, cassava is affected by the whitefly in the Palearctic region but not in South America (see Chapter 2).

Direct feeding injury and soiling due to honeydew exuded by the whitefly are generally obscured by its role as a vector of plant viruses. In fact, with the exception of cotton and a very few crops, plant-protection measures are mostly directed to prevent virus spread.

Greathead (1986) updated the information in Mound and Halsey (1978) and listed 506 plant species belonging to 74 families. The compilation presented here lists 540 plant species belonging to 77 families. One host species, *Oryza sativa,* in Greathead's list has been omitted since the whitefly collected on rice, identified earlier as *B. tabaci*, was later described as *Bemisia graminis* by David and Winstone (1988). No subspecies or varieties have been included in the list. Another deviation from Greathead's list is the placement of *Cleome* spp. in Cleomaceae instead of Capparidaceae, following Singh et al., 1990.

While many families are represented by a single species that serves as host of *B. tabaci,* there are as many as 99 species in Leguminosae at the other extreme. It may be pointed out that 50% of the total number of host plants belong to only five families, namely, Leguminosae, Compositae, Malvaceae, Solanaceae and Euphorbiaceae. Plant families have been ranked in Table 4.1 according to the number of plants recorded as hosts of *B. tabaci*. It is followed by a detailed list in which the families and species in each are arranged alphabetically (Table 4.2).

Table 4.1.   Ranking of plant families as hosts of *B. tabaci*

Family	No. of host species
Leguminosae	99
Compositae	62
Malvaceae	37
Solanaceae	37
Euphorbiaceae	35
Convolvulaceae	20
Verbenaceae	18
Cucurbitaceae	17
Labiatae	16
Amaranthaceae	15
Cruciferae	15
Rosaceae	12
Moraceae	10
Chenopodiaceae	9
Oleaceae	8
Gramineae	7
Tiliaceae	7
Umbelliferae	5
5 families, each with 4 species	20
12 families, each with 3 species	36
13 families, each with 2 species	26
29 families, each with 1 species	29
Total—77	540

Table 4.2.   List of host plants of *Bemisia tabaci*

Acanthaceae	*Adhatoda vasica, Asystasia gangetica, Ruellia patula, R. prostrata*
Aceraceae	*Acer macrophyllum*
Amaranthaceae	*Achyranthes aspera, Alternanthera* sp., *Amaranthus blitum, A. caudatus, A. gangeticus, A. graecizans, A. hybridus, A. spinosus, A. tricolor, A. viridis, Amaranthus* sp., *Cleosia clistata, C. plumosa, Digera arvensis* (= *alternifolia*), *Gomphrena globosa*
Anacardiaceae	*Odina asplentifolia*
Annonaceae	*Annona muricata, A. reticulata, A. squamosa, Fissistigma oldhamii*
Araceae	*Anthurium andreaeanum, Colocasia antiquorum, Typhonium trilobatum*
Aristolochiaceae	*Aristolochia bracteolata, A. cymbifera* (= *labiosa*), *A. punjabensis*
Asclepiadaceae	*Cynanchum acutum, Leptadenia heterophylla, Pergularia extensa*
Balsaminaceae	*Impatiens balsamina*
Bignoniaceae	*Spathodea campanulata*
Bombacaceae	*Bombacopsis glabra, Ceiba* sp.

Boraginaceae	*Helitropium europaeum, H. ovalifolium, H. sudanicum*
Cannabinaceae	*Cannabis sativa*
Capparidaceae	*Boscia senegalensis, Cadaba rotundifolia, Capparis* sp.
Caprifoliaceae	*Lonicera erusca, L. japonica*
Caricaceae	*Carica papaya*
Caryophyllaceae	*Dianthus chinensis, Saponaria vaccaria*
Chenopodiaceae	*Beta vulgaris, Chenopodium album, C. amaranticolor, C. ambrosioides, C. murale, C. quinoa, Chenopodium* sp., *Cochlospermum planchoni, Spinacea oleracea*
Chrysobalanaceae	*Chrysobalanus orbicularis*
Cistaceae	*Cistus salvifolius*
Cleomaceae	*Cleome chelidonii, C. gynandra, C. viscosa, Cleome* sp.
Commelinaceae	*Commelina benghalensis*
Compositae	*Acanthospermum hispidum, Ageratum conyzoides, Artemisia vulgaris, Aspilia africana, Aspilia* sp., *Aster tataricus, Aster* sp., *Bidens pilosa, Blainvillea rhomboidea, Blumea lacera, B. neilgherrensis, Calendula officinalis, Carthamus oxyacantha, C. tinctorius, Centaurea africana, Centaurea* sp., *Chromolaena odorata, Chrysanthemum argenteum, C. coronarium, C. indicum, C. sinense, Chrysanthemum* sp., *Cirsium arvense, Conyza aegyptiaca, Coreopsis tinctoria, Cosmos bipinnatus, C. sulphureus, Eclipta erecta (= alba, prostrata), Emilia javanica (= coccinea), E. sonchifolia, Erigeron linifolius (= conyza, crispus), Eupatorium cannabinum, E. chinense, E. glandulosum, Galinsoga parviflora, Gerbera jamesonii, Helianthus annuus, H. debilis, H. tuberosus, Inula viscosa, Lactuca canadensis, L. sativa, L. scariola, Launaea asplenifolia, Mikania condata, Parthenium argentatum, Pseudelephantopus spiralis, Serratula quinquefolia, Sonchus arvensis, S. cornutus, S. oleraceus, Sonchus* sp., *Tagetes erecta, T. patula, Vernonia anthelmintica, V. cinerea, Vernonia* sp., *Vicoa vestita, Xanthium pungens, X. strumarium (= brasilicum), Zinnia angustifolia, Z. elegans,*
Convolvulaceae	*Convolvulus arvensis, Convolvulus* sp., *Ipomoea aquatica (= reptans), I. batatas, I. blepharosepala, I. cairica, I. cardiosepala, I. carnea, I. cordofana, I. hederacea, I. involucarata, I. nil, I. palmata, I. purga, I. purpurea, I. quinquefolia, I. rubrocaerulea, I. sagittata, Jacquemontia tamnifolia, Turbina corymbosa (= mollissima)*
Cruciferae	*Brassica alboglabra, B. campestris, B. caulorapa, B. chinensis, B. juncea, B. napus, B. oleracea, B. rapa, Capsella bursa-pastoris, Eruca sativa, Nasturtium officinale, Raphanus sativus, Raphanus* sp., *Sinapis arvensis, Zilla myagroides*
Cucurbitaceae	*Benincasa hispida, Citrullus colocynthis, C. lanatus, Coccinia indica, Cucumis melo (= maderaspatanus), C. sativus, Cucurbita maxima, C. moschata, C. pepo, Ecballium elaterium, Lagenaria siceraria, L. vulgaris, Luffa acutangula, L. aegyptiaca (= cylindrica), Momordica charantia, Trichosanthes anguina, T. dioica*
Ericaceae	*Arbutus menzeisii*

Euphorbiaceae	*Acalypha hispida, A. indica, A. marginata, Bridelia ferruginea, Chamaesyce hypericifolia, Chrozophora tinctoria, Croton bonplandanum, C. lobatus, C. sparsiflorus, Euphorbia aegyptiaca, E. convolvuloides, E. falcata, E. geniculata, E. helioscopia, E. heterophylla, E. hirta, (= pilulifera), E. hirtella, E. hypericifolia, E. peplus, E. prostrata, E. prunifolia, E. pulcherrima, Jatropha curcass, J. gossypifolia, J. multifida, Macaranga tanarius, Manihot esculenta (= utilissima), M. glaziovii, Manihot sp., Mercurialis annua, Micrococca mercurialis, Phyllanthus maderaspatensis, P. niruri, Ricinus communis, Trewia nudiflora*
Fagaceae	*Quercus agrifolia, Q. densiflora*
Flacourtiaceae	*Rawsonia lucida*
Geraniaceae	*Erodium sp., Pelargonium odoratissimum, Pelargonium sp.*
Gramineae	*Coix lacryma-jobi, Cynodon dactylon, Hemarthria compressus (= fasciculata), Oplismenus burmannii, Pennisetum americanum (= Penicillaria spicata), Saccharum officinarum, Zea mays*
Grossulariaceae	*Ribes cynosbati, R. gracile, R. grossularia*
Guttiferae	*Psorospermum corymbiferum*
Labiatae	*Anisomeles ovata, Elsholtzia cristata (= patrini), Lamium purpureum, Lamium sp., Leucas ciliata, L. stelligera, Mentha longifolia, M. sativa, M. sylvestris, Nepeta ruderalis, Ocimum basilicum, O. gracile, O. sanctum, Origanum sp., Salvia splendens, Stachys* spp.
Lauraceae	*Persea gratissima, Umbellularia californica*
Leguminosae	*Acacia nilotica, Acacia sp., Albizia lebbeck, Arachis hypogaea, Astragalus sinicus, Bauhinia purpurea, B. racemosa, B. tomentosa, B. variegata, Butea frondosa, Caesalpinia pulcherrima, Cajanus cajan, C. indicus, Calopogonium sp., Canavalia ensiformis, Cassia fistula, C. javanica, C. occidentalis, C. senna, C. tora, Cassia sp., Centrosema pubescens, Centrosema sp., Cicer arietinum, Clitoria ternatea, Crotalaria juncea, C. pycnostachya, C. saltiana, Crotalaria sp., Cyamopsis psoralioidea, C. tetragonoloba, Dalbergia sissoo, Desmodium intortum, D. latifolium (= lasiocarpum), D. triquetrum, Dolichos biflorus, D. lablab, Erythrina indica, E. suberosa, Glycine hispida, G. javanica, G. koidzumii, G. max, Glycine sp., Indigofera hirsuta, Indigofera sp., Lathyrus articulatus, Lens esculenta, Lespedeza bicolor, Lotus arabicus, Lupinus hartwegii, L. perennis, Macrotyloma uniflorum, Medicago denticulata, M. hispida, M. sativa, Melilotus indica (= parviflora), Millettia drastica, Mucuna cochinchinensis, Mucuna sp., Parkinsonia aculeata, Phaseolus atropurpureus, P. calcaratus, P. lathyroides, P. longepedunculatus, P. lunatus, P. vulgaris, Piliostigma thonningii, Pisum arvense, P. sativum, Platysepalum vanderysti, Prosopis stephaniana, Psoralea bituminosa, Pterocarpus erinaceus, Pueraria sp., Rhynchosia memnonia, R. minima, Sesbania bispinosa, S. macrocarpa, S. sesban, Stylosanthes gracilis, Tephrosia appollinea, T. purpurea, Teramnus uncinatus, Trifolium alexandrinum, Vicia dasycarpa, V. faba, Vigna aconitifolia, V. catjang, V. luteola, V. mungo, V. radiata, V. repens, V. sesquipedalis, V. sinensis, V. unguiculata, Vigna sp., Voandzeia subterranea*
Linaceae	*Linum usitatissimum, Reinwardtia trigyna*

Loganiaceae	Sp. indet
Lythraceae	*Lawsonia alba*
Malvaceae	*Abutilon avicennae, A. bidentatum, A. figarianum (= graveolens), A. glaucum (= pannosum), A. grandiflorum, A. indicum, A. zanzibaricum, Abutilon* sp., *Althaea cannabina, A. rosea, Gossypium arboreum, G. barbadense, G. herbaceum, G. hirsutum, Gossypium* sp., *Hibiscus cannabinus, H. esculentus, H. mutabilis (= sinensis), H. rosa-sinensis, H. sabdariffa, H. ternifoliolus, Hibiscus* sp, *Malva nicaensis, M. sylvestris, Malvastrum coromandelianum, Malvaviscus arboreus, Sida alba, S. asperifolia, S. carpinifolia, S. cordifolia, S. grewioides, S. rhombifolia, S. veronicaefolia (= humilis), Urena lobata, Wissadula amplissima*
Menispermaceae	*Stephania japonica*
Moraceae	*Broussonetia papyrifera (= Morus australis), Ficus carica, F. palmata, F. religiosa, F. sycomorus, Ficus* sp., *Maclura aurantiaca, Morus alba, M. indica, Morus* sp.
Moringaceae	*Moringa oleifera (= pterygosperma)*
Musaceae	*Musa sapientum, Musa* sp.
Myrtaceae	*Eugenia* sp., *Psidium guajava*
Nyctaginaceae	*Boerhavia repens (diffusa)*
Oleaceae	*Forsythia suspensa, Jasminum humile, J. officinale, J. pubigerum, J. sambac, Jasminum* sp., *Lingustrum vulgare, Olea eropaea*
Oxalidaceae	*Oxalis corniculata*
Passifloraceae	*Barteria bagshawi, Passiflora edulis*
Pedaliaceae	*Sesamum indicum, S. orientale, Sesamum* sp.
Periplocaceae	*Periploca graeca*
Plantaginaceae	*Plantago* sp.
Plumbaginaceae	*Plumbago europaea*
Polygonaceae	*Antigonon leptopus, Polygonum persicaria, Rumex* sp.
Portulacaceae	*Portulaca oleracea*
Proteaceae	*Helicia ochinchinensis*
Punicaceae	*Punica granatum*
Ranunculaceae	*Clematis lingusticifolia, Ranunculus langsdorfii (= japonicus), R. muricatus*
Rhamnaceae	*Rhamnus californica, R. crocea, Ziziphus mauritiana, Z. spinachristi*
Rosaceae	*Fragaria vesca, Heteromeles arbutifolia, Potentilla* sp., *Pyrus calleryana, P. communis, P. malus, P. mamorensis, Rosa centrifolia, R. gallica (= bourbonia), R. indica (= chinensis), Rosa* sp., *Rubus fruticosus*
Rubicaceae	*Gardenia jasminoides, Morinda tinctoria*
Rutaceae	*Citrus* sp., *Ruta* sp.
Salicaceae	*Salix* sp.
Scrophulariaceae	*Capraria biflora, Scoparia dulcis, Veronica* sp.

Solanaceae	*Capsicum annuum, C. frutescens, Cestrum nocturnum, Datura alba, D. fastuosa, D. innoxia (= D. metel), D. stramonium, D. suaveolens (= gardneri), Datura sp., Hyoscyamus desertorum, H. niger, Lycium chinense, Lycopersicon lycopersicum (= esculentum), L. pennellii, L. pimpinellifolium, Nicandra physalodes, Nicotiana glauca, N. glutinosa, N. plumbaginifolia, N. rustica, N. tabacum, Petunia hybrida, P. violacea (= phoenicea), Petunia sp., Physalis angulata, P. floridana, P. heterophylla, P. minima, P. peruviana, Solanum dubium, S. melongena, S. nigrum, S. tuberosum, S. verbascifolium, S. vilosum, S. xanthocarpum, Withania somnifera*
Sterculiaceae	*Glossostemon bruguieri, Guazuma tomentosa, Theobroma cacao*
Thymeliaceae	*Daphne gnidium*
Tiliaceae	*Corchorus acutangulus, C. aestuans, C. capsularis, C. olitorius, C. trilocularis, Grewia asiatica, Triumfetta rhomboidea*
Tropaeolaceae	*Tropaeolum majus*
Ulmaceae	*Celtis australis, Trema guineensis, Ulmus campestris*
Umbelliferae	*Apium graveolens, Caucalis latifolia, Coriandrum sativum, Daucus carota, Eryngium sp.*
Urticaceae	*Urtica urens, Villebrunnea frutescens (= Boehmeria frutescens)*
Verbenaceae	*Callicarpa sp., Clerodendrum inerme, C. infortunatum, C. splendens, C. villosum, Duranta plumieri, D. repens, Holmskioldia sanguinea, Lantana camara, Lippia gemminata, L. nodiflora, Nycanthes arbor-tristis, Verbena bonariensis, V. officinalis, Verbena sp., Vitex angus-castus, V. keniensis, V. negundo*
Violaceae	*Viola tricolor, Viola sp.*
Zingiberaceae	*Elettaria cardamomum*
Zygophyllaceae	*Tribulus terrestris*

REFERENCES

David, B.V. and Winstone, A.A. (1988). A new whitefly, *Bemisia graminis* sp. nov. (Aleyrodidae: Homoptera) from India. *Entomon* **13** (1): 33–35.

Greathead, A.H. (1986). Host plants. In: *Bemisia tabaci—a Literature Survey* (M.J.W. Cock, ed.). C.A.B. International Institute of Biological Control, U.K., pp. 17–25.

Mound, L.A. and Halsey, S.H. (1978). *Whitefly of the World. A Systematic Catalogue of the Aleyrodidae (Homoptera) with Host Plant and Natural Enemy Data.* British Museum (Natural History). John Wiley & Sons, London, 340 pp.

Singh, U., Wadhwani, A.M. and Johri, B.M. (1990). *Dictionary of Economic Plants in India.* Indian Council of Agricultural Research, New Delhi, 288 pp.

5

Bionomics

The information available on the development duration, fecundity, survival, longevity and sex ratio of *Bemisia tabaci*, as well as on the various factors determining population dynamics of the whitefly is presented. Accumulated over some sixty years, this information includes studies conducted in the field as well as in the laboratory under natural or experimentally manipulated conditions. Further, the biology of the whitefly was studied on various host plants, but primarily on cotton. Understandably, the data are highly disparate, as will be evident from the critical survey below.

Duration of Development

Duration of development is the length of time between oviposition and the emergence of an adult. It is the sum of duration of the egg stage, the three nymphal instars and that of the pupal stage. Let it be recalled that the stage referred to here as 'pupa' includes that described as the 'fourth-instar nymph' in Chapter 2. While a large number of workers have furnished information on the development duration, few have provided stage-wise breakup, particularly of the nymphal stages. Besides, the information available is highly variable due to great diversity of experimental conditions. An attempt has been made here to enhance comparability of the data by categorising it from different aspects.

Egg: The incubation period reportedly varies widely, mainly due to various environmental conditions, especially temperature. Under outdoor conditions the incubation period has been reported to range between 3–5 days during summer and 7–33 days during winter (Table 5.1).

Mohanty and Basu (1987) reared *B. tabaci* on four different host plants throughout the year under glasshouse conditions in Delhi. The egg stage lasted 2–4 days during March–October (av. max. temp. 32.1°–43.8°C; av. min. temp. 17.4–29.0°C) on *Lantana camara,* cotton and tobacco, versus 2–5 days on brinjal (egg-plant, aubergine). During November–February (av. max. temp. 25.7–30.1°C; av. min. temp. 10.4–12.8°C), the incubation period was 6–10 days on *L. camara* and brinjal, but 7–8 days on cotton and 8–10 days on tobacco.

Data on the effect of different ranges of experimentally fluctuating temperatures on the incubation period of eggs is furnished in Table 5.2.

Several workers have studied the incubation period of *B. tabaci* eggs at particular constant temperatures (Table 5.3). The data furnished therein show that the period was minimum (3.7 days) at 28°C and maximum (22.5 days) at 16.7°C. Gerling et al. (1986) have furnished a graphic

Table 5.1. Incubation period (in days) of eggs of *Bemisia tabaci* under outdoor conditions

Place	Host	Incubation period	Reference
Punjab	Cotton	3–33 (Min.April–Sept Max. Dec–Jan)	Husain and Trehan (1933)
Northern Bihar, India	Tobacco	3–4 (During summer) 7–10 (During winter)	Pruthi and Samuel (1942)
Egypt	Lubia	5 (During Aug–Sept) 29–33°C	Khalifa and El-Khidir (1964)
Israel	Sweet-potato	3–39 (Min. during June–Sept) daily mean temp. 28.4°C (Max. during Dec–Jan) daily mean temp. 14.3°C	Azab et al. (1971)

Table 5.2. Incubation period (in days) of eggs of *Bemisia tabaci* under experimentally fluctuating temperatures

Host	Temperature range (in °C)	Incubation period	Reference
Sweet-potato	22.3–28.0	10.7–7.1	El-Helaly et al. (1971)
Cotton	24.4–40.6 (av. 31.1)	5.8	Butler et al. (1983)
	27.2–42.8 (av. 34.8)	5.6	
	26.7–43.3 (av. 35.3)	5.3	
Cotton	15.0–25.0 (av. 20.8)	8.5	Horowitz (1983)
	22.0–30.0 (av. 26.7)	6.8	
	25.0–35.0 (av. 30.8)	5.2	

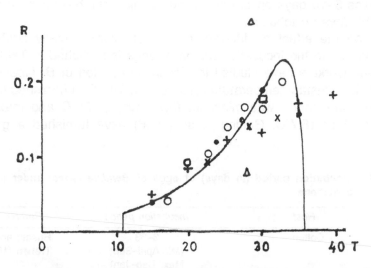

Fig. 5.1. Developmental rates (*R*) of *B. tabaci* eggs at constant temperature (*T*) (After Gerling et al., 1986). • von Arx et al. (1983); O Bulter et al. (1983); x El-Helaly et al. (1971); Δ El-Helaly et al. (1977); + Gameel (1978); □ Horowitz (1983).

comparison of some data on rates of development of *B. tabaci* eggs at constant temperatures (Fig. 5.1).

Verma et al. (1990) reared freshly laid eggs of *B. tabaci* on green gram (*Phaseolus radiatus*) at different constant temperatures (10, 14, 23, 27, 30 and 36°C) in a growth chamber under continuous light and 80 ± 5% relative humidity. They found 10°C to be the minimum threshold for incubation and the eggs did not hatch at 36°C. Besides mean incubation period, relative rate of development and percentage of hatching, they have also given a thermal summation of the developmental period (Table 5.4).

Table 5.3.   Mean incubation periods of eggs of *Bemisia tabaci* at different constant temperatures

Temperature in °C	Host	Mean incubation period (in days)	Reference
16.7	Cotton	22.5	Butler et al. (1983)
25.0	Cotton	7.6	Butler et al. (1983)
28.0	Cauliflower	3.7	El-Helaly et al. (1977)
30.0	Cotton	5.3	Horowitz (1983), as cited by Gerling et al. (1986)
31.0	Sweet-potato	5.9	El-Helaly et al. (1971)
32.5	Cotton	5.0	Butler et al. (1983)

The rate of development as well as the percentage of hatching was maximum at 27°C. Hence Verma et al. (1990) concluded that 90.61– 103.40 days-degrees are required for proper hatching of the eggs. Obviously, the authors did not consider the percentage of hatching as the main criterion, which was much higher at 71.52 degrees than at 103.40.

The effect of the same constant conditions on the incubation period of the eggs on various plants was studied by Lopez-Avila (1986). He stated that under constant conditions of 25°C, RH 75%, light : dark 16 : 8 hours, the duration of the egg stage was 6.14 days on bean plants, 6.37 days on tobacco plants, 6.9 days on lantana, 7.30 days on tomato and 7.67 days on cotton.

Nymphal and Pupal Stages: Duration of these stages varies and has generally been correlated with temperature or seasonal factor. Although the life cycle of B. tabaci has been studied by many workers, data on the duration of individual stages are relatively scant, some of which are presented in Table 5.5.

Mohanty and Basu (1987) presented elaborate data on duration of the different immature stages of B. tabaci, reared continuously on four host species for one year under glasshouse conditions in Delhi. They found the duration of the immature stage to be much longer during winter (Nov– Feb) than during other seasons (Mar–Oct) (Table 5.6).

It has already been mentioned that all the data furnished above with regard to pupal development refer to the stage between the third-instar nymph and adult emergence. Separate figures for the fourth-instar nymph and pupa have been provided by Lopez-Avila (1986). Under constant conditions of 25°C, RH 75% and light : dark 16:8 hours, the fourth instar lasted 3.8 days on Lantana camara, 3.4 days on bean, 2.2 days on tobacco, 2.1 days on cotton and 2.0 days on tomato. The corresponding figures for the pupal stage were 4.5 days on tobacco, 4.4 days on bean, 2.4 days on tomato, 2.3 days on L. camara and 1.7 days on cotton.

Table 5.4. Effect of constant temperatures on the development of eggs of B. tabaci

Temperature (°C)	Mean incubation period (days)	Relative rate of development*	Thermal summation**	Hatching (%)
10	25.0	0.040	–	8.0
14	17.88	0.056	71.52	82.0
23	6.97	0.143	90.61	84.0
27	4.86	0.206	82.62	92.0
30	5.17	0.193	103.40	60.0
36	No hatching			

* 1 : developmental period (days)
** Day-degrees above minimum temperature threshold of 10°C.

Some data on development rates of *B. tabaci* nymphs at constant temperatures was graphically presented by Gerling et al. (1986) (Fig. 5.2).

Total Developmental Period

The total duration of the immature stages of *B. tabaci* reportedly varies widely and is correlated with climate and host-plant conditions. Rapid development during summer and the adverse effect of winter on the development rate clearly show the whitefly to be thermophilic. Records

Table 5.5. Duration of development (in days) of the immature stages of *Bemisia tabaci* under field conditions and at constant temperatures in the laboratory (after Gerling et al., 1986)

	Field conditions				Laboratory conditions		
Reference	Pruthi & Samuel (1942)		Khalifa & El-Khidir (1964)	Azab et al. (1971)	El-Helaly et al. (1971)	El-Helaly et al. (1977)	Horowitz (1983)
Host plant	Tobacco		Lubia	Sweet-potato	Sweet-potato	Cauli-flower	Cotton
Season/ Temp.	Summer	Dec	Aug–Sept (29–33˚C)	Summer (daily mean temp 28.5˚C)	31˚C	28˚C	30˚C
Egg stage	3–4	7–10	5.0	4.7	5.9	3.7	5.3
N 1	3–5	8–10	2.4	2.4	3.0	3.5	2.5
N 2	2–6	6–9	1.8	2.0	2.0	1.9	3.0
N 3	2–4	6–9	2.5	2.3	1.9	2.0	2.6
P	2–5	4–6	4.0	4.3	4.7	7.1	4.3
Total	18	39	15.6	16.4	17.5	18.3	17.7
Rate*	0.055	0.026	0.064	0.061	0.057	0.054	0.056

* Rate = 1 : duration.

Table 5.6. Duration of different immature stages (in days) of *B. tabaci* reared simultaneously on four host plants round the year (Mohanty and Basu, 1987)

Host	Egg		N 1		N 2		N 3		P	
	*M–O	**N–F	M–O	N–F	M–O	N–F	M–O	N–F	M–O	N–F
Lantana	2–4	6–10	2–4	6–8	2–4	3–8	2–4	4–8	3–6	6–10
Brinjal	2–5	6–10	2–6	6–9	2–5	6–9	2–5	4–9	3–6	8–10
Cotton	2–4	6–8	2–5	8–11	3–0	8–11	2–3	6–8	3–6	6–11
Tobacco	2–4	8–10	3–5	6–10	2–4	6–10	3–4	6–10	4–5	7–11

*M–O = March–Oct: Av. max. temp. 32.1–43.8˚C;
          Av. min. temp. 17.4–29.0˚C.
**N–F = Nov–Feb: Av. max. temp. 25.7–30.1˚C;
          Av. min. temp. 10.4–12.8˚C.

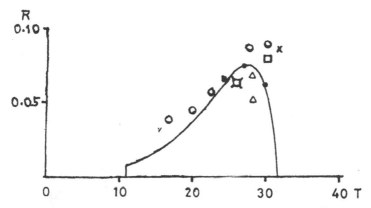

Fig. 5.2. Developmental rates (R) of B. tabaci nymphs at constant temperatures (T) (after Gerling et al., 1986) • von Arx et al. (1983); O Butler et al. (1983); × El-Helaly et al. (1971); Δ El-Helaly et al. (1977) ☐ Horowitz (1983).

of the shortest period of 11 days during summer (Pruthi and Samuel, 1942) and the longest period of 107 days during winter (Husain and Trehan, 1933) are both from India.

Misra and Lamba (1929) reported the total developmental period (TDP) to range from 12–27 days on cotton at an average temperature of 28.9°C and 87% RH. The TDP ranged between 11 days during April and 39 days during winter on tobacco in northern Bihar, India (Pruthi and Samuel, 1942). Khalifa and El-Khidir (1964) found the mean period to be 15.6 days on lubia in the Sudan during Aug–Sept (29–33°C), while the same on tomato in Rajasthan, India, was 22.8 days when the mean daily maximum and minimum temperatures ranged between 31.0–31.7°C and 17.0–21.6°C, respectively. The TDP for sweet-potato in Egypt ranged between 14–20 (mean 16.4 days) during June–Sept and 74–75 (mean 74.6 days) during Dec–March (Azab et al., 1971). The life cycle under Pantnagar (U.P., India) conditions ranged from 13.20 days during April–Nov and 24–72 days during Nov–March (Nene, 1972).

Mohanty and Basu (1987) presented more elaborate data of their findings during one year's continuous rearing of B. tabaci on four species of host plants that revealed variations due to seasons as well as hosts (Table 5.7).

Summing up the entire range of variations in developmental period, Mohanty and Basu (1987) found the seasonal factor to have a profound effect while the effect of hosts was not substantial. However, month-wise break-up of eleven experiments revealed adequate host-wise differences, especially during November and to a lesser extent during February (Fig. 5.3).

Data on the TDP under experimentally fluctuating temperatures is limited and those cited by Gerling et al. (1986) presented in Table 5.8.

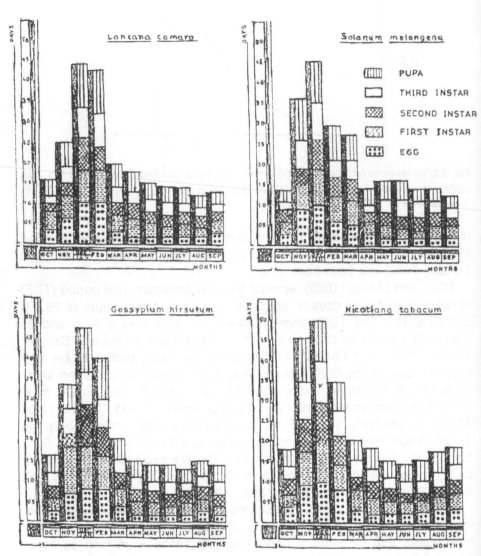

Fig. 5.3. Month-wise break up of the duration of egg and nymphal stages of *B. tabaci*, reared simultaneously on four plant species round the year (Mohanty and Basu, 1987).

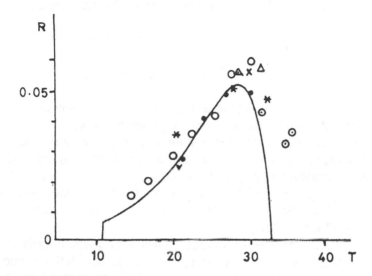

Fig. 5.4. Developmental rates (R) of *B. tabaci* from eggs to adults at constant and fluctuating temperatures (after Gerling et al., 1986).
Constant temperatures: ● von Arx et al. (1983); O Butler et al. (1983); Δ El-Helaly et al. (1971); ▲ El-Helaly et al. (1977); × Horowitz (1983). Fluctuating temperatures: ⊙ Butler et al. (1983); * Horowitz (1983).

Table 5.7. Duration of life cycle (from egg to adult) of *B. tabaci* on four hosts at different times of the year (Mohanty and Basu, 1987)

Month	Temp. in °C		Developmental duration (egg to adult) in days				Differences between max. and min. duration (in days)
	Av. max.	Av. min.	L. camara	Brinjal	Cotton	Tobacco	
March	35.2	17.4	20	27	20	20	7
April	38.6	21.5	18	14	15	18	4
May	43.8	25.7	15	16	14	15	2
June	43.5	29.0	14	16	14	14	2
July	34.3	26.4	14	14	13	15	2
Aug	33.9	26.7	12	14	15	17	5
Sept	32.5	23.6	13	12	14	18	6
Oct	32.1	22.1	16	14	16	18	4
Nov	30.1	12.8	25	36	33	45	20
Dec–Jan	26.0	10.5	43	45	47	49	6
Feb	27.2	11.6	42	29	40	34	13
Difference between max. and min. duration (in days)			31	33	34	35	
				Range: 31–35			Range: 2–20

This data was graphically compared with some other at constant temperatures (Fig. 5.4) by Gerling et al. (1986).

Coikesen and Sekeroglu (1987) studied the development of *B. tabaci* on cotton seedlings in the laboratory in Turkey at two fluctuating temperatures and one constant temperature. Their findings are presented in Table 5.9.

Regression analysis indicated a linear relationship between the development rate of each stage and the temperature used.

Developmental durations at constant temperatures are evident from Table 5.5, which provides data of rearing on single plant species. Coudriet et al. (1985) furnished findings of their rearing of the whitefly on seventeen species of host plants under the same temperature. Lopez-Avila (1986) also reared *B. tabaci* on four different hosts under the same constant temperature (Table 5.10).

The data of Coudriet et al. (1985) shows very marked variations due to the host factor, with development on sweet-potato, lettuce, cucumber etc. being much faster than on carrot, broccoli (*B. campestris*) and tomato. The difference between the two extremes, that between sweet-potato and carrot, works out to as much as 40%. Host-correlated variations in the

Table 5.8. Duration of total developmental period (in days) of *B. tabaci* under experimentally fluctuating temperatures

Reference		Butler et al. (1983)			Horowitz (1983)		
Host plant		Cotton			Cotton		
Temperature	('C)	24.4–40.6	27.2–42.8	26.7–43.3	15–25	22–30	25–35
Average*		(31.1)	(34.8)	(35.3)	(20.8)	(26.7)	(30.8)
Egg-adult (days)		22.4	26.2	27.5	26.9	22.0	21.0
Rate**		0.044	0.038	0.036	0.037	0.05	0.047

* For data of Butler et al., the average temperatures are as given in the publication. For those of Horowitz:

$$\frac{max \times 14 + min \times 10}{24}$$

** 1 : duration.

Table 5.9. Durations of the total developmental period (in days) of *B. tabaci* under two experimentally fluctuating temperatures and one constant temperature

Temperature (in 'C)	Egg-adult (in days)	* Calculated rate of development
12–20 (av. 16.8)	68	0.015
18–24 (av. 21.3)	36	0.028
25 (constant)	24.2	0.041

* 1 : duration

data of Lopez-Avila (1986), though evident, are not so pronounced, being limited to less than 20% between the extremes.

Adults

Adult Emergence: The maximal emergence has been reported to occur between 0800 and 1200 hours by several workers (Husain and Trehan, 1933; Azab et al., 1971; Butler et al., 1983; Musuna, 1985).

Adult eclosion under constant conditions has been discussed by Byrne and Bellows (1991). As much as 90% of the adults emerged between 0600 and 0930 hours under a constant temperature of 29.5 ± 0.6°C and a photoperiod of 14 : 10 (L : D). Studies under a series of constant temperatures revealed a significant inverse correlation between the time of median emergence and temperature. There was no emergence at temperatures below 17 ± 0.3°C. Few emerged during darkness. The peak time of emergence was delayed when temperature fluctuations occurred.

According to G.D. Butler (cited by Gerling et al. (1986); pers. comm.) the sex ratio of the emerging adults was unstable, favouring the males

Table 5.10. Mean developmental durations (in days) from egg to adult on different hosts at constant temperatures (in °C).

Temperature	Host	Mean development time (days)	References
26.7 ± 1°C	Sweet-potato	18.6	Coudriet et al. (1985)
	Lettuce	19.4	
	Cucumber	20.6	
	Brinjal (aubergine)	20.9	
	Squash	21.3	
	Alfalfa	21.4	
	Cotton	21.7	
	Phaseolus vulgaris	21.8	
	Watermelon	22.3	
	Cantaloupe	22.3	
	Parthenium argentatum	23.2	
	Pepper	23.4	
	Cyamopsis tetragonoloba	23.9	
	Linum usitatissimum	23.9	
	Tomato	27.3	
	Brassica oleracea	29.7	
	Carrot	29.8	
25.0°C	Bean	21.5	Lopez-Avila (1986)
	Tobacco	22.4	
	Cotton	23.0	
	Tomato	23.5	
	Lantana	25.3	

initially. Then it reached unity at about 0930 hours but in half-hour counts fluctuated between 31 and 80% females.

Sex Ratio: *Bemisia tabaci* is arrhenotokous and is known to lay unfertilised eggs which give rise to males only (Husain and Trehan, 1933; Azab et al., 1971; Mound, 1983; Sharaf and Batta, 1985). Unmated females produce male offspring (XO) while mated females produce both males and females (XO and XX). Virgin females may initiate field populations, provided they live long enough to mate with their male progeny. The conventional estimation of sex ratios by counting existing field populations may not, therefore, reflect the actual rate of fertilisation of the females. Since both sexes are usually found together, most of the females are assumed to be fertilised.

The ratio of males and females changes under various conditions, as reported by several workers, but most field counts have been taken during the period of abundance of the whitefly. Some workers, notably Pruthi and Samuel (1942), Azab et al. (1971) and Horowitz (1983) have made year-round counts.

The proportion of males to females was high during March–August, low during September–February and particularly low during November–February on tobacco in northern Bihar (Pruthi and Samuel, 1942). In Egypt the females were much more predominant than the males throughout the year on lantana (Azab et al., 1971). Horowitz (1983) found females to be predominant from June to August, followed by male predominance during October, immediately after the late summer population peaks on cotton in Israel.

Under controlled conditions, Sharaf and Batta (1985) found a remarkable increase in number of adult females with a decrease in temperature from 25 to 14°C. The male : female ratio of 1 : 1.8 at 25°C changed drastically to 1 : 3.1 at 14°C. Rearing of *B. tabaci* for more than ten generations on bean plants at 25°C showed the male : female ratio to be 1 : 2.15 (Lopez-Avila, 1986).

Mating Behaviour: Avidov (1956) observed copulation to take place within 1–8 hours of adult emergence during summer and within three days during fall and spring. Most mating occurs during the first day after emergence (Khalifa and El-Khidir, 1964; Azab et al., 1971).

Li et al. (1989) studied the courtship and mating behaviour of *B. tabaci* and found it to be complex. Within the first 10 hours of emergence, the females are attracted to males but do not allow them to initiate courtship. Thereafter courtship starts with the male circling the female several times before placing an antenna or foretarsus on the edge of her wing. If there is no refusal on her part, he then positions himself parallel to her and their antennae are held at a 24° angle to the horizontal axis of the head.

The male drums the flagellum of the female antennae with his own while moving his abdomen up and down. Next he positions his abdomen beneath hers at a 25° angle and tries to grasp her terminalia with his opened claspers. If the female accepts this advance, she pulls back the terminal flap covering the gonophore. The abdomen of the male along with the aedeagus is bent upward at nearly a 90° angle, bringing the latter parallel to the longitudinal axis of her body upon insertion into the gonophore. Copulation lasts from 125 to 265 seconds and is terminated by the female, who frees herself from the male by pushing him away with her legs. Polygamy and polyandry occur in B. tabaci.

Preoviposition Period: Azab et al. (1971) found the preoviposition period to vary from 1–6 days on sweet-potato plants in an outdoor insectary in Egypt. Data provided by other workers under field conditions show the upper limit of this period to be much shorter.

Sharaf and Batta (1985) found the preoviposition period to be 3.6 days at 25°C versus 4.9 days at 14°C. The findings of Lopez-Avila (1986) do not accord with the earlier data. He found that at 25°C B tabaci starts oviposition within 24 hours of emergence. Butler et al. (1983) reported the preoviposition period of B. tabaci in the field as ranging from 1–8 days at temperatures above 20°C.

Fecundity: Fecundity has usually been measured as the number of eggs per female. Various workers have mentioned the maximum number and average number of eggs laid per female. Some have provided information on the average number of eggs per day per female. The rate of reproduction has also been estimated by counting the nymphal progeny (see Avidov, 1956). Such figures may reasonably be expected to be lower than the true fecundity in terms of eggs per female and to show considerable variation, because of being arrived at by various workers under different conditions and on different crops, but mainly cotton.

Husain and Trehan (1933) found the maximum number of eggs laid by a single female in captivity on cotton, to be 119 over a period of 18 days. The average number of eggs per female was 28 in 1929 and 43 in 1930. The average number of eggs laid during a 24-hour period was 6 and 8 in two different years, with the maximum being 16. Pruthi and Samuel (1942) recorded 27 to 206 eggs per female on tobacco, laid in 3 to 12 days, with the maximum in 24 hours being 56.

The fecundity figures arrived at through studies in India, are considerably lower than those reported by workers from Israel, Egypt and Sudan. Studies on the biology of B. tabaci on egg-plant in Israel showed that single females can lay 300 or more eggs, with the average number per female exceeding 50 (Avidov, 1956). The mean number of eggs per female on lubia in the Sudan during summer was 108 (Khalifa and El-Khidir,

1964), while that on cotton during September–November averaged 160.4 (Gameel, 1974). Azab et al. (1971) stated that the number of eggs per female on sweet-potato during summer in Egypt ranged from 48 to 394 with a mean of 161.

Several authors have studied the fecundity of *B. tabaci* under laboratory conditions and the data obtained varies widely. Butler et al. (1983) found that the average number of eggs per female at 26.7 and 32.2°C was 81 and 72, respectively. Of the eggs laid at 26.7°C, 68% hatched against 75% of those laid at 32.2°C. Von Arx et al. (1983) studied developmental biology in the laboratory on cotton, using *B. tabaci* material from Sudan. The mean number of eggs per female at 27°C was 127.5. Hassan (1982), cited by Gerling et al. (1986), found the corresponding number to be more than 309 at 25–26°C. He also used whitefly material from Sudan with cotton as the host. The mean number of eggs per female presented by Horowitz (1983) was considerably less—95.5 at 30°C and 93.3 at 22–30°C.

The high fecundity of the Sudanese *B. tabaci* drew the attention of researchers. Investigations by Dittrich et al. (1986) emphasised resistance to DDT and simultaneous stimulation of fertility by DDT residues as the major causes for aggravation of the whitefly problem as a primary pest of cotton. This aspect will be discussed later in this chapter.

Adult Longevity: Studies conducted by various workers under field and laboratory conditions have yielded diverse longevity figures. However, they generally agree on two broad points. First, the adults live longer during winter than in summer and second, the females live longer than the males.

Husain and Trehan (1933) found adults to live in captivity on cotton for an average of 2.5 days in summer and up to 24 days in November. Pruthi and Samuel (1942) found males to live on tobacco for 4 days in summer and 7 days in winter, the corresponding lifespan of females being 8 and 12 days, respectively. Both these records are from northern India. The average longevity of males and females during summer (29–33°C) on lubia in Egypt has been reported to be 6 and 18.5 days, respectively (Khalifa and El-Khidir, 1964).

The above longevity figures appear to be quite low compared to those furnished by some workers. For instance, in Israel longevity of the males on egg-plant was 4 days in summer and 34 days in winter while the average lifespan of females was 17 days in summer and 55.3 days during winter (Aviodov, 1956). Azab et al. (1971) reared *B. tabaci* on sweet-potato in an outdoor insectary in Egypt. The adult males lived for 2–17 days and females for 8–60 days. The average longevity during summer and winter (mean daily temperatures 28.5 and 14.2°C, respectively) was

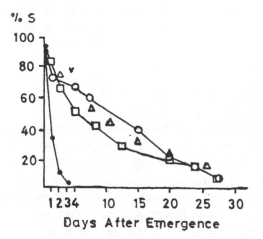

Fig. 5.5. Per cent survival (S) of *B. tabaci* adults at 4 different constant humidities and a temperature of 30–22°C in the laboratory (Horowitz, 1983) (After Gerling et al., 1986).

● 21%   □ 30%   Δ 80%   O 90%

4 and 13.7 days for the males and 13.7 and 57.3 days for the females, revealing a much longer lifespan during winter. Longevity of the males and females on cotton in the Sudan during September–December was found to be 13.2 and 61.5 days, respectively (Gameel, 1978 as cited by Gerling et al., 1986).

Cohen (1982) found adults to die soon after coming into contact with surfaces preheated to 35°C or more.

Information on adult longevity under constant temperatures is also available. In Arizona, Butler et al. (1983) studied development of *B. tabaci* on seedling cotton in constant-temperature cabinets. They found that males lived an average of 7.6 and 11.7 days at 26.7 and 32°C, respectively. The corresponding figures for females were 8.0 and 10.4 days. The most interesting part of the data is the longer lifespan of the males at 32°C, which is a rare phenomenon.

While going through the array of literature on the bionomics of *B. tabaci*, it becomes quite evident that the manipulation of environmental conditions for experiments has been virtually limited to temperature variations. According to Gerling et al. (1986), only Horowitz (1983) tested the longevity of adult females at a predetermined temperature regime of 30–22°C (day/night, 14/10 hours, respectively) and various humidities between 21 and 90%. The drastic effect of 21% RH on survival is evident from Fig. 5.5. More recently, Cohen (1990) has cited the unpublished data of Berlinger et al. providing valuable information on the effect of different humidity levels at different temperatures on adult survival. They reported reduced survival with an increase in temperature, decrease in RH and increased exposure time at temperatures between 30 and 35°C. Relative humidity and exposure time had little influence at 25 or 41°C. Survival was relatively high at 25°C under all combinations of RH (100, 80, 50 and 20%) and exposure time (2, 4 and 6 hours). On the other hand, at 41°C survival was only 2–7% after 2 hours exposure at all RH levels.

Number of Generations Per Year: From a survey of the literature, the number of generations of *B. tabaci* per year seems to range between 10–15. The lowest figure in the range was reported by Monsef and Kashkooli (1978) from the Iranian province of Fars, who recorded 10–11 generations of this important pest of cotton. While Azab et al. (1971) recorded 11 generations in Egypt, Avidov (1956) reported 11–12 generations in coastal plains and 15 in the Jordan valley. Husain and Trehan (1933) and Pruthi and Samuel (1942) found 12 overlapping generations, while Nene (1972), and Pimpale and Summanwar (1984) encountered as many as 15 overlapping generations; all these records are from India.

Influence of Various Factors on Biology

Temperature: The prevalence of *B. tabaci* as a summer pest in tropical and subtropical countries indicates that the whitefly is thermophilic. The data presented in the previous pages clearly shows the developmental period to be considerably lengthened during winter. The figures reported by various authors vary widely but the thermophilic trend is quite apparent. Some generalisation regarding developmental threshold temperatures can be drawn from the information available on adult longevity, fecundity, preimaginal developmental and survival rates, which appear to occur near 10°C (Byrne and Bellows, 1991).

Linear regression has indicated that developmental thresholds for *B. tabaci* are 10°C (lower) and 32.2°C (upper). These compare favourably with thresholds derived from environmental chamber studies adopting linear approximation techniques (Zalom et al., 1985).

In the temperature range to which whiteflies are subjected, a non-linear approach is needed to describe developmental rates as a function of constant temperatures (Butler et al., 1983; von Arx et al., 1983). While Butler et al. (1983) used the symmetrical function of Stinner et al. (1974), von Arx et al. (1983) preferred the asymmetrical function of Logan et al. (1976). Gerling et al. (1986) presented three graphs, comparing the developmental rates of egg (Fig. 5.1), nymph-to-adult (Fig. 5.2), and egg-to-adult (Fig. 5.4) given by various authors with those of the model of von Arx et al. (1983). The asymmetrical curves and the various points thereon provide confirmation of numerous findings that a sharp drop in developmental rates of all stages occurs at temperatures exceeding 30–33°C. While egg development is slowed down at about 33°C, nymphal and egg-to-adult developmental rates already reach their peaks at 29°C. Trophic influences may account for this difference. The lower and upper developmental thresholds are 11 and 33°C, respectively. Rate of development is maximal at 28°C. At that temperature development from egg to adult takes 20 days.

Although the possibilities of survival and reproduction drop sharply at temperatures above 32°C, the whitefly has been noted as a pest under much higher temperature regimes. This might be due to favourable microclimatic conditions, offering protection against an otherwise very hot macroclimate. Secondly, cooling off at night may help the whitefly to survive in such areas (Gerling et al., 1986).

Laboratory tests have shown that temperatures above 46°C are lethal to the adults (Avidov, 1956). Development took longer and there was evidence of aestivation at temperatures fluctuating between 27 and 43°C (Butler et al., 1983). Eggs failed to hatch at a constant temperature of 36°C (Butler et al. 1983; Verma et al. 1990).

The adults live much longer under winter than under summer conditions (Husain and Trehan, 1933; Pruthi and Samuel, 1942; Azab et al., 1971; Nene, 1972). The whitefly overwinters as an active adult (Avidov, 1956; Gerling, 1984) when it lives for 1–2 months.

Humidity: Avidov (1956) considered low humidity the major mortality factor in Israel, leading to cessation of oviposition and adult mortality. Low humidities of 20% RH or less during hot weather have been reported to be highly detrimental to the immature stages (Avidov, 1956; Gameel, 1978).

Very low and very high relative humidities (< 20 and > 85%) play an important role in regulating populations of B. tabaci (Horowitz, 1986). The impact of both extremes of RH is apparently most severe on hatching eggs, crawlers and very young nymphs that have yet to settle down. Once established, the nymphs may be more resistant to the extremes of humidity.

Gerling et al. (1986) cited the findings of Horowitz (1983) on the effect of relative humidity on fecundity, survival of immature stages and longevity of adults (Figs. 5.6 and 5.7). Populations were held at fluctuating temperatures of 22–30°C and 85 or 45% RH. At 85% RH, more eggs were laid early in the lives of females, but their oviposition dropped after the 11th day, going below that at 45% RH, resulting ultimately in a shorter oviposition period and fewer eggs per female at the higher humidity (Fig. 5.6). There was, however, no difference in longevity at the two regimes.

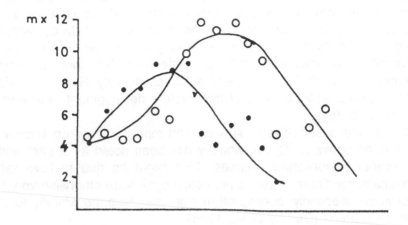

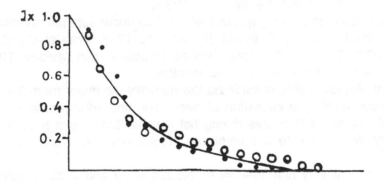

Fig. 5.6. Life table data of *mx* (no. of female progeny per ovipositing female) and l*x* (survival) for *B. tabaci* at a temperature of 30–22˚C, day/night 14–10 h, respectively, and two relative humidities in the laboratory (Horowitz, 1983) (after Gerling et al., 1986).

• 45% RH, O 85% RH.

Horowitz's tests to determine the effect of RH upon survival of immatures during development from egg to adult at temperatures between 30–22˚C (day/night, 14/10 h, respectively) and three constant humidity levels of 31, 80 and 90%, showed great differences. Survival was maximum at 31% RH, being markedly higher than that at the other two humidity levels throughout the period of development (Fig. 5.7). The effect of humidity

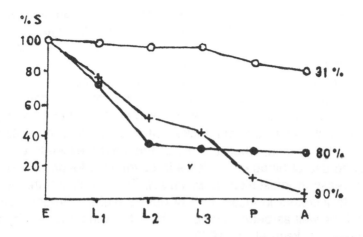

Fig. 5.7. Per cent survival (S) of *B. tabaci* during development from egg to adult (E-A) at a temperature of 30–22°C, day/night, 14–10 h, respectively and 3 constant relative humidities in the laboratory (Horowitz, 1983) (after Gerling et al., 1986).

on adults of *B. tabaci* has already been discussed under adult longevity (Fig. 5.5).

Rainfall: In the Sudan heavy rains were usually followed by a drop in population levels (Khalifa and El-Khidir, 1964; Gameel, 1978). Studies by Seif (1981) on seasonal fluctuation of adult population of whitefly on cassava on the Kenya coast, suggested rainfall to have an indirect effect. Ohnesorge et al. (1981) found oviposition to be impaired by rain. In Venezuela, the main factor affecting populations of *B. tabaci* was found to be the rainfall pattern. During the rainy season numbers were low, increasing rapidly in the drier months (Anzola and Lastra, 1985). Mohanty and Basu (1991) found trap catches to be negatively correlated with rainfall.

Photoperiod: El-Helaly et al. (1977) found considerably faster development under long-day conditions (16/8, light/dark) compared to an 8/16 L/D regime. However, this finding is of academic interest only since the difference between light and dark conditions over the year ranges between 2–5 hours at the most in regions where *B. tabaci* is prevalent. In subtropical countries, reduction in photoperiod during winter is associated with appreciable fall in temperature, which accounts for lengthening of the developmental period.

Plant Quality: The females of *B. tabaci* prefer young leaves for feeding and oviposition (Husain and Trehan, 1933; Avidov, 1956; Khalifa and El-Khidir, 1964; Gameel, 1974; Ohnesorge et al., 1980).

Husain et al. (1936) suggested that there is a correlation between the attack of *B. tabaci* and the pH of the cotton leaves. Berlinger et al. (1983) found a definite, pH-linked leaf-age effect with regard to attractiveness to *B. tabaci* adults. They found the adults to discriminate between pH values of the level of 0.25, showing a clear preference for media with pH values of 6.0–7.25 offered *in vitro*. Caged adults preferred 120-day-old cotton leaves with pH 6.8 to 60-day-old leaves with pH 5.9. These findings may explàin the fact that *B. tabaci* attacks cotton plants in commercial fields only late in the season, when the pH of the leaves exceeds 6.

Increased use of nitrogen fertilisers in cotton was found to result in an overall increase in infestation by *B. tabaci*. The population increase was attributed to increase in insect fertility due to higher nitrogen content of the leaves, as well as better protection from the wind afforded by denser plant canopy (Jackson et al., 1973).

Horowitz (1983) found that females collected in the field as pupae and allowed to oviposit under field conditions in June, laid on average 81.4 eggs while those of September averaged only 23.9. The difference in average temperatures during the two periods was too small (28 ± 2°C) to account for the highly significant difference in fecundity. Thus it appeared that age structure of the leaves, likely to change over time, may have affected fecundity. Von Arx et al. (1983) found fecundity of *B. tabaci* to be dependent on leaf age.

Byrne and Draeger (1989) compared crawler survival on young (5-leaf stage) with that on mature (> 25-leaf stage) lettuce. Mortality of the crawlers was 100% on mature lettuce plants as against 58.1% on young ones. Since eight out of 10 first-instar nymphs penetrated phloem tissue of both young and old lettuce plants, they ascribed this difference to the nutritional status of the phloem tissue of both plant stages.

Climatic conditions are known to affect the morphology and physiology of plants which, in turn, affect behaviour and development of insects. In the Jordan valley, Ohnesorge et al. (1981) found a dysynchronism between leaf aging and development of *B. tabaci*. Under a low-temperature regime, whitefly development could not keep pace with leaf aging, resulting in failure of a major part of the population to complete development within the period the leaves lasted. A host which is congenial in one season may not be so in another. Mohanty (1985) reared *B. tabaci* on healthy seedlings of *Lantana camara*, brinjal (egg-plant), cotton and tobacco in an insect-proof nursery at different times of the year in Delhi. He released the same number of adults in each cage and pupal cases on the leaves of the plants were counted four weeks later. The average number of pupal cases per leaf on each host species during different periods of the year is given in Table 5.11.

During December–January *L. camara* alone harboured a sizeable population, that on other hosts being negligible.

Effects of Insecticidal Treatments: Dittrich et al. (1986) presented evidence of the pronounced effect of insecticidal treatments on the fecundity of *B. tabaci*. Frequently treated populations of the whitefly were found to have a very high fecundity (309.0 ± 115.2 eggs per female). Laboratory experiments were conducted to determine the role of DDT residue in fertility stimulation, using caged pairs of whiteflies that had been exposed to DDT residues from the egg stage. The data showed an accelerated egg deposition in accordance with the residue level, even though higher concentrations caused decline in mean lifetime (Table 5.12).

The findings on insecticidal resistance in Sudanese whiteflies and the function of DDT in accelerating the population by increasing fertility, tend to offer an explanation for the elevation of *B. tabaci* from a secondary pest of cotton in the Sudan until the late 1970s to the status of a major one.

Increase in *B. tabaci* populations on cotton after DDT spray, despite high adult mortality, was attributed to an increase in nitrogen content of the leaves due to the spray (Saad, 1975; Weisser, 1980; cited by Berlinger, 1986). The same explanation was given by Ripper (1964) to account for

Table 5.11. Host preference of *B. tabaci* in quantitative terms of pupae developed per leaf during different periods of the year (Mohanty, 1985)

Period of the year	Average number of pupal cases per leaf			
	Brinjal	Cotton	L. camara	Tobacco
June	166	139	467	443
July	784	140	412	301
August	254	189	511	160
September	495	289	697	230
October–November	168	23	115	22
December–January	7	0	96	6

Table 5.12. Bionomics of two strains of *B. tabaci* on cotton leaf discs with various levels of DDT residue (Dittrich et al., 1986)

Treatment	Concentration of DDT (ppm)	Mean lifetime of females (days)	Total eggs per female
S strain (DDT susceptible)			
Control	0	29.4 ± 8.8	309.0 ± 115.2
DDT	1	28.6 ± 7.0	344.8 ± 119.9
R strain (DDT resistant)			
Control	0	37.6 ± 3.4	257.3 ± 172.9
DDT	5	30.7 ± 8.8	261.9 ± 93.1
DDT	10	26.7 ± 8.5	286.3 ± 97.7

increase in *B. tabaci* populations following spraying with Sevin. Besides changes in the concentrations of nutrients within the leaf, the other possibilities include hormoligosis (increased response sensitivity to environmental changes under subharmful stress factor) (Luckey, 1968) and increased productivity under stress factor.

Discussion

The data presented above, often reflects significant differences in findings by various workers which might be related to different sets of physical and biotic variables. Some of the variables, especially temperature, have been studied in great detail.

The findings allow some generalisation regarding developmental threshold temperatures, the lower and upper limits of which appear to be near 10° and 32°C, respectively. The prevalence of the whitefly under much higher temperature regimes seems to be due to favourable microclimatic conditions and cooling off at night.

According to the comprehensive life table for *B. tabaci* on cotton, worked out by Horowitz et al. (1984), mortality is highest during the crawler and young nymphal stages, mainly due to climatic factors. Preimaginal survival of *B. tabaci* varies inversely with relative humidity. Very low and very high relative humidities (< 20 and > 85%) are highly detrimental, especially to hatching eggs, crawlers and very young nymphs. The whitefly appears to be more sensitive to very low humidities than to very high ones. Extremely high temperatures and both high and low relative humidities play an important role in regulating population of *B. tabaci* (Horowitz, 1986). Why or how high humidities act adversely is still incompletely understood (Gerling et al., 1986). It may be pointed out in this connection that proper understanding of the effect of different humidity levels at different temperatures is essential for gaining insight into the ecology of the whitefly.

Reportedly, heavy rains have usually been followed by a drop in population levels of the whitefly. The adverse effect is understandably more drastic on the adult than the immature stages, which are firmly attached to the lower surface of leaves. The impact of rainfall on population levels seems to depend on the frequency, duration and nature of the rainfall. In Delhi, trap catches showed progressive fall with the advent of the monsoon. Catches started to rise after the rainy season and peaked during October (Mohanty and Basu, 1991).

The influence of the photoperiods that are prevalent in the subtropics during the summer has not been studied (Gerling et al., 1986). The present author believes that whatever impact the photoperiods might have on the whitefly, it is indirect and effected through the host plants.

The effect of host-plant species on developmental duration is much less pronounced than seasonal effect, especially in localities subjected to high summer and low winter temperatures. Differences due to host plants are generally marginal and not as drastic as encountered by Coudriet et al. (1985) (see Table 5.10). Unfortunately, information on host plants (cultivar, rearing method) and the whitefly (origin, plant species reared upon) is generally lacking in the literature, thereby precluding analysis.

Limited studies on trophic influence and plant quality show these to be important parameters, having a major influence on the life-table statistics (von Arx et al., 1983). Horowitz (1983) found highly significant differences in fecundity, apparently due to age structure of the leaves. The impact of the nutritional status of the host on crawler mortality was exhibited by cent per cent mortality of the crawlers on mature lettuce leaves against 58.1% on young ones (Byrne and Draeger, 1989). Clearly, the host-plant-related aspect deserves serious attention to gain insight into the behaviour of the whitefly adult, explaining leaf selection.

Whitefly population growth has been found to be much faster on plants preferred for feeding and oviposition than on unpreferred hosts. However, some recent findings strongly indicate that host preference may evolve rapidly. The transfer of B. tabaci from lantana to cotton and rearing for three generations resulted in significant increase in fecundity on cotton. The same was found when B. tabaci was transferred from cotton to lantana. The results suggest that transfer from lantana to cotton leads to selection of individuals that develop and reproduce well on cotton. Since such host alterations occur annually under natural conditions in Israel, the findings tend to corroborate the low populations of B. tabaci during the first part of the cotton season despite favourable temperature and crop conditions (Gerling and Or, unpublished, cited by van Lenteren and Noldus, 1990).

The Sudanese strain of B. tabaci is known to have a much higher fecundity and longevity than strains from other countries. Interestingly enough, B. tabaci in Egypt laid on average, more than 100 eggs per female, but unlike the Sudanese strain did not live longer than its conspecifics in most countries. While there are strong indications that the high fecundity and longevity of the Sudanese strain are the outcome of repeated insecticidal treatments, the same explanation does not hold true for B. tabaci in Egypt, where insecticidal pressure is not known to be higher than that in Israel or in Arizona (Gerling et al., 1986).

The data presented by various authors on developmental duration, longevity and fecundity show enough variation to suggest the possibility of existence of local strains of the whitefly. Severe outbreaks of B. tabaci in various parts of the world during the last decade and differences in the range of host plants in different locations, suggest that genetic differences within and between populations of the whitefly are not limited to variation induced by insecticides (Gerling et al., 1986). Collaborative research by taxonomists and population geneticists is required to resolve the issue of *B. tabaci* strains which have to be detected and characterised. Some recent findings have already indicated that adaptation (through selection) of local populations of *B. tabaci* to an initially poor host plant can occur within a few generations.

Lastly, one should be cautious about interpretation of autecological data, as rightly pointed out by van Lenteren and Noldus (1990). Many reports lack information on plant varieties, nutrient conditions and differences due to different growing seasons. Furthermore, the growing evidence of the existence of different strains of the whitefly, and even the possibility of involvement of a morphologically indistinguishable from *B. tabaci* but genetically distinct species, underscores the futility of gross generalisation.

REFERENCES

Anzola, D. and Lastra, R. (1985). Whitefly population and its impact on the incidence of tomato yellow mosaic virus in Venezuela. *Phytopathologische Zeitschrift* 112 (4): 363–366.

Avidov, Z. (1956). Bionomics of the tobacco whitefly (*Bemisia tabaci* Gennad.) in Israel. *Ktavim* (English edition) 7 (1): 25–41.

Azab, A.K., Megahed, M.M. and El-Mirsawi, H.D. (1971). On the biology of *Bemisia tabaci* (Genn.) (Hemiptera-Homoptera: Aleyrodidae). *Bull. Soc. Entomol. d'Egypte* 55: 305–315.

Berlinger, M.J. (1986). Host plant resistance to *Bemisia tabaci*. *Agric. Ecosys. Environ.* 17: 69–82.

Berlinger, M.J., Magal, Z. and Benzioni, A. (1983). The importance of pH in food selection by the tobacco whitefly *Bemisia tabaci*. *Phytoparasitica* 11: 151–160.

Butler, G.D., Jr, Henneberry, T.J. and Clayton, T.E. (1983). *Bemisia tabaci* (Homoptera: Aleyrodidae): Development, oviposition, and longevity in relation to temperature. *Ann. Entomol. Soc. Amer.* 76: 310–313.

Byrne, D.N. and Draeger, E.A. (1989). Effect of plant maturity on oviposition and nymphal mortality of *Bemisia tabaci* (Homoptera: Aleyrodiade). *Environ. Entomol.* 18: 429–432.

Byrne, D.N. and Bellows, T.S. (1991). Whitefly biology. *Ann. Rev. Ent.* 36: 431–451.

Cohen, S. (1982). Control of whitefly vectors of virus by colour mulches. In: *Pathogens, Vectors and Plant Diseases, Approaches to Control* (K.F. Harris and K. Maramorosch, eds.). Academic Press, New York, pp. 45–56.

Cohen, S. (1990). Epidemiology of whitefly-transmitted viruses. In: *Whiteflies: Their Bionomics, Pest Status and Management* (D. Gerling, ed.) Intercept, Wimborne, England, pp. 211–225.

Coikesen, T. and Sekeroglu, E. (1987). [Effects of changes in temperature on the development of the cotton whitefly, *Bemisia tabaci* (Genn.) (Homoptera: Aleyrodidae)]. Degisik Ortam Sicakliklarinin pamuk beyazsinegi, *Bemisia tabaci* (Genn.) (Homoptera, Aleyrodidae), nin gelismesine etkisi. *Turkiyë Entomoloji Dergisi* 11 (3): 163–168.

Coudriet, D.L., Prabhaker, N., Kishaba, A.N. and Meyerdirk, D.E. (1985). Variation in developmental rate on different hosts and overwintering of the sweet-potato whitefly *Bemisia tabaci* (Homoptera: Aleyrodidae). *Environ. Entomol.* **14**: 516–519.

Dittrich, V., Hassan, S.O. and Ernst, G.H. (1985). Sudanese cotton and the whitefly: a case study of the emergence of a new primary pest. *Crop Protection* **4**: 161–176.

Dittrich, V., Hassan, S.O. and Ernst, G.H. (1986). Development of a new primary pest of cotton in the Sudan: *Bemisia tabaci*, the whitefly. *Agric. Ecosys. Environ.* **17**: 137–142.

El-Helaly, M.S., El-Shazli, A.Y. and El-Gayar, F.H. (1971). Biological studies of *Bemisia tabaci* Genn. (Homopt., Aleyrodidae) in Egypt. *Zeitschrift für Angewandte Entomologie* **69**: 48–55.

El-Helaly, M.S., Ibrahim, E.G. and Rawash, I.A. (1977). Photoperiodism of the whitefly *Bemisia tabaci* Gennadius (Aleyrodidae; Homoptera). *Zeitschrift für Angewandte Entomologie* **83**: 393–397.

Gameel, O.I. (1974). Some aspects of the mating and oviposition behaviour of the cotton whitefly *Bemisia tabaci* (Genn.). *Rev. Zool. Afric.* **88**: 784–788.

Gameel, O.I. (1978). The cotton whitefly *Bemisia tabaci* (Genn.) in the Sudan Gezira. Third CIBA-GEIGY seminar on the strategy for cotton pest control in the Sudan, 8–10 May, Basel, Switzerland, pp. 111–131.

Gerling, D. (1984). The overwintering mode of *Bemisia tabaci* and its parasitoids in Israel. *Phytoparasitica* **12**: 109–118

Gerling, D., Horowitz, A.R. and Baumgärtner, J. (1986). Autecology of *Bemisia tabaci*. *Agric. Ecosys. Environ.* **17**: 5–19.

Hassan, O. (1982). Investigations of DDT residues on cotton leaves on the fertility of the cotton whitefly *Bemisia tabaci* (Gennadius) (Homoptera: Aleyrodidae). M.Sc. Thesis, University of Reading, England, 37 pp.

Horowitz, A.R. (1983). Population dynamics of the tobacco whitefly (*Bemisia tabaci* Gennadius) on cotton. Ph.D. Thesis, Tel Aviv University, Israel, 213 pp.

Horowitz, A.R. (1986). Population dynamics of *Bemisia tabaci* (Gennadius), with special emphasis on cotton fields, *Agric. Ecosys. Environ.* **17**: 37–47.

Horowitz, A.R., Podoler, H. and Gerling, D. (1984). Life table analysis of the tobacco whitefly *Bemisia tabaci* (Gennadius) in cotton fields in Israel. *Acta Oecologica, Oecologia Applicata* **5**: 221–233.

Husain, M.A. and Trehan, K.N. (1933). Observations on the life-history, bionomics and control of the whitefly of cotton (*Bemisia gossypiperda* M. & L.). *Indian J. Agric. Sci.* **3**: 701–753.

Husain, M.A., Puri, A.N. and Trehan, K.N. (1936). Cell sap acidity and the incidence of whitefly *Bemisia gossypiperda* on cottons. *Curr. Sci.* **4**: 486–487.

Jackson, J.E., Burhan, H.P. and Hassan, H.M. (1973). Effects of season, sowing date, nitrogenous fertilizer and insecticide spraying on the incidence of insect pests in the Sudan Gezira. *J. Agri. Sci.* **81**: 491–505.

Khalifa, A. and El-Khidir, E. (1964). Biological study on *Trialeurodes lubia* and *Bemisia tabaci* (Aleyrodidae). *Bull. Soc. Entomol. d'Egypte* **48**: 115–129.

Li, T., Vinson, S.B. and Gerling, D. (1989). Courtship and mating behaviour of *Bemisia tabaci* (Homoptera: Aleyrodidae). *Environ. Entomol.* **18**: 800–806.

Logan, J.A., Willkind, D.J., Hoyt, S.C. and Tanigoshi, L.K. (1976). An analytical model for description of temperature-dependent rate phenomena in arthropods. *Environ. Entomol.* **5**: 1133–1140.

Lopez-Avila, A. (1986). Taxonomy and biology. In: *Bemisia tabaci: A Literature Survey of the Cotton Whitefly with an Annotated Bibliography* (M.J.W. Cock, ed.). C.A.B. International Institute of Biological Control, U.K., pp. 27–35.

Luckey, T.D. (1968). Insecticide hormoligosis. *J. Econ. Entomol.* **61**: 7–12.

Misra, C.S. and Lamba, K.S. (1929). The cotton whitefly (*Bemisia gossypiperda*, n. sp.). *Bull. Agric. Res. Inst., Pusa* **96**, 7 pp.

Mohanty, A.K. (1985). Effect of physical and biotic factors on intraspecific variation in morphology, biology and disease-transmitting ability of whitefly vector, *Bemisia tabaci* (Genn.). Ph.D. Thesis, Indian Agricultural Research Institute, New Delhi, 125 pp.

Mohanty, A.K. and Basu, A.N. (1987). Biology of the whitefly vector, *Bemisia tabaci* Genn., on four host plants throughout the year. *J. Ent. Res.* **11**: 15–18.

Mohanty, A.K. and Basu, A.N. (1991). Seasonal variations in the aerial populations of the whitefly vector *Bemisia tabaci* under Delhi conditions. *Indian Phytopath.* **44**: 494–496.

Monsef, A.A. and Kashkooli, A. (1978). Die Baumvollveissfliege *Bemisia tabaci* Gen. in der Provinz Fars und die Kontrolle. *Entomologie et Phytopathologie Appliquees* **46** (1\2): 66–77 (in Persian, German summary pp. 4–5).

Mound, L.A. (1983). Biology and identity of whitefly vectors of plant pathogens. In: *Plant Virus Epidemiology. The Spread and Control of Insect-Borne Viruses* (R.T. Plumb and J.M. Thresh, eds.). Blackwell Scientific Publications, U.K., pp. 305–313.

Musuna, A.C.Z. (1985). A technique for monitoring whitefly, *Bemisia tabaci* (Genn.), in cotton in Zimbabwe. *Agric. Ecosys. Environ.* **17**: 29–35.

Nene, Y.L. (1972). A survey of viral disease of pulse crops in Uttar Pradesh: final technical report. *Res. Bull. G.B. Pant Univ. Agric. & Tech.* **4**, 191 pp.

Ohnesorge, B., Sharaf, N. and Allawi, T. (1980). Population studies on the tobacco whitefly *Bemisia tabaci* Genn. (Homoptera: Aleyrodidae) during the winter season. I. The spatial distribution on some host plants. *Zeitschrift für Angewandte Entomologie* **90**: 226–232.

Ohnesorge, B., Sharaf, N. and Allawi, T. (1981). Population studies on the tobacco whitefly *Bemisia tabaci* Genn. (Homoptera: Aleyrodidae) during the winter season. II. Some mortality factors of the immature stages. *Zeitschrift für Angewandte Entomologie* **92**: 127–136.

Pimpale, T.D. and Summanwar, A. (1984). Studies on different stages in the life cycle and influence of season on the duration of different generations of the whitefly, *Bemisia tabaci* Genn. *Pestology* **8** (12): 15–19.

Pruthi, H.S. and Samuel, C.K. (1942). Entomological investigation on the leaf-curl disease of tobacco in northern India. V. Biology and population of the whitefly vector (*Bemisia tabaci* Genn.) in relation to the incidence of the disease. *Indian J. Agric. Sci.* **12**: 35–57.

Ripper, W.E. (1964). Side effects of pesticides on plant growth. *Proc. Seventh British Weed Conference*, pp. 1040–1057.

Seif, A.A. (1981). Seasonal fluctuation of adult population of the whitefly, *Bemisia tabaci*, on cassava. *Insect Science and its Application* **1**: 363–364.

Sharaf, N. and Batta, Y. (1985). Effect of some factors on the relationship between the whitefly *Bemisia tabaci* Genn. (Homopt., Aleyrodidae) and the parasitoid *Eretmocerus mundus* Mercet (Hymenopt., Aphelinidae). *Zeitschrift für Angewandte Entomologie* **99**: 267–276.

Stinner, R.E., Gutierrez, A.P. and Butler, G.D., Jr. (1974). An algorithm for temperature dependent growth simulations. *Canadian Ent.* **106**: 519–524.

van Lenteren, J.C. and Noldus, L.P.J.J. (1990). Whitefly-plant relationship: Behavioural and ecological aspects. In: *Whiteflies: Their Bionomics, Pest Status and Management* (D. Gerling, ed.). Intercept, Wimborne, England, pp. 47–89.

Verma, A.K., Ghatak, S.S. and Mukhopadhyay, S. (1990). Effect of temperature on development of whitefly (*Bemisia tabaci*) (Homoptera: Aleyrodidae) in West Bengal. *Indian J. Agric. Sci.* **60** (5): 332–336.

von Arx, R., Baumgärtner, J. and Delucchi, V. (1983). Developmental biology of *Bemisia tabaci* (Genn.) (Sternorrhynca, Aleyrodidae) on cotton at constant temperatures. *Mitteilungen der Schweizerischen Entomologischen Gesellchaft* **56**: 389–399.

Zalom, F.G., Natwick, E.T. and Toscano, N.C. (1985). Temperature regulation of *Bemisia tabaci* (Homoptera: Aleyrodidae) population in Imperial Valley cotton. *J. Econ. Ent.* **78** (1): 61–64.

6

Sampling Techniques for Population Studies of *Bemisia tabaci*

Sampling is the basic requirement for estimating the numbers of an insect within a crop, varying with weather conditions, cultural practices, the activities of its natural enemies and dispersal and for assessing the effects of various control measures. Knowledge of spatial patterns is an essential prerequisite for any sampling plan. Ideally, sampling should be based on an intimate knowledge of the biology, ecology and the resultant spatial pattern of the whitefly. According to the objective of the study, sampling may concentrate on adults of *Bemisia tabaci* or the last two nymphal instars including the so-called 'pupae' or red-eyed nymphs. Eggs and the first two nymphal instars are generally disregarded in ordinary surveys since they are hard to detect (Ohnesorge and Rapp, 1986a). While Ohnesorge and Rapp (1986b) have reviewed the monitoring of *B. tabaci*, Ekbom and Rumei (1990) have discussed the sampling and spatial patterns of whiteflies.

Sampling of Adult Whiteflies

Indirect Estimation by Trapping: Adult whiteflies are characteristically attracted to yellow surfaces (see Chapter 8). Various types of traps have been used, based on this visual response (Berlinger, 1980; Melamed-Madjar et al., 1982; Sharaf, 1982; Gerling and Horowitz, 1984; Butler et al. 1985); yellow sticky traps have become a major tool in monitoring the adult population of *B. tabaci*. Various trapping surfaces such as yellow plastic sheets, plates or Petri dishes have been used, after coating with some sticky substance, either grease, tanglefoot or other diluted adhesive. Such traps can be used again after counting the whiteflies, by removing the adhesive material with a detergent and recoating.

While flat traps of various shapes and sizes have generally been used (Butler et al., 1986), cylindrical types (Byrne et al., 1986; Youngman et al., 1986), have given satisfactory results.

During spring and summer, horizontally placed traps gave higher catches than those placed vertically (Sharaf, 1982; Gerling and Horowitz, 1984); vertical traps were somewhat more effective during winter (Sharaf, 1982).

The optimal placement sites of the traps, their shapes and sizes have to be determined according to the size of the host plant, whitefly phenology and environment. Traps fixed at ground level gave higher catches in fallow fields than in cotton fields. Traps placed in open spaces in cotton fields due to germination failure, caught more whiteflies compared to those placed at sites with dense vegetation (Gerling and Horowitz, 1984). On the other hand, catches within the field and 4 m away from the border were the same when the traps were placed at plant height (Melamed-Madjar et al., 1982).

Catches on yellow traps are influenced by temperature and photophase (Byrne and von Bretzel, 1987; Bellows et al., 1988). Both high and low temperature may reduce trap catches drastically and rainy weather inhibits flight. Basu (unpublished) noted trap catches to be greatly reduced under overcast conditions even when there was no rain and conditions were not otherwise uncongenial.

Good correlation between catches on yellow sticky traps and actual populations has been found in some systems (Gerling and Horowitz, 1984). Hence such traps are very useful for monitoring whitefly populations, which calls for their use in practical integrated management systems.

An alternative to colour traps are suction samplers that suck in mobile stages of insects by a strong air current into a bag. The opening of the suction tube delimits the area to be sampled, thereby allowing an absolute population estimate (Southwood, 1978). Although suction samplers enable relatively large areas to be sampled, they are generally heavy and awkward to use. Besides, the high sucking force and the risk of injury to the whiteflies during removal from the collector bag are not congenial to monitoring a representative percentage of virus-carrying insects in field populations. To overcome this difficulty, Cohen et al. (1988) designed a simple system. A collection device based on a cordless rechargeable vehicle vacuum cleaner was modified to collect whiteflies directly into clear sleeve cages fitted with removable plastic caps. The device was found convenient for using the cages directly as inoculation chambers, to measure population densities and also to monitor movement with prior application of tracer fluorescent dyes.

Direct Count of Adults: Estimation of absolute population densities by direct count of adults is a difficult problem as the spatial patterns of whitefly adults are usually aggregated and they readily fly away if disturbed during scouting. Accordingly, direct counting has to be done early in the morning when the adults are least mobile (Hill, 1968; Seif, 1981; Gerling and Horowitz, 1984). However, population counts of the adults on cotton in Zimbabwe were consistently higher during 0900–1200 h than during 0500–0630 h, although the differences were not significant. The high numbers of adults located on plants during mid-morning possibly coincide with peak emergence of adults from pupae (Musuna, 1986). For adult counting on cotton, the sample unit per plant comprises the first two fully expanded main terminal leaves and one leaf at mid-level of the plant. Each sample leaf is rotated gently by the petiole so as not to disturb the adult whiteflies on the under-surface of the leaves (Musuna, 1986). To count adults on mung bean (*Vigna radiata*), Rangaraju and Chenulu (1980) successfully used a bell-jar. Each sample plant was covered with a bell-jar of suitable height and diameter and slightly disturbed. The whiteflies left the plant and rested on the inner wall of the bell-jar before moving upward towards the light, where they could be easily counted. The authors considered the method suitable for any type of crop small enough to be covered with a bell-jar.

Comparisons of yellow traps to other sampling methods showed a high correlation, at least during part of the season. A highly significant correlation between number of adults caught on yellow traps and number of nymphs in leaf samples until mid-August, was reported by Melamed-Madjar et al. (1982). Horowitz (1983) found a high correlation between adults caught on yellow traps and those sampled by the direct visual method.

Comparisons between vacuum sampling and direct counting of adults on cotton plants in Israel showed a highly significant relation (Horowitz, 1983; Gerling and Horowitz, 1984). However, the numbers of adults recorded on a yellow sticky trap, those sampled by vacuum collection or by direct count, sometimes reveal discrepancies. Gerling and Horowitz (1984) recorded adult populations throughout the cotton season with yellow traps and vacuum collectors at three sites. Although the population trends reflected by yellow traps were the same as for suction sampling, peak catches with one coincided with a decline by the other. Ohnesorge and Rapp (1986b) offered a hypothetical explanation for the discrepancies. The whiteflies trapped with horizontal yellow traps at ground level were considered by them to be migratory adults apparently caught preferentially. The higher catches on fallow fields in spite of the cloth screen to prevent approach from surrounding vegetation, lent support to this assumption. The higher catches on the vertical traps during the winter season seemed to represent the non-migratory whiteflies resting within the vegetation canopy. Thus the available information indicates that the optimal placement of the trap should be horizontal at ground level for monitoring migratory whiteflies, and adjacent to new plant growth for local dispersal.

Sampling of Immature Stages

Sampling the sedentary immature stages gives more reliable estimates of the absolute population density and detailed work in this aspect has been done by von Arx et al. (1984) and Ohnesorge and Rapp (1986a). The accuracy of the estimates depends on the choice of leaves to be sampled and the manner in which the individuals are to be assessed.

Within plants, eggs and young nymphs occur on the uppermost and young leaves, while older nymphs and pupae are found on older leaves. In view of this, efforts have been made to link phenological plant models to models of whitefly development, to pinpoint the possible area of occurrence of any particular growth stage of the insect. Even on the same plant, the sampling location for a particular immature stage understandably differs at different periods of the growing season.

Counting all the nymphs on a leaf is certainly the most reliable method but too time-consuming to be practised.

Stratified sampling of cotton plants (Schultz et al., 1967; Ohnesorge et al., 1980, 1981; van Gent, 1982) and of tomato plants (Sharaf, 1981) has been done by taking leaves from the upper, middle and lower parts of the plants. Either all the nymphs on a leaf were counted or just the nymphs on one part of the leaf counted or estimated. Restricting the counts to one sector of the leaf could result in an incorrect estimate of the whitefly population level due to non-random distribution of the immature stages within the cotton plants. Obviously, non-random techniques would provide more reliable estimates. Fowler (1956) sampled leaves of high and low infestation and Mound (1965) the eighth leaf from the top. Melamed-Madjar et al. (1982) found the most infested leaf to be located at the fifth and sixth nodes of the main stem from the top in June and the seventh and eighth nodes in July. Gerling et al. (1980) sampled the leaf harbouring the maximum pupae while von Arx et al. (1984) sampled the leaf on the main stem with maximum red-eye nymphs. Since the leaves on the main stem harbour nearly 50% of the whitefly at the peak levels of population density in the Sudan, von Arx et al. (1984) disregarded the side branches. On the other hand, sampling of the side branches might be necessary in the Middle East where infestation on cotton continues until late in the season.

Spatial patterns for nymphs of *B. tabaci* on cotton have been statistically described by von Arx et al., (1984), applying the numerical and sequential sampling theory (Iwao, 1977; Kuno, 1977; Sheperd, 1980).

They calculated the number of leaves required to obtain a given precision level at different population densities and also devised a sequential sampling plan. They found that sampling of about 400 leaves would be required for a precision level of 10%, even at high whitefly densities. These findings underscore the need for developing time-saving sampling procedures. It has been suggested that a presence-absence (incidence) sampling plan would be of great use for *B. tabaci* (Butler et al., 1986).

It is amply clear from the foregoing discussion that the development of any sampling method for *B. tabaci* essentially requires intimate knowledge of the spatial patterns. The latter, in turn, depends on the growth habit and nutritional status of the host or host cultivar, environmental conditions and the resultant behaviour of the whitefly, and proximity to sources of infestation. Studies on *B. tabaci* have shown aggregated distribution for both adult and immature stages. This aggregation occurs not only at different levels of a plant, but also at different sectors of the same leaf. A linear relationship was found between the mean crowding index and mean density of *B. tabaci* pupae for two cotton varieties in the Sudan (von Arx et al., 1984) and for adults among cotton plants in Israel (Horowitz, 1983). The proper timing for sampling has to be determined on the basis of the developmental period of *B. tabaci* and growth patterns of the host plant. In order to generalise spatial patterns, counts have to be done at different levels of population density, at different locations and under various environmental conditions. Such basic data would enhance the accuracy of the statistical descriptions, a prerequisite to designing satisfactory sampling plans with optimal sample sizes, allowing error terms to be estimated.

REFERENCES

Bellows, T.S., Perring, T.N., Arakawa, K. and Farrar, C.A. (1988). Patterns in diel flight activity of *Bemisia tabaci* in cropping systems in southern California. *Environ. Entomol.* 17: 225–228.

Berlinger, M.J. (1980). A yellow sticky trap for whiteflies: *Trialeurodes vaporariorum* and *Bemisia tabaci* (Aleurodidae). *Entomol. Experim. Appli.* 27: 98–102.

Butler, G.D., Henneberry, T.J. and Natwick, E.T. (1985). *Bemisia tabaci*: 1982 and 1983 populations in Arizona and California cotton fields. *Southwestern Entomol.* 10: 20–25.

Butler, G.D., Henneberry, T.J. and Hutchison, W.D. (1986). Biology, sampling and population dynamics of *Bemisia tabaci*. In: *Agricultural Zoology Reviews* (E.G. Russell, ed.). Intercept, Wimborne, England, 1, 387 pp.

Byrne, D.N. and von Bretzel, P.K. (1987). Similarity in flight activity rhythms in coexisting species of Aleyrodidae, *Bemisia tabaci* and *Trialeurodes abutilonea*. *Entomol. Experim. Appli.* **43**: 215–219.

Byrne, D.N., von Bretzel, P.K. and Hoffman, C.J. (1986). Impact of trap design and placement when monitoring for the banded-winged whitefly and the sweet-potato whitefly (Homoptera: Aleyrodidae). *Environ. Entomol.* **15**: 300–304.

Cohen, S. Duffus, J.E. and Berlinger, M.J. (1988). Epidemiological Studies of Whitefly-transmitted Viruses in California and Israel. Final Report BARD Project No. I-589-83, ARO, Bet Dagan, Israel, 91 pp.

Ekbom, B.S. and Rumei, X. (1990). Sampling and spatial patterns of whiteflies. In: *Whiteflies: Their Bionomics, Pest Status and Management* (D. Gerling, ed.). Intercept, Wimborne, England, pp. 107–121.

Fowler, H.D. (1956). Some physiological effects of attack by whitefly (*Bemisia gossypiperda*) and of spraying parathion on cotton in the Sudan Gezira. *Empire Cotton Growing Review* **33**: 288–299.

Gerling, D. and Horowitz, A.R. (1984). Yellow traps for evaluating the population levels and dispersal patterns of *Bemisia tabaci* (Gennadius) (Homoptera: Aleyrodidae). *Ann. Entomol. Soc. Amer.* **77**: 753–759.

Gerling, D., Motro, U. and Horowitz, R. (1980). Dynamics of *Bemisia tabaci* (Gennadius) (Homoptera: Aleyrodidae) attacking cotton in the coastal plain of Israel. *Bull. Entomol. Res.* **70**: 213–219.

Hill, B.G. (1968). Occurrence of *Bemisia tabaci* (Genn.) in the field and its relation to the leaf curl disease of tobacco. *South African J. Agric. Sci.* **11** (3): 583–594.

Horowitz, A.R. (1983). Population dynamics of the tobacco whitefly (*Bemisia tabaci* Gennadius) on cotton. Ph.D. Thesis, Tel Aviv University, Israel, 213 pp.

Iwao, S. (1977). The m-m statistics as a comprehensive method for analyzing spatial patterns of biological populations and its application to sampling problems. In: *Studies on Methods of Estimating Population Density, Biomass and Productivity in Terrestrial Animals* (M. Morisita, ed.) JIBP Synthesis, University of Tokyo Press, Tokyo, Vol. 17 pp. 21–46.

Kuno, E. (1977). Sequential sampling of population density by quadrant sampling. In: *Studies on Methods of Estimating Population Density, Biomass and Productivity in Terrestrial Animals* (M. Morisita, ed.). JIBP Synthesis, University of Tokyo Press, Tokyo, Vol. 17 13–21.

Melamed-Madjar, V., Cohen, S., Chen, M., Tam, S. and Rosilio, D. (1982). A method for monitoring *Bemisia tabaci* and timing spray application against the pest in cotton fields in Israel. *Phytoparasitica* **10**: 85–91.

Mound, L.A. (1965). Effect of leaf hair on cotton whitefly populations in the Sudan Gezira. *Empire Cotton Growing Review* **42**: 33–40.

Musuna, A.C.Z. (1986). A method for monitoring whitefly, *Bemisia tabaci* (Genn.), in cotton in Zimbabwe. *Agric. Ecosys. Environ.* **17**: 29–35.

Ohnesorge, B. and Rapp, G. (1986a). Methods for estimating the density of whitefly nymphs *Bemisia tabaci* (Genn.) in cotton. *Tropical Pest Management* **32**: 207–211.

Ohnesorge, B. and Rapp, G. (1986b). Monitoring *Bemisia tabaci*: A review. *Agric. Ecosys. Environ.* **17**: 21–27.

Ohnesorge, B., Sharaf, N. and Allawi, T. (1980). Population studies on the tobacco whitefly *Bemisia tabaci* Genn. (Homoptera: Aleyrodidae) during the winter season. I. The spatial distribution on some host plants. *Zeitschrift für Angewandte Entomologie* **90**: 226–232.

Ohnesorge, B., Sharaf, N. and Allawi, T. (1981). Population studies on the tobacco whitefly *Bemisia tabaci* Genn. (Homoptera: Aleyrodidae) during the winter season. II. Some mortality factors of the immature stages. *Zeitschrift für Angewandte Entomologie* **92**: 127–136.

Rangaraju, R. and Chenulu, V.V. (1980). A new method for counting whitefly (*Bemisia tabaci* Genn.) population in mung bean (*Vigna radiata* (L.) Wilczek). *Curr. Sci.* **49**: 825–826.

Schultz, L.R., Jackson, J.E. and Faulkner, R.C. (1967). Studies on the sowing date of cotton in the Sudan Gezira. II. The relationship between sowing date of cotton and the incidence of insect pests. *J. Agric. Sci., Cambridge* **69**: 317–327.

Seif, A.A. (1981). Seasonal fluctuation of adult population of the whitefly, *Bemisia tabaci*, on cassava. *Insect Sci. and Appl.* **1**: 363–364.

Sharaf, N.S. (1981). Studies on whiteflies on tomatoes in the Jordan Valley. II. Seasonal abundance of the immature stages of the tobacco whitefly *Bemisia tabaci* Genn. (Homoptera: Aleyrodidae). *Dirasat* **8**: 127–146.

Sharaf, N.S. (1982). Determination of the proper height, direction, position and distance of a yellow sticky trap for monitoring adult sweetpotato whitefly populations (*Bemisia tabaci* Genn., Homoptera: Aleyrodidae). *Dirasat* **9**: 169–182.

Sheperd, M. (1980). Sequential sampling plans for soybean arthropods. In: *Sampling Methods in Soybean Entomology* (M. Kogan and D.C. Herzog, eds.). Springer-Verlag, New York, pp. 79–93.

Suthwood, T.R.E. (1978). *Ecological Methods.* Chapman and Hall, London.

van Gent, R.V. (1982). Investigations on Parasites as a Component of Integrated Pest Control of Whitefly in Cotton. FAO/UNDP Gezira Res. Stn. Agric. Res. Corp. Wad Medani Sudan, Working Paper No. 8, 39 pp.

von Arx, R., Bumgärtner, J. and Delucchi, V. (1984). Sampling of *Bemisia tabaci* (Genn.) (Sternorrhyncha: Aleyrodidae) in Sudanese cotton fields. *J. Econ. Ent.* **77**: 1130–1136.

Youngman, R.R., Toscano, N.C., Jones, V.P., Kido, K. and Natwick, E.T. (1986). Correlations of seasonal trap counts of *Bemisia tabaci* (Homoptera: Aleyrodidae) in southeastern California. *J. Econ. Ent.* **79**: 67–70.

7

Population Dynamics

Studies on population dynamics of *Bemisia tabaci* have received attention in recent years, matching its growing stature as a very formidable pest, especially of cotton, in different countries where the whitefly was of little significance earlier. The whitefly is so polyphagous and widespread in tropical and subtropical regions that it is extremely difficult, if not impossible, to generalise the patterns of population development. Before discussing the diverse information in the literature on the population dynamics of the whitefly, let us look at the various biotic and physical factors which influence it.

Factors Influencing Populations

Migration of Adults/Host Factor: *Bemisia tabaci* is a weak flier and hence dispersed mainly by the action of the wind. Most movements within a crop occur at a low level to locate fresh feeding or oviposition sites (Gerling and Horowitz, 1984). When the crop as a whole becomes unfavourable due to maturity or harvesting, a large-scale dispersal to search for suitable hosts takes place. While emigration may be large scale at certain times, immigration is usually small scale. Trap catches under Delhi conditions for several years invariably showed mass dispersal of *B. tabaci* between two cropping seasons (Mohanty and Basu, 1991; Basu, unpublished). Immigration, on the other hand, is not a locust-like mass movement from one crop to another but, as aptly depicted by Cock (1986), a dispersal-colonisation-population growth-outbreak sequence.

The seasonal migration of whiteflies from one host plant to another has been reported by various authors. Husain and Trehan (1933), who studied the whitefly problem of cotton in the Punjab, India, found the first adults of the year to emerge around mid-January, usually on weeds such as *Convolvulus arvensis* and *Euphorbia* spp., or cultivated plants such as *Brassica* spp., from which infestation spread to okra, cucurbits and ratoon cotton, and thence to the cotton crop as soon as it germinated in April. Reproduction continued freely on cotton throughout the summer, peaking in August and dropping suddenly from September–October. Towards the end of the cotton season, the whitefly migrated back to *Brassica* etc., on which the immature stages overwintered. These observations led Husain et al. (1936) to distinguish three phases of migration during the course of the year: (i) migration from cotton to the winter alternative hosts; (ii) migration from the winter hosts to the spring ones; and (iii) migration from the spring hosts to cotton. Cucurbits and ratoon cotton, they concluded, served as intermediate sources of the whitefly.

It seems worthwhile to cite another migration pattern, also in northern India but south-east of the Punjab, in the context of crops other than cotton. During a survey of the viral maladies of grain legumes in Uttar Pradesh, Nene (1972) observed four phases of migration under Pantnagar conditions: (i) Adults left mature crops of urd bean, mung bean and soybean in October and colonised various winter vegetables, lentil, peas, pigeon-pea and winter ornamentals, on which they were found in goodly numbers during November through February. But development and multiplication remained very slow due to low temperatures. (ii) By February end or early March, the whitefly migrated to spring soybean, urd bean, mung bean, sweet-potato (nursery) and sunflower, and multiplied faster with a rise in temperature on these crops as well as vegetables, beans and ornamentals until maturation of the hosts. (iii) The adults then migrated in May to summer crops of urd bean, mung bean, soybean, cowpea, okra and other summer vegetables and multiplied rapidly during May–July. (iv) The seasonal cycle was completed when the whitefly migrated to the main *kharif* season crops of urd bean, mung bean, soybean, cowpea, *Cajanus cajan*, okra, sunflower etc. and exploited these crops until October end.

It is evident from the above that the seasonal activities of *B. tabaci* depend on the agroclimatic conditions of an area. For instance, in the plains of West Bengal in eastern India, where both summer and winter are milder than in the Punjab and Uttar Pradesh, *B. tabaci* is found throughout the year on various cultivated crops and weeds (Anon., 1988). The seasonal changes there are not drastic enough to curb its activity to any marked extent and dispersals seem to be determined by physiological conditions of the hosts.

The importance of various host plants, such as melons, potato, sunflower, soybean and various weeds, as sources of infestation for cotton has been pointed out by many authors (Pruthi and Samuel, 1942; Trehan, 1944; Khalifa and El-Khidir, 1964; Gameel, 1970; Habibi, 1975; Melamed-Madjar et al., 1979; van Gent, 1982). In fact, under most agroclimatic systems, alternative cultivated plants or weeds are available nearby to provide shelter to the whiteflies that leave the mature or otherwise inhospitable hosts.

In the cotton production system of the south-western United States, *B. tabaci* seems to need only short-range migration once established in an area where hosts are continuously available. The whitefly overwinters between cropping seasons as actively developing populations (Coudriet et al., 1986) on winter weeds such as cheeseweed and sow thistle from October to March. In the spring, sunflower, *Helianthus annuus* and *Convolvulus arvensis* become more important. A similar situation has been encountered in the Near East (Gameel, 1969; Gerling, 1984). Although weeds play an important role in maintaining whitefly populations, cultivated hosts are often more important (Byrne et al., 1990). Melons are planted in the south-western United States during March and again in July. Cotton is usually planted in April and this highly preferred crop gives rise to large numbers of *B. tabaci* throughout the summer. In autumn, when the crop is terminated, large numbers of migratory morphs leave in search of suitable hosts. The largest population is air-borne around the first part of October (Bellows et al., 1988; Byrne and von Bretzel, 1987), which coincides with the lettuce-growing season, planted first in September with the last harvesting in March.

The cotton-lettuce production cycle in the south-western United States closely resembles other agricultural systems, such as the soybean-bean system in Central America and the cotton-tomato system in Israel (Byrne et al., 1990). The incidence of *B. tabaci* in bean fields (*Phaseolus vulgaris*) in Cuba showed a distinctly regular pattern and regression analysis was used to describe the population dynamics in relation to temperature sums. Immigration continues for only 10–20 days from sowing and older crops are not colonised (Heyer et al., 1989).

Mature crops commonly serve as sources for neighbouring young crops. Such sources are particularly important in areas where an overlapping sequence of crops is grown as in tropical countries.

In dry climates irrigation facilities enable raising a crop outside its normal growing season. The dry season crop helps whiteflies by serving as a source for the rainfed crop.

The characteristics of the host plant not only influence the biology of the whitefly, but also define the spatial qualities of the system under study. Trophic influences determine not only survival and fecundity, but also density-dependent immigration rates (Baumgärtner and Yano, 1990). The more the whitefly aggregates on young leaves, the more a population build-up per plant is prevented by density-dependent emigration.

Climatic Conditions: Climatic conditions are perhaps the most important of the factors that influence population dynamics of *B. tabaci*. A temperature range of 27–30°C promotes rapid development of the whitefly (Avidov, 1956; Butler et al., 1983; Gerling et al., 1986) but this period and the number of progeny depend on the host. However, there is apparently no correlation between developmental duration and the number of progeny (Coudriet et al., 1985, 1986).

In Israel, low humidity was found to be the major mortality factor (Avidov, 1956), causing cessation of oviposition before death of the adults. Gameel (1970) attributed the occasional low populations in the Sudan to high temperatures (43–45°C) and low humidity levels (8–17%), or to low temperatures and low humidities. Population studies on the Kenya coast by Seif (1981), indicated the presence of whitefly on cassava year round with marked seasonal fluctuations in population levels. Through multiple regression, he found that climatic factors account for about 51% of the variation in population levels. While temperature and relative humidity interaction was highly correlated, solar radiation and rainfall had no significant effect. However, rainfall had a significant effect through the host plant. Lal (1981) found high humidity and stable maximum temperatures (29.4–32.9°C) to be congenial for whitefly development on cassava in Kerala, India. In Nigeria, Vetten and Allen (1983) noted the pronounced effect of season on numbers of whitefly emerging, the maximum being recorded in April–May, following the onset of rains after the dry season (Dec–Jan). The population declined with continued heavy rainfall. A period of moderate rainfall combined with high day temperature appeared to favour high populations. Sharaf (1982a) reported decline in whitefly populations on tomato due to extreme conditions prevalent during spring in Jordan, either directly or indirectly through effect on the host plants. In Egypt, the population on tomato is low during winter and increases during dry periods, peaking during August–October. Late sowings in April were severely affected while early sowings in March were not (Khalifa and El-Khidir, 1964; Shaheen, 1983). High humidity and rainfall and relatively low temperatures during July to October in southern India were found uncongenial to the whitefly and the worst effects of the yellow mosaic disease could be avoided by sowing horse gram during this period (Muniyappa, 1983). Studies in Parbhani in western India revealed maximum temperature and sunshine hours to be positively correlated with whitefly population, while relative humidity, rainfall and rainy days correlated negatively (Puri, 1991). The fluctuations in whitefly populations on fall cucumber in Iraq from one year to another or during the same week in different years were attributed to adult reproductive activity, which correlated positively with temperature (El-Serwiy et al., 1984).

The decline in population density to the lowest level during late winter in the Jordan valley was investigated by Ohnesorge et al. (1981). They considered the decline to be partly due to a 'dilution effect' as the whitefly population was distributed among an ever-increasing amount of food-plant foliage. Oviposition was found to be impaired by rain and low temperatures. The maximum mortality of the immature stages was due to failure of whitefly development to keep pace with ageing of the leaves, the latter dying before completion of development by the former. On food plants with long-lasting leaves, such as cauliflower and *Lantana* sp., *B. tabaci* showed a good survival compared to 100% mortality on plants with short-lived leaves such as squash.

Natural Enemies: Information on the role of the natural enemies on population dynamics of the whitefly is limited and mostly anecdotal (Cock, 1986). The only detailed studies on this aspect pertain to cotton in Israel (Gerling, 1984; Gerling et al., 1980; Horowitz et al., 1984). In the coastal plain of Israel, the percentage of parasitism of *B. tabaci* did not increase with the numbers of whitefly on cotton (Gerling et al., 1980). Synchronised generations of *B. tabaci* were set up on cotton bushes by manipulating infestation with cages and monitoring was done to accumulate life-table data. Key factor analysis revealed that the natural enemies, mainly *Eretmocerus mundus* and *Encarsia lutea*, attacked a large number of whiteflies but were not the key mortality factor (Horowitz et al., 1984).

Monitoring of overwintering populations of the whitefly and its two major parasitoids in Israel showed marked variation between sample dates, between localities, between plant species, between plants of the same species and between leaves of the same plant (Gerling, 1984). Maximum parasitisation was usually encountered on plants such as *Lantana camara*, which maintained populations of *B. tabaci* for long periods. The relatively stable situation provided by such hosts seems to be necessary for full manifestation of the regulatory potential of the parasitoids.

In the Sudan Gezira, the influence of natural enemies on whitefly population dynamics is poorly understood but they appear to be of minor importance (von Arx et al., 1983b; Baumgärtner et al., 1986).

Baumgärtner and Yano (1990) have pointed out that a general assessment of the role of natural enemies of aleyroids may be premature. They cited the example of the viburnum whitefly, *Aleurotrachelus jelinekii*. A key factor analysis on the life tables of the species revealed no density-dependent factor and accordingly no regulatory effect of natural enemies. The life system of the univoltine species appeared instead to be controlled by major disturbances affecting adult survival and fecundity (Southwood and Reader, 1976). However, density-dependent mechanisms could be detected by a new analysis, emphasising details of within-plant distribution and within-generation processes (Hassell et al., 1987; Hassell, 1987).

Population Growth on Cotton

Studies on population dynamics of B. tabaci have most often been centred round the cotton crop. Population fluctuations on cotton have been studied by various workers under diverse agroclimatic conditions (Husain et al., 1936; Gerling, 1967; Schultz et al., 1967; Gameel, 1969; Jackson et al., 1973; Gerling et al., 1980; Melamed-Madjar et al., 1982; van Gent, 1982; Horowitz, 1983; Butler et al., 1985). In spite of differences in environmental conditions and sampling techniques, four phases of the seasonal population curves are discernible (Horowitz, 1986). The first phase is that of moderate growth, which is followed by the exponential growth phase. The next or third is the stabilised phase and the fourth the phase of natural decline.

Moderate growth occurs early in the season when colonisation is initiated by a small number of adults and the whitefly numbers are low during the first part of the cotton season (May until July) in Israel, although temperatures and host conditions are favourable for rapid growth. The moderate growth seems to be due to the time taken by whiteflies from other hosts to adapt on cotton. This assumption gains strength from the host-transfer experiments by Gerling and Or (unpublished, cited by van Lenteren and Noldus, 1990), who found significant increase in fecundity on cotton, when B. tabaci from Lantana camara was reared for three generations on cotton.

Favourable conditions, such as reasonably high temperatures and suitable nutritional status of host plants, promote rapid development, leading to the exponential phase of growth. Exponential growth is usually followed by an outbreak of the pest population (Horowitz, 1983; Butler et al., 1985).

The stabilised phase is apparently the outcome of competition for food and space which become progressively limited. Duration of the stabilised phase, when discernible, may vary considerably. In a few cases it was very short but in some lasted about two months.

The natural decline is brought about by senescence of the ageing plants, lower temperatures and possibly by increase in parasitoid populations (Gerling et al., 1980; van Gent, 1982; von Arx et al., 1983b).

Baumgärtner and Yano (1990) recognised three major approaches in conventional analysis for gaining insight into the population dynamics of aleyroids. In the first approach, widely used, population densities and age structure through time are studied in the field as well as in greenhouses, and empirically related to exogenous factors such as plant quality and natural enemies. Besides cropping season, such studies cover the off-season too. The second approach to evaluating the importance of the ecological factor through experiments under controlled conditions, has been attempted by only a few workers. The influence of both constant temperature and age of host plant on *B. tabaci* was studied by von Arx et al. (1983a). Zalom et al. (1985) plotted the number of *B. tabaci* on a physiological time scale, expressed in day-degrees above the lower threshold of development, and used an exponential model to compute population densities in cotton fields. Thus temperature and host plant factors were the key elements in explaining population dynamics of *B. tabaci.* The third approach to construction and analysis of age-specific life tables is a more quantitative and more comprehensive method, as shown below.

Life-Table Analysis/Models: Life-table analyses for *B. tabaci* were made in the Sudan (von Arx et al., 1983b) and in Israel (Horowitz et al., 1984) to determine the main mortality factors affecting the whitefly pest on cotton.

Studies on a population of *B. tabaci* with overlapping generations and a changing age structure in the Sudanese cotton fields were conducted by von Arx et al. (1983b). Preliminary simulation experiments indicated that weather conditions in the Sudan Gezira are favourable for whitefly development until December, when the first bolls of the cotton variety Barac open. A non-linear analytical model after Logan et al. (1976) was used to determine the developmental rates of eggs, nymphs and adults of *B. tabaci.* Besides mortality factors such as adverse temperature and natural enemies, host plant physiology and density-dependent migration were incorporated in the model. Most of the relevant parameters were estimated through experiments under controlled conditions (von Arx et al., 1983a). The model showed that besides emigration and an unexplained late season mortality, temperature and nutritional status of the host plant were the most important factors regulating the life system of *B. tabaci.* They found the withdrawal of irrigation at the time of cotton-boll opening to be a valuable control practice for minimising the population level of *B. tabaci* and protecting opening bolls from honeydew. Thus the inclusion of the host factor facilitates not only prediction of changes in food quality, but also characterisation of spatial features for multitrophic interactions.

In the model of von Arx et al. (1983b), either immigration or both immigration and emigration rates have been estimated by adjusting the model predictions to observe densities. According to Baumgärtner and Yano (1990), this is an unsatisfactory approach because parameter estimation is done with the same data set as that used for validation.

Another approach to field life-table studies is the use of successive artificial infestations, as done by Horowitz et al. (1984). Artificially separated generations of *B. tabaci* were obtained by infesting young cotton leaves in the field by confining groups of females within small clip-on cages attached to leaves. The numbers of live, dead and parasitised whiteflies in relation to age distribution, were recorded from the samples of leaves collected at 3-day intervals following each infestation. The empty puparia in the samples collected at the end of each generation, provided a good estimate of whitefly or parasitoid emergence. A similar procedure was repeated under controlled conditions, serving as a control to the field population.

The key factor, the variation of which has the greatest impact on the total generation mortality (KT), was evaluated by calculating the regression of each k value on KT (Podoler and Rogers, 1975) when the highest regression coefficient indicated the key factor. While mortality of the crawler and egg stages/(k_1) was identified as the key factor during the first season, mortality of the first instar proved to be the key factor during the next two seasons. Mortality during the crawler and first-instar stages was assumed to be mainly due to climatic factors. Parasitism was not a decisive mortality factor and acted upon stages later than the first instar under the conditions prevailing during the study. However, parasitism was found to increase at certain periods, contributing measurably to the total mortality.

Horowitz (1986) drew some general conclusions from the life tables mentioned above: (i) a very high mortality occurs during the crawler and first-instar stages; (ii) extreme high temperatures and both high and low humidities (> 85% and < 20%) are detrimental to the population of whitefly (see Chapter 5); (iii) reduction of whitefly numbers late in the growing season seem to be partly due to host plant quality and emigration; and (iv) natural enemies did not have a large impact on the populations of B. tabaci.

Borad and Puri (1991) conducted life-table analysis for B. tabaci in unprotected cotton and brinjal fields at Parbhani, India, following the procedures of Horowitz et al. (1984). Discrete generations of the whitefly were maintained by artificial infestations at 3 and 2 successive dates in cotton and brinjal, respectively. The highest mortality was recorded during the egg and crawler stages and to a lesser extent during the pupal stage. Climatic factors were mainly responsible for mortality during the different developmental stages. Parasitism was found to be moderate and not a decisive mortality factor. A higher percentage of individuals reached the adult stage in brinjal fields than in cotton.

All aleyroid population models consider overlapping generations to take into account time-varying age structure, with the exception of one on the univoltine Aleurotrachelus jelinekii with discrete generations.

Baumgärtner and Yano (1990) reviewed the dynamic simulation models for aleyroid systems, grouping them according to driving variables and system structure. They denoted the three groups of population models as A, B and C.

Model A represents a population model with temperature as the driving variable, temperature and plant species being the important factors. Models belonging to this category have been developed to study the dynamics of *Trialeurodes vaporariorum* on a number of host plants under greenhouse conditions.

Model B, comprising aleyroid-plant population models, shows different attempts to include the influence of host plants in a more explicative way than in model A, and is very sensitive to stress-induced changes in food quality as well as to temperature. Besides, predicted infestation patterns depend on both immigration rates and dispersal within the plants. Studies on the dynamics of *B. tabaci* cited earlier, fall in category B.

Model C is an aleyroid-parasitoid population model with temperature and plant influences as driving variables. Contrary to A and B, natural enemy activity in C drives the aleyroid system in cyclic oscillations.

Conclusions

In spite of great economic importance, information on population dynamics of *B. tabaci* is limited. The great adaptability of this highly opportunistic whitefly, its wide distribution, extensive host range, occurrence of local races, and complexity of the diverse agroecosystems to which it belongs, defy superficial attempts to gain insight into this aspect.

Bemisia tabaci has a high intrinsic rate of increase and growth is exponential as long as physiological conditions of the host and temperature remain congenial. Population growth rate can be estimated on cotton by simulation models based on autecological information but there is scope for improvement of the models developed so far. For example, Hassell (1987) has shown that the application of stochastic variation, especially with regard to spatial distribution and within-patch survival, leads to conclusions different from those arrived at through conventional analysis of generation-specific life tables. Baumgärtner and Yano (1990) have advocated comparison of mathematical qualities, keeping in view the objective of the model to be developed, since researchers have generally not felt it necessary to justify their preference for various simulation methods used.

Proper understanding of the immigration and emigration rates of the whitefly and its natural enemies is an area that requires serious attention.

The important role of natural enemies in reduction of populations of *T. vaporariorum* under greenhouse conditions has been well established and successful biological control programmes have been developed (van Lenteren and Woets, 1988). As regards *B. tabaci*, the reasons for the shortcomings of the parasitoids and predators have to be investigated. Direct and indirect relationship between host plant, whitefly and natural enemies should be studied to gain insight into the tritrophic system. The inclusion of parasitism, predation and competition would make models more realistic. Adequate experimental background would enable parameter estimation for comprehensive models on trophic interactions.

The inclusion of spatial dynamics and the effect of management practices would enhance the predictive value of models.

REFERENCES

Anonymous (1988). Epidemiology and Control of Some Whitefly Transmitted Virus Diseases of Pulses and Vegetables: Final Report of Research Scheme. Bidhan Chandra Krishi Viswavidyalaya, Kalyani, India, 90 pp.

Avidov, Z. (1956). Bionomics of the tobacco whitefly (*Bemisia tabaci* Gennad.) in Israel. *Ktavim* (English edition) 7 (1): 25–41.

Baumgärtner, J. and Yano, E. (1990). Whitefly population dynamics and modelling. In: *Whiteflies: Their Bionomics, Pest Status and Management* (D. Gerling, ed.). Intercept, Wimborne, England, pp. 123–146.

Baumgärtner, J., Delucchi, V., von Arx, R. and Rubli, D. (1986). Whitefly (*Bemisia tabaci* Genn., Stern.: Aleyrodidae) infestation patterns as influenced by cotton, weather and Heliothis: hypothesis testing by using simulation models. *Agric. Ecosys. Environ.* 17: 49–59.

Bellows, T.S., Perring, T.N., Arakawa, K. and Farrar, C.A. (1988). Patterns in diel flight activity of *Bemisisa tabaci* in cropping systems in southern California. *Environ. Entomol.* 17: 225–228.

Borad, V.K. and Puri, S.N. (1991). Life table studies of *Bemisia tabaci* (Gennadius) on cotton and brinjal under field conditions by artificial infestation. *Indian J. Ecol.* 18: 186–189.

Butler, G.D., Henneberry, T.J. and Clayton, T.E. (1983). *Bemisia tabaci* (Homoptera: Aleyrodidae): Development, oviposition, and longevity in relation to temperature. *Ann. Entomol. Soc. Amer.* 76: 310–313.

Butler, G.D., Henneberry, T.J. and Natwick, E.T. (1985). *Bemisia tabaci*: 1982 and 1983 populations in Arizona and California cotton fields. *Southwestern Entomologist* 10 (1): 20–25.

Byrne, D.N. and von Bretzel, P.K. (1987). Similarity in flight activity rhythms in coexisting species of Aleyrodidae, *Bemisia tabaci* and *Trialeurodes abutilonea*. *Entomol. Experim. Appl.* 43: 215–219.

Byrne, D.N., Bellows, T.S. and Parrella, M.P. (1990). Whiteflies in agricultural systems. In: *Whiteflies: Their Bionomics, Pest Status and Management* (D. Gerling, ed.) Intercept, Wimborne, England, pp. 227–261.

Cock, M.J.W. (ed.) (1986). *Bemisia tabaci: A Literature Survey.* C.A.B. International Institute of Biological Control, U.K., 121 pp.

Coudriet, D.L., Prabhaker, N., Kishaba, A.N. and Meyerdirk, D.E. (1985). Variation in developmental rate from different hosts and overwintering of the sweet-potato whitefly, *Bemisia tabaci* (Homoptera: Aleyrodidae). *Environ. Entomol.* **14**: 516–519.

Coudriet, D.L., Mayerdirk, D.E., Prabhaker, N. and Kishaba, A.N. (1986). Bionomics of sweet-potato whitefly (Homoptera: Aleyrodidae) on weed hosts in the Imperial Valley, California. *Environ. Entomol.* **15**: 1179–1183.

El-Serwiy, S., El-Haidari, H. and Saad, A. (1984). Population density of the whitefly *Bemisia tabaci* (Gennadius), (Homoptera: Aleyrodidae) on fall cucumber in Iraq. *Agric. Water Resources Research* **3** (2): 78–87 (Arabic), 135 (English).

Gameel, O.I. (1969). Studies on whitefly parasites Encarsia *lutea* Masi and *Eretmocerus mundus* Mercet (Hymenoptera, Aphelinidae). *Rev. Zool. Bot. Afric.* **79**: 65–77.

Gameel O.I. (1970). The effects of whitefly on cotton. In: *Cotton Growth in the Gezira Environment* (M.A. Sidding and L.C. Hughes, eds.). Agricultural Research Corp., Wad Medani, pp. 265–280.

Gerling, D. (1967). Bionomics of the whitefly-parasite complex associated with cotton in southern California (Homoptera: Aleyrodidae; Hymenoptera: Alphelinidae). *Ann. Entomol. Soc. Amer.* **60**: 1306–1321.

Gerling, D. (1984). The overwintering mode of *Bemisia tabaci* and its parasitoids in Israel. *Phytoparasitica* **12**: 109–118.

Gerling D. and Horowitz, A.R. (1984). Yellow traps for evaluating the population levels and dispersal patterns of *Bemisia tabaci* (Gennadius) (Homoptera: Aleyrodidae). *Ann. Entomol. Soc. Amer.* **77**: 753–759.

Gerling, D., Motro, U. and Horowitz, R. (1980). Dynamics of *Bemisia tabaci* (Gennadius) (Homoptera: Aleyrodidae) attacking cotton in the coastal plain of Israel. *Bull. Entomol. Res.* **70**: 213–219.

Gerling, D., Horowitz, A.R. and Baumgärtner, J. (1986). Autecology of *Bemisia tabaci. Agric. Ecosys. Environ.* **17**: 5–19.

Habibi, J. (1975). The cotton white-fly *Bemisia tabaci* Genn. Bioecology and methods of control. *Entomol. Phytopath. Appl.* **38**: 13–36.

Hassell, M.P. (1987). Detecting regulation in patchily distributed animal populations. *J. Animal Ecol.* **56**: 705–713.

Hassell, M.P., Southwood, T.R.E. and Reader, P.M. (1987). The dynamics of the viburnum whitefly (*Aleurotrachelus jelinekii*): a case study of population regulation. *J. Animal Ecol.* **56**: 283–300.

Heyer, W., Lok, M.L.C. and Cruz, B. (1989). [The population dynamics of the cotton whitefly *Bemisia tabaci* Genn. in bean fields in the Republic of Cuba]. Zur populations dynamik der Mottenschildlaus *Bemisia tabaci* Genn. in Bohnenbestarden der Republic Kuba. *Archiv für Phytopathologie und Pflanzenschutz* **25** (5): 473–479.

Horowitz, A.R. (1983). Population dynamics of the tobacco whitefly (*Bemisia tabaci* Gennadius) on cotton. Ph.D. Thesis, Tel Aviv University, Israel, 213 pp.

Horowitz, A.R. (1986). Population dynamics of *Bemisia tabaci* (Gennadius), with special emphasis on cotton fields. *Agric. Ecosys. Environ.* **17** : 37–47.

Horowitz, A.R., Podoler, H. and Gerling, D. (1984). Life table analysis of the tobacco whitefly *Bemisia tabaci* (Gennadius) in cotton fields in Israel. *Acta Oecologica, Oecologia Applicata* **5**: 221–233.

Husain, M.A. and Trehan, K.N. (1933). Observations on the life history, bionomics and control of the white-fly of cotton (*Bemisia gossypiperda* M. & L.). *Indian J. Agric. Sci.* **3**: 701–753.

Husain, M.A., Puri, A.N. and Trehan, K.N. (1936). Cell sap acidity and the incidence of whitefly *Bemisia gossypiperda* on cottons. *Curr. Sci.* **4**: 486–487.

Jackson, J.E., Burhan, H.O. and Hassan, H.M. (1973). Effects of season, sowing data, nitrogenous fetiliser and insecticide spraying on the incidence of insect pests on cotton in the Sudan Gezira. *J. Agirc. Sci.* **81**: 491–505.

Khalifa, A. and El-Khidir, E. (1964). Biological study on *Trialeurodes lubia* and *Bemisia tabaci* (Aleyrodidae). *Bull. Soc. Entomol. d'Egypte* **48**: 115–129.

Lal, S.S. (1981). An ecological study of the whitefly, *Bemisia tabaci* (Genn.) population on cassava *Manihot esculenta* Crantz. *Pestology* **5**: 11–17.

Logan, J.A., Wollkind, D.J., Hoyt, S.C. and Tanigoshi, L.K. (1976). An analytical model for description of temperature dependent rate phenomena in arthropods.. *Environ. Entomol.* **5**: 1133–1140.

Melamed-Madjar, V., Cohen, S., Chen, M., Tam, S. and Rosilio, D. (1979). Observations on populations of *Bemisia tabaci* Gennadius (Homoptera: Aleyrodidae) on cotton adjacent to sunflower and potato in Israel. *Israel J. Entomol.* **13**: 71–78.

Melamed-Madjar, V., Cohen, S., Chen, M., Tam, S. and Rosilio, D. (1982). A method for monitoring *Bemisia tabaci* and timing spray applications against the pest in cotton fields in Israel. *Phytoparasitica* **10**: 85–91.

Mohanty, A.K. and Basu, A.N. (1991). Seasonal variations in the aerial populations of the whitefly vector *Bemisia tabaci* under Delhi conditions. *Indian Phytopath.* **44**: 494–496.

Muniyappa, V. (1983). Epidemiology of yellow mosaic disease of horsegram (*Macrotyloma uniflorum*) in southern India. In: *Plant Virus Epidemiology. The Spread and Control of Insect-Borne Viruses* (R.T. Plumb and J.M. Thresh, eds.). Blackwell Scientific Publications, Oxford, U.K., pp. 331–335.

Nene, Y.L. (1972). A survey of viral diseases of pulse crops in Uttar Pradesh: final technical report. *Res. Bull., G.B. Pant Univ. Agric. Tech.* **4**, 191 pp.

Ohnesorge, B., Sharaf, N. and Allawi, T. (1981). Population studies on the tobacco whitefly *Bemisia tabaci* Genn. (Homoptera, Aleyrodidae) during the winter season. II. Some mortality factors of the immature stages. *Zeitschrift für Angewandte Entomologie* **92**: 127–136.

Podoler, H. and Rogers, D. (1975). A method for the identification of key factors from lifetable data. *J. Animal Ecol.* **44**: 85–114.

Pruthi, H.S. and Samuel, C.K. (1942). Entomological investigations on the leaf-curl disease of tobacco in northern India. V. Biology and population of the whitefly vector (*Bemisia tabaci* Genn.) in relation to the incidence of the disease. *Indian J. Agric. Sci.* **12**: 35–57.

Puri, S.N. (1991). *Bemisia tabaci* (Gennadius) problem in Marathwada: some contributions in development of integrated management strategy. Marathwada Agricultural University, Parbhani, India, 13 pp.

Schultz, L.R., Jackson, J.E. and Faulkner, R.C. (1967). Studies on the sowing date of cotton in the Sudan Gezira. II. The relationship between sowing date of cotton and the incidence of insect pests. *J. Agric. Sci., Cambridge* **69**: 317–327.

Seif, A.A. (1981). Seasonal fluctuation of adult population of the whitefly, *Bemisia tabaci*, on cassava. *Insect Sci. Appl.* **1**:363–364.

Shaheen, A.H. (1983). Some ecological aspects of the whitefly, *Bemisia tabaci* Genn., on tomato. *Bull. Soc. Entomol. d'Egypte* **62**: 83–87.

Sharaf, N.S. (1982a). Factors limiting the abundance of the tobacco whitefly (*Bemisia tabaci* Genn., Homoptera, Aleyrodidae) on tomatoes during the spring season in the Jordan valley. *Disarat* **9**: 97–103.

Southwood, T.R.E. and Reader, P.M. (1976). Population census data and key factor analysis for the Viburnum whitefly, *Aleurotrachelus jelinekii* (Frauenf.), on three bushes. *J. Animal Ecol.* **3**: 313–325.

Trehan, K.N. (1944). Further notes on the bionomics of *Bemisia gossypiperda* M. & L., the white-fly of cotton in the Punjab. *Indian J. Agric. Sci.* **14**: 53–63.

van Gent, R.V. (1982). Investigations on Parasites as a Component of Integrated Pest Control of Whitefly in Cotton. FAO/UNEP Gezira Res. Stn. Agric. Res. Corp., Wad Medani Sudan, Working Paper No. 8, 39 pp.

van Lenteren, J.C. and Noldus, L.P.J.J. (1990). Whitefly–plant relationships: Behavioural and ecological aspects. In: *Whiteflies: Their Bionomics, Pest Status and Management* (D. Gerling, ed.). Intercept, Wimborne, England, pp. 47–89.

van Lenteren, J.C. and Woets, J. (1988). Biological and integrated control in greenhouses. *Ann. Rev. Entomol.* **33**: 239–269.

Vetten, H.J. and Allen, D.J. (1983). Effect of environment and host on vector biology and incidence of two whitefly-spread diseases of legumes in Nigeria. *Ann. Appl. Biol.* **102**: 219–227.

von Arx, R., Baumgärtner, J. and Dulucchi, V. (1983a). Developmental biology of *Bemisia tabaci* (Gennadius) on cotton at constant tempratures. *Mitteilungen der Schweizerischen Entomologischen Gesellschaft* **56**: 389–399.

von Arx, R., Baumgärtner, J. and Delucchi, V. (1983b). A model to simulate the population dynamics of *Bemisia tabaci* (Gennadius) (Stern.: Aleyrodidae) on cotton in the Sudan Gizira. *Zeitschrift für Angewandte Entomologie* **96**: 341–361.

Zalom, F.G., Natwick, E.T. and Toscano, N.C. (1985). Temperature regulation of *Bemisia tabaci* (Homoptera: Aleyrodidae) populations in Imperial Valley cotton. *J. Econ. Ent.* **78**: 61–64.

8

Behavioural and Ecological Aspects of Host Selection and Spatial Distribution

A thorough understanding of the interactions between *Bemisia tabaci* and its host plants is necessary for a meaningful approach to solving white-fly-related problems. This chapter deals with some important aspects of the broad field of whitefly-plant relationships. It covers the behavioural and ecological aspects connected with host location; selection of host species and parts of plant for feeding and oviposition; and the spatial distribution within and between host plants. Host-plant-related variation in developmental duration of *B. tabaci* and related autecological information have already been discussed in Chapter 5.

Host Selection for Landing

It appears from literature that colour is the only factor in host location by *B. tabaci* from a distance. Husain and Trehan (1940) found the adults to be most strongly attracted to yellowish-green, followed in decreasing order by yellow, red, orangish-red, dark green and purple. Mound (1962) found the whitefly to be attracted to two ranges of wavelengths of transmitted light, the blue/ultraviolet and the yellow parts of the spectrum. He specu-lated that the short wavelengths (blue/UV) induced migratory behaviour, while attraction to longer wavelengths might facilitate host location. The whitefly seems to be attracted either to the short or longer wavelengths but not to both at the same time. Berlinger (1980) reported *B. tabaci* to be strongly attracted to a surface reflecting yellow in the range 500–700 nm. Cohen (1982) found the attraction to a yellow reflecting surface so strong that the adults would alight on it, regardless of the surface tempera-ture. A similar fatal attraction to a yellow incandescent bulb was noted by Berlinger (1986) when used for trapping experiments. Attraction to yellow has been reported by several other workers also, including Ahmad and Harwood (1973) and Sharaf (1982) and can be explained by the marked preference of *B. tabaci* for young leaves, which are yellower than older ones. Adults of *Trialeurodes vaporariorum* have been known to respond to photospectra comparable to those of new leaves (MacDowall, 1972).

Apart from visual aspects, Mound (1962) also studied olfaction but found no reaction to odour of the host plant or to conspecific individuals. Berlinger (1977, unpublished, cited by Berlinger, 1986) also found no reaction to olfactory stimuli. Thus no long-distance reaction to host characteristics other than colour has been found to influence landing. Since the adults of *B. tabaci* seem to be very short sighted (Cohen, 1982), they remain close to the soil surface (Cohen and Berlinger, 1986).

Host Selection After Landing

The nymphal stages of *B. tabaci* are sessile and mobility during the entire development period is limited to the exploratory crawling of the first-instar nymphs for a brief period. The crawlers have very limited dispersal capacities on the leaf after they hatch from the eggs. Thus selection of a proper site for oviposition by the female is vital for growth and survival of the offspring. *B. tabaci* females feed and oviposit on the same leaves, as do most whiteflies.

No studies explicitly address selection behaviour of *B. tabaci* on the plant or in choice situations with various plant species (van Lenteren and Noldus, 1990). According to unpublished observations of Berlinger (1983, cited by Berlinger, 1986), it is quite certain that selection of host or medium is made only after the fly has pierced the plant or membrane and probed it with its stylets and not by contact with its tarsi. If the plant is found suitable, the whitefly settles down for feeding and egg-laying; if not, it takes off (Berlinger et al., 1983b). The host selection behaviour is best known for the greenhouse whitefly, *Trialeurodes vaporariorum.* Electrical penetration graph of *T. vaporariorum* probing in cucumber leaf strongly indicates that rejection of a host plant, which occurs within a few minutes, cannot be based on probing the phloem. Whiteflies seem to distinguish between species of host primarily by probing the apoplast of the mesophyll just below the epidermis, rather than by probing the phloem (van Lenteren and Noldus, 1990).

Pollard (1955) made a morphological study of the penetration behaviour of *B. tabaci* on cotton. He found that penetration of the epidermis is predominantly intercellular, but intracellular and stomatal modes of entry also occur. The stylets usually follow an intercellular path through the parenchyma and plasmolysis of parenchyma cells adjacent to the stylets rarely occurs. The primary objective is the phloem tissue, which is not blocked and there is no wound response. He concluded that the most important reason for the occurrence of the nymphs on the lower leaf surface is nearness to the phloem since the stylets cannot reach it from the upper surface.

Besides proximity of phloem to the lower surface, other suggested explanations for the occurrence of whiteflies on the underside of leaves are: thinness of lower cuticle (Hargreaves, 1915; Pollard, 1955); protection from rain and also safe disposal of excreta from the dorsally placed anus (Hargreaves, 1915).

Whiteflies have typical homopteran mouthparts with two pairs of minute stylets, the outer mandibular pair tightly enclosing the maxillary pair except at the base. Electron microscopic studies of *T. vaporariorum*, revealed the stylets to be similar to those of other homopterans (Forbes, 1972). As in aphids, the maxillary stylets are not symmetrical and are interlocked by a series of ridges and grooves to form the larger food canal and the smaller salivary canal between their apposed inner surfaces. As in aphids, the central duct in each mandibular stylet contains two dendrites and the maxillary stylets are not innervated.

Scanning electron microscopy of the apex of the labium of six species of whiteflies, including *B. tabaci* and *T. vaporariorum*, revealed the presence of seven pairs of sensilla in each, symmetrically positioned on either side of the labial groove (Walker and Gordh, 1989). The exact function of these sensilla is yet to be worked out but logically they cannot be chemoreceptors, as otherwise probing the apoplast of the mesophyll would not be necessary for final host acceptance. Our knowledge of the sensory mechanisms of homopteran feeding, attained through studies on aphids and leafhoppers during the last two decades, strongly suggests that chemoreception via the feeding apparatus is limited to the 'epipharyngeal organ' (Weber, 1930), better termed the *precibarial chemosensilla* (Backus and McLean, 1982). It is through these chemosensilla that aphids, leafhoppers and probably whiteflies and other homopterans taste plant sap and hence they are vitally important for mediating host selection. This is the personal view of the present author, based on logical analysis of the information available on the two better studied homopteran groups mentioned above. Ultrastructural and cytochemical studies of the feeding apparatus of whiteflies are desperately needed. They would provide a basis for better understanding of virus-vector relationships and brighten the future prospects of developing host-plant resistance.

Leaf Age and Nutrition: Leaf age is a major factor influencing host selection by *B. tabaci* since the females prefer young leaves for oviposition (Khalifa and El-Khidir, 1964; Avidov and Harpaz, 1969; Gameel, 1977;

Ohnesorge et al., 1980). On soybean cultivars, *B. tabaci* laid more eggs on young leaves than on mature ones (Rossetto et al., 1977). Better acquisition of virus by whiteflies from young leaves suggests better feeding behaviour on such sources that contain the highest concentration of soluble nitrogen (Mound, 1983). Site selection for feeding and oviposition are strongly interlinked. Young leaves may serve as the best compromise, meeting nutritional requirements of the adults and providing conditions for optimal development of the immatures (van Lenteren and Noldus, 1990). Since whitefly nymphs are sessile except for a brief period after hatching, oviposition on young leaves that will outlast the period of immature development, is essential for survival of the progeny. Rote and Puri (1991) reported a highly significant positive correlation between whitefly population and nitrogen content of the cotton leaf.

Leaves of different ages may vary widely in nutritional quality. Joyce (1958) found that numbers of *B. tabaci* correlated positively with leaf nitrogen. Husain et al. (1936) suggested a correlation between the attack of *B. tabaci* and the pH levels of the cotton leaves on the basis of their observations in which various cultivars, seasons and localities with different types of soil were compared. The relative incidence of the whitefly corresponded with the trend of the pH curve, indicating partiality towards higher pH values. Studies by Berlinger et al. (1983b) showed significant increase in pH levels of cotton plants with plant age (50–150 days), from 5.6 to 6.8. The whitefly could differentiate between pH values of the level of 0.25 and showed clear preference for pH values of 6.0–7.25 offered *in vitro*. Caged adults preferred 120-day-old cotton leaves with pH 6.8 to 60-day-old leaves with pH 5.9. Mohanty and Basu (1985, unpublished) found 20% sucrose solution preferred over 10% and 5% concentrations offered *in vitro*. Of the different pH levels tested, 6.6 was found to be optimal.

Horowitz (1983) obtained ample indication of the effect of age structure of cotton leaves on fecundity, which was drastically reduced in September compared to that in June. The difference in average temperature during the two periods was too small to account for the adverse effect on fecundity. Von Arx et al. (1983) found fecundity to be dependent on leaf age. Byrne and Draeger (1989) provided strong evidence of the nutritional status of the host on crawler mortality, which was cent per cent on mature lettuce leaves, compared to 58.1% on young ones. Since eight out of 10 crawlers penetrated phloem tissue of both young and old lettuce plants, the absolute mortality on mature lettuce plants was attributed to the poor nutritional status of the phloem tissue.

Studies by Byrne and Miller (1990) have illuminated the nutritional aspect of *B. tabaci* as well as on excretion. The unprecedented emergence of *B. tabaci* as a pest in Florida, especially of poinsettia, and its expanded host range led them to trace the reasons.

The phloem sap of poinsettia contains 15 amino acids, of which 14 occur in pumpkin phloem sap. Almost all these amino acids were present in the honeydew produced by the two strains on the two hosts and approximately half were found at significantly lower levels in the honeydew produced on the two hosts. These findings indicate that these amino acids are metabolised either by the whitefly or by the symbionts housed in their mycetocytes (Hook and Griffiths, 1980). Honeydew produced on two hosts contained six additional amino acids not found in the phloem sap. These included glutamine, the most predominant, which exceeded 50% of the total amino acid content.

The carbohydrates found in phloem sap were common transport sugars, such as sucrose, and their constituents. The honeydew of whiteflies on both hosts also contained melezitose, a trisaccharide common in the honeydew of aphids. The most noteworthy discovery was the presence of trehalose, a disaccharide not previously associated with insect honeydew. While both whitefly strains processed phloem sap and produced honeydew in the same manner, the Florida strain produced significantly larger quantities. This indicated its ability to process more sap and the potential of gaining access to more amino acids, in short supply in the phloem sap of some plants, allowing this strain to broaden its host range.

The honeydew of *B. tabaci* feeding on poinsettia did not contain uric acid or hypoxanthine although xanthine occurred at a low level. This suggests that certain amino acids may be used to discharge nitrogenous compounds. Although several may be involved, glutamine is a likely candidate (Byrne and Miller, 1990).

Ilyas et al. (1991) reported a highly significant positive relationship between whitefly incidence and nitrogen content and pH of the leaf, while the leaf chlorophyll content correlated negatively.

Leaf Hairiness: Leaf hairiness is an important factor, strongly influencing host selection by *B. tabaci*. It is generally agreed that hairy varieties of cotton harbour larger populations of the whitefly than glabrous ones (Pollard and Saunders, 1956; Mound, 1965; Omran and El-Khidir, 1978; Baloch et al., 1982; Bindra, 1983; Khalifa and Gameel, 1983; Butler and Henneberry, 1984; Butler and Wilson, 1984, Ozgur and Sekeroglu, 1986; Butler et al., 1988). Mound (1965) attributed this to the microclimatic effect due to sheltered conditions amongst the leaves. He found no difference, at least in the early stages of infestation, between hairy and glabrous varieties with regard to fecundity of *B. tabaci*, the action of predators and parasitoids or interspecific competition. On the other hand, Omran and

El-Khidir (1978) correlated this phenomenon with the strong preference of *B. tabaci* for egg-laying at the base of the leaf hairs. Sippell et al. (1983) suggested the role of hairs in affecting the search efficiency of parasitoids. Hairiness of cucumber and *Gerbera* has been established to affect the search ability of *Encarsia formosa* Gahan, a parasitoid of *T. vaporariorum* (Hulspas-Jordaan and van Lenteren, 1978; Li et al., 1987).

Whiteflies usually do not occur on the youngest leaves of host plants (van Lanteren and Noldus, 1990). *Bemisia tabaci* does not oviposit on the very hairy top leaves of hairy cotton varieties (Mound, 1965); moderate hairiness seems to be preferable. *Lycopersicon hirsutum* and *L. hirsutum* f. *glabratum* accessions were found to be unsuitable for *B. tabaci* (Kisha, 1981; Berlinger et al., 1983a) as well as to *T. vaporariorum* (Gentile et al., 1968), because of the glandular leaf hairs. *Solanum pennelli*, a related species that can be crossed with tomato, is highly resistant to *B. tabaci* and *T. vaporariorum*, due solely to its sticky exudation from glandular hairs covering the leaves and stems (Gentile et al., 1968; Berlinger et al., 1983a; Berlinger, 1986).

Ilyas et al. (1991) found a highly significant positive correlation between all the morphological characters of cotton leaf, namely, hair density, hair length and mid-rib thickness, and whitefly incidence. They concluded that leaf hair density and hair length were equally important characters and influence the whitefly population combinedly. While several cotton varieties with low hair density showed low populations, the *desi* cultivars with high hair density harboured low populations because of their shorter length.

Leaf Shape and Microclimate: Besides hairiness, modification of leaf shape in cotton has been found to have a strong influence on whitefly incidence. The resistance of okra and super-okra types of foliage was related by Sippell et al. (1983) to unfavourable microclimate due to better air movement, lower air humidity and probably higher temperatures within the reduced canopy. Similarly, Butler et al. (1988) suggested that whitefly numbers on smooth and okra-type leaves could be explained by more air and light, higher temperature and lower humidity due to openness of the canopy.

Spatial Distribution

There are two main ways by which *B. tabaci* moves: a short active movement, covering distances measurable in terms of metres (Melamed-Madjar et al., 1979; Fauquet et al., 1986); and passive movement over much longer distances controlled mainly by the wind (Varma, 1963; Melamed-Madjar et al., 1982; Sharaf, 1982; Gerling and Horowitz, 1984; Thresh,

1984; Berlinger and Dahan, 1986; Fargette et al., 1986; Fauquet et al., 1986; Youngman et al., 1986).

Short-distance flights occur within the plant canopy (Avidov, 1956; Ohnesorge et al., 1980) and among the neighbouring plants at least to a distance of 5 m (Melamed-Madjar et al., 1979). By this active flight, newly emerged adults leave the older lower leaves on which they developed to reach the younger upper leaves for feeding and oviposition. A similar flight pattern has also been shown when they land on a non-preferred host and leave the same in search of a suitable one. During such short flights, mostly in the form of a loop, they usually alight on the upper surface and then creep to the lower surface of the leaf (Berlinger, 1986).

Long-distance movements occur when whitefly adults take off from their host, are caught up in an air current and drift passively for varying distances until they chance to settle on yellowish-green objects. Take-off may be induced by the physiological condition of the leaf (Rathi, 1972, cited by Nene, 1972) and its senescence (Avidov and Harpaz, 1969). In the dispersal phase, they are sensitive to short wavelengths of transmitted light and the stimulus possibly leads to flying towards the sky. Glick and Noble (1961) captured whiteflies at a height of 305 m in traps attached to an aeroplane. While studying aerial transport of B. tabaci in the Sudan Gezira, Joyce (1983) found trapping of airborne whiteflies to be consistent with a model of passive transport. Convection currents in the morning evidently carried· the whitefly to a height of at least 1600 m, while cessation of convection late in the afternoon was accompanied by increased densities at lower levels.

Bemisia tabaci is a poor flier and the longest flight distance has been found to be 7 km by trapping marked whiteflies (Cohen and Ben-Joseph, 1986; Cohen et al., 1988). Whiteflies have higher wing-beat frequencies and lower wing loading than aphids (Byrne et al., 1988) and in contrast to aphids, B. tabaci mostly fly close to the ground (Gerling and Horowitz, 1984; Byrne et al., 1986). Whiteflies have limited ability to direct their flight and direction of movement is determined by wind. They tumble along very close to the ground during movement among crops and weed hosts (Byrne et al., 1990).

Byrne and Houck (1989) reported two morphs to exist within populations of B. tabaci—a migratory and a trivial flying morph. They found a number of differences in alary characteristics between non-migratory individuals within a bean field and migratory individuals from trap plants several metres away from the field. Movement of the trivial flying morph in search of suitable feeding and oviposition sites takes place on a smaller spatial scale, within their original habitat. As long as conditions remain favourable, most whiteflies seem to stay on the plants on which they originated (Gerling and Horowitz, 1984). Even the migrators are poor fliers, the longest distance covered, as already mentioned, being 7 km only. They are routinely seen over fallow ground in extremely high numbers (Gerling and Horowitz, 1984; Byrne et al., 1986). The factor (factors) determining the ratio between the two morphs is (are) yet to be ascertained.

The available information presented in this chapter reveals wide gaps in knowledge of the sensory mechanisms of the whitefly mediating host selection, feeding and dispersal, as well as its nutritional requirements. Studies on these basic aspects are greatly needed for selection or manipulation of host plants to make them less acceptable to whiteflies.

REFERENCES

Ahmad, M. and Harwood, R.F. (1973). Studies on a whitefly-transmitted yellow mosaic of urd bean (*Phaseolus mungo*). *Plant Disease Reporter* 57: 800–802.

Avidov, Z. (1956). Bionomics of the tobacco whitefly (*Bemisia tabaci* Genn.) in Israel. *Katvim* (English edition) 7 (1): 25–41.

Avidov, Z. and Harpaz, I. (1969). *Plant Pests of Israel.* Israel University Press, Jerusalem, 549 pp.

Backus, E.A. and McLean, D.L. (1982). Sensory systems and feeding behaviour of leafhoppers. I. The aster leafhopper, *Macrosteles fascifrons* Stål. *J. Morph.* 172: 361–379.

Baloch, A.A., Soomro, B.A. and Mallah, G.H. (1982). Evaluation of some cotton varieties with known genetic markers for their resistance/tolerance against sucking and bollworm complex. *Turkiyë Bitki Koruma Dergisi* 6 (1): 3–14.

Berlinger, M.J. (1980). A yellow sticky trap for whiteflies: *Trialeurodes vaporariorum* and *Bemisia tabaci* (Aleyrodidae). *Entomol. Experim. Appl.* 27: 98–102.

Berlinger, M.J. (1986). Host plant resistance to *Bemisia tabaci. Agric. Ecosys. Environ.* 17: 69–82.

Berlinger, M.J. and Dahan, R. (1986). Flight patterns of *Bemisia tabaci*, a vector of plant viruses. Abstract, International Conference on Tropical Entomology (Nairobi, Kenya), p. 23.

Berlinger, M.J., Dahan, R. and Shevach-Urkin, E. (1983a). Breeding for resistance in tomato to the tobacco whitefly, *Bemisia tabaci. Phytoparasitica* 11: 132 (abstract).

Berlinger, M.J., Magal, Z. and Benzioni, A. (1983b). The importance of pH in food selection by the tobacco whitefly, *Bemisia tabaci. Phytoparasitica* 11: 151–160.

Bindra, O.S. (1983). Insect resistance in cotton in Sudan. In: *Durable Resistance in Crops* (F. Lamberti, J.M. Waller and N.A. van der Graff, eds.). Plenum Press, New York, pp. 227–229.

Butler, G.D. and Henneberry, T.J. (1984). *Bemisia tabaci*: Effect of cotton leaf pubescence on abundance. *Southwestern Entomologist* 9 (1): 91–94.

Butler, G.D. and Wilson, F.D. (1984). Activity of adult whiteflies (Homoptera: Aleyrodidae) within plantings of different cotton strains and cultivars as determined by sticky-trap catches. *J. Econ. Ent.* **77**: 1137–1140.

Butler, G.D., Rimon, D. and Henneberry, T.J. (1988). *Bemisia tabaci* (Homoptera: Aleyrodidae): Populations on different cotton varieties and cotton stickiness in Israel. *Crop Protection* **7**: 43–47.

Byrne, D.N., Bellows, T.S. and Parrella, M.P. (1990). Whiteflies in agricultural systems. In: *Whiteflies: Their Bionomics, Pest Status and Management* (D. Gerling, ed.). Intercept, Wimborne, England, pp. 227–261.

Byrne, D.N., von Bretzel, P.K. and Hoffman, C.J. (1986). Impact of trap design and placement when monitoring for the bandedwinged whitefly and the sweet-potato whitefly (Homoptera: Aleyrodidae). *Environ. Entomol.* **15**: 300–304.

Byrne, D.N., Buchmann, S.L. and Spangler, H.G. (1988). Relationship between wing loading, wingbeat frequency and body mass in homopterous insects. *J. Experim. Biol.* **135**: 9–23.

Byrne, D.N. and Draeger, E.A. (1989). Impact of plant maturity on oviposition and nymphal mortality of the sweet-potato whitefly, *Bemisia tabaci* (Gennadius) (Homoptera: Aleyrodidae). *Environ. Entomol.* **18**: 429–432.

Byrne, D.N. and Houck, M.A. (1989). Morphometric identification of wing polymorphism in *Bemisia tabaci* (Gennadius) (Homoptera: Aleyrodidae). *Ann. Entomol. Soc. Amer.* **83**: 487–493.

Byrne, D.N. and Miller, W.B. (1990). Carbohydrate and amino acid composition of phloem sap and honeydew produced by *Bemisia tabaci*. *J. Insect Physiol.* **36**: 433–439.

Cohen, S. (1982). Control of whitefly vectors of viruses by colour mulches. In: *Pathogens, Vectors and Plant Diseases, Approaches to Control* (K.F. Harris and K. Maramorosch, eds.). Academic Press, New York, pp. 45–56.

Cohen, S. and Ben-Joseph, R. (1986). Preliminary studies of the distribution of whiteflies (*Bemisia tabaci*), using fluorescent dust to mark the insects. *Phytoparasitica* **14**: 152–153.

Cohen, S. and Berlinger, M.J. (1986). Transmission and cultural control of whitefly-borne viruses. *Agric. Ecosys. Environ.* **17**: 89–97.

Cohen, S., Kern, J., Harpaz, I. and Ben-Joseph, R. (1988). Epidemiological studies of the tomato yellow leaf curl virus (TYLCV) in the Jordan valley, Israel. *Phytoparasitica* **16** (3): 259–270.

Fargette, D., Fauquet, C., Lecoustre, R. and Thouvenel, J.C. (1986). Primary and secondary spread of African cassava mosaic virus. *Proc. Workshop on Epidemiology of Plant Virus Diseases (Orlando, FL)*, pp. VII-19–21

Fauquet, C., Fargette, D., van Helden, M., Vanhalder, I. and Thouvenel, J.C. (1986). Field dispersal of *Bemisia tabaci* vector of African cassava mosaic virus. *Proc. Workshop on Epidemiology of Plant Virus Diseases (Orlando, FL)*, pp. VII-10–12.

Forbes, A.R. (1972). Innervation of the stylets of the pear psylla, *Psylla pyricola* (Homoptera: Psyllidae), and the greenhouse whitefly, *Trialeurodes vaporariorum* (Homoptera: Aleyrodidae). *J. Ent. Soc. B.C.* **69**: 27–30.

Gameel, O.I. (1977). *Bemisia tabaci*. In: *Diseases, Pests and Weeds in Tropical Crops* (J. Kranz, H. Schmutterer and W. Koch, eds.). Paul Parey, Berlin, pp. 320–322.

Gentile, A.G., Webb, R.E. and Stoner, A.K. (1968). Resistance in *Lycopersicon* and *Solanum* to greenhouse whiteflies. *J. Econ. Ent.* **61**: 1355–1357.

Gerling, D. and Horowitz, A.R. (1984). Yellow traps for evaluating the population levels and dispersal patterns of *Bemisia tabaci* (Gennadius) (Homoptera: Aleyrodidae). *Ann. Entomol. Soc. Amer.* **77**: 753–759.

Glick, P.A. and Noble, L.W. (1961). Airborne movement of the pink bollworm and other arthropods. *USDA Bull.* **1255**: 1–20.

Hargreaves, E. (1915). The life-history and habits of the greenhouse whitefly (*Aleyrodes vaporariorum* Westd.) *Ann. Appl. Biol.* 1: 303–334.

Hook, E.J. and Griffiths, G.W. (1980). Ultracellular symbionts of the Homoptera. *Ann. Rev. Ent.* 25: 161–187.

Horowitz, A.R. (1983). Population dynamics of the tobacco whitefly (*Bemisia tabaci* Gennadius) on cotton. Ph.D. thesis, Tel Aviv University, Israel, 213 pp.

Hulspas-Jordaan, P.M. and van Lenteren, J.C. (1978). The relationship between host-plant leaf structure and parasitization efficiency of the parasitic wasp *Encarsia formosa* Gahan (Hymenoptera: Aphelinidae). *Mededelingen van de Faculteit Landbouwwetenschappen Rijksuniversiteit Gent* 43: 431–440.

Husain, M.A., Puri, A.N. and Trehan, K.N. (1936). Cell sap acidity and the incidence of whitefly (*Bemisia gossypiperda*) on cottons. *Curr. Sci.* 4: 486-487.

Husain, M.A. and Trehan, K.N. (1940). Final report on the scheme of investigations on the whitefly on cotton in the Punjab. *Indian J. Agric. Sci.* 10: 101–109.

Ilyas, M., Puri, S.N. and Rote, N.B. (1991). Effects of some morphophysiological characters of leaf on incidence of cotton whitefly. *J. Maharashtra Agric. Univ.* 16 (3): 386–388.

Joyce, R.J.V. (1958). Effect of the cotton plant in the Sudan Gezira on certain leaf-feeding insect pests. *Nature* 182: 1463–1464.

Joyce, R.J.V. (1983). Aerial transport of pest and pest outbreaks. *EPPO Bull.* 13: 111–119.

Khalifa, A. and El-Khidir, E. (1964). Biological study on *Trialeurodes lubia* and *Bemisia tabaci*. *Bull. Soc. Entomol. d'Egypte* 48: 115–129.

Khalifa, H. and Gameel, Y. (1983). Breeding cotton cultivars resistant to the whitefly *Bemisia tabaci* (Genn.). In: *Durable Resistance in Crops* (F. Lamberti, J.M. Waller and N.A. van der Graff, eds.). Plenum Press, New York, pp. 231–236.

Kisha, J.S.A. (1981). Observations on the trapping of the whitefly *Bemisia tabaci* by glandular hairs on tomato leaves. *Ann. Appl. Biol.* 97: 123–127.

Li, Z.H., Lammes, F., van Lenteren, J.C., Huisman, P.W.T., van Vianen, A. and de Ponti, O.M.B. (1987). The parasite-host relationship between *Encarsia formosa* Gahan (Hymenoptera, Aphelinidae) and *Trialeurodes vaporariorum* (Westwood) (Homoptera, Aleyrodidae). XXV. Influence of leaf structure on the searching activity of *Encarsia formosa*. *J. Appl. Ent.* 104: 297–304.

MacDowall, F.D.H. (1972). Phototactic action spectrum for whitefly and the question of colour vision. *Canadian Entomologist* 104: 299–307.

Melamed-Madjar, V., Cohen, S., Chen, M., Tam, S. and Rosilio, D. (1979). Observations on populations of *Bemisia tabaci* Gennadius (Homoptera: Aleyrodidae) on cotton adjacent to sunflower and potato in Israel. *Israel J. Entomol.* 13: 71–78.

Melamed-Madjar, V., Cohen, S., Chen, M., Tam, S. and Rosilio, D. (1982). A method for monitoring *Bemisia tabaci* and timing spray applications against the pest in cotton fields in Israel. *Phytoparasitica* 10: 85–91.

Mound, L.A. (1962). Studies on the olfaction and colour sensitivity of *Bemisia tabaci* (Genn.) (Homoptera, Aleyrodidae). *Entomol. Experim. Appl.* 5: 99–104.

Mound, L.A. (1965). Effect of leaf hair on cotton whitefly populations in the Sudan Gezira. *Empire Cotton Growing Review* 42: 33–40.

Mound, L.A. (1983). Biology and identity of whitefly vectors of plant pathogens. In: *Plant Virus Epidemiology: The Spread and Control of Insect-Borne Viruses* (R.T. Plumb and J.M. Thresh, eds.) Blackwell Scientific Publications, Oxford, U.K., pp. 305–313.

Nene, Y.L. (1972). A survey of viral diseases of pulse crops in Uttar Pradesh: Final Technical Report. *Res. Bull., G.B. Plant Univ. Agric. Tech.* 4, 191 pp.

Ohnesorge, B., Sharaf, N. and Allawi, T. (1980). Population studies on the tobacco whitefly *Bemisia tabaci* Genn. (Homoptera: Aleyrodidae) during the winter season. I. Spatial distribution on some host plants. *Zeitchrift für Angewandte Entomologie* 90: 226–232.

Omran, H.H. and El-Khidir, E. (1978). Über die Bevorzugung von Blatthaaren zur Eiablage bei *Bemisia tabaci* (Genn.) (Hom., Aleyrodidae). *Azeiger für Schadilingskunde Pflanzenschutz Umweltschutz* **51** (11): 175.

Ozgur, A.F. and Sekeroglu, E. (1986). Population development of *Bemisia tabaci* (Homoptera, Aleyrodidae) on various cotton cultivars in Cukurova, Turkey. *Agric. Ecosys. Environ.* **17**: 83–88.

Pollard, D.G. (1955). Feeding habits of cotton whitefly, *Bemisia tabaci* Genn. (Homoptera, Aleyrodidae). *Ann. Appl. Biol.* **43**: 664–671.

Pollard, D.G. and Saunders, J.H. (1956). Relations of some cotton pests to jassid resistant sakel. *Empire Cotton Growing Review* **33**: 197–202.

Rossetto, D., Costa, A.S., Miranda M.A.C., Nagai, V. and Abramides, E. (1977). Differencas na oviposicao de *Bemisia tabaci* em variedades de soja. *Anais Soc. Entomol. do Brasil* **6** (2): 256-263.

Rote, N.B. and Puri, S.N. (1991). Population dynamics of whitefly *Bemisia tabaci* (Gennadius) on cotton and its relationship with weather parameters. *J. Cotton Res. Devel.* **5** (2): 181–189.

Sharaf, N.S. (1982). Determination of the proper height, direction, position and distance of a yellow sticky trap for monitoring adult sweet-potato whitefly populations (*Bemisia tabaci* Genn.: Homoptera: Aleyrodidae). *Dirasat* **9**: 169–182.

Sippell, S.W., Bindra, O.S. and Khalifa, H. (1983). Resistance in cotton to whitefly (*Bemisia tabaci*). In: *10th Internat. Cong. Plant Protection 1983*. Volume 2. *Proc. Conf. Brighton, England, 20–25 November, 1983, Plant Protection for Human Welfare*, p. 841.

Thresh, J.M. (1984). Plant virus dispersal. In: *The Movement and Dispersal of Agriculturally Important Biotic Agents* (D.R. MacKenzie, C.S. Barfield, G.G. Kennedy, R.D. Berger and D.J. Toranto, eds.). Claitor's Publishing Division, Baton Rouge, Louisiana, pp. 51–106.

van Lenteren, J.C. and Noldus, L.P.J.J. (1990). Whitefly-plant relationships: Behavioural and ecological aspects. In: *Whiteflies: Their Bionomics, Pest Status and Management*: (D. Gerling ed.) Intercept, Wimborne, England, pp. 47–89.

Varma, P.M. (1963). Transmission of plant viruses by whiteflies. *Bull. Natl. Inst. Sci. India* **24**: 11–33.

von Arx, R., Baumgärtner, J. and Delucchi, V. (1983). A model to simulate the population dynamics of *Bemisia tabaci* Genn. (Stern: Aleyrodidae) on cotton in the Sudan Gezira. *Zeitschrift für Angewandte Entomologie* **96**: 341–361.

Walker, G.P. and Gordh, G. (1989). The occurrence of apical labial sensilla in the Aleyrodidae and evidence for a contact chemosensory function. *Entomol. Experim. Appl.* **51**: 215–222.

Weber, H. (1930). *Biologie Der Hemipteren*. Springer, Berlin.

Youngman, R.R., Toscano, N.C., Jones, V.P., Kido, K. and Natwick, E.T. (1986). Correlations of seasonal trap counts of *Bemisia tabaci* (Homoptera: Aleyrodidae) in southeastern California. *J. Econ. Ent.* **79**: 67–70.

9

Plant Resistance to *Bemisia tabaci*

Plant resistance to *Bemisia tabaci* or any other insect may be explained as perceptible reduction in population growth due to genetic characteristics of the host plant compared to a standard variety. Resistance is a natural phenomenon and is the rule rather than the exception. Otherwise, plants would not be resistant to most of the phytophagous insects occurring in the same habitat. Susceptibility is generally the outcome of specialisation of insects, greatly aided by human involvement in improving agriculture. Wiping out natural vegetation for expansion of agriculture, introduction of new genotypes of numerous crops and their intensive cultivation, extended growing season for some crops, and the ill effects of overriding dependence on chemical control, have created new pest and disease problems or greatly aggravated the problems which were minor earlier. All these underscore host-plant resistance as a safe and relatively stable tactic since it adds to other control options without being influenced by them.

The two major categories of resistance to insects are antixenosis and antibiosis, which often occur together. Kogan and Ortman (1978) advocated use of the term antixenosis instead of 'non-preference', used by Painter (1951). Resistance due to antixenosis is associated with behavioural aspects, whereas antibiosis denotes the host to be incongenial for growth, multiplication and survival of the insect.

Although complete resistance or immunity is the ideal, it has rarely been found and employed. Even partial resistance, more often encountered, may prove to be very useful because it tends to be more durable. This important trait is highly desirable for the development of stable agroecosystems, especially in the tropics (Buddenhagen and de Ponti, 1983; Kennedy et al., 1987) where populations of whitefly often reach alarming proportions very rapidly when conditions are congenial. Introducing partial resistance requires more sophisticated testing methods, which are generally lacking.

Studies on resistance to *B. tabaci* have virtually been limited to screening available crop cultivars. Besides cotton and tomato, varietal screening has been done for various crops that include grain legumes, beans, potato and cassava. Details of such tests have not been provided, nor felt necessary. Cock (1986) has cited some references. Elaborate breeding programmes to evolve varieties by combining resistance with desirable agronomic tests have been very limited. Aside from a temporary breeding programme of this sort in the Sudan Gezira (Sippell et al., 1983), long-term breeding projects on tomato in Israel and in the Netherlands seem to be the only attempts in this direction (de Ponti et al., 1990).

Methods of Testing Resistance

The first step towards detection of resistance is large-scale screening of a wide collection of varieties and breeding lines and related plant species to ascertain possible sources of resistance. This is done by a free-choice test or a non-choice test. In the free-choice test adults are allowed access to two or more leaves or plants. No such freedom is allowed in the non-choice experiments, whereby adults are kept confined to a certain leaf or plant. The free-choice test is meant to show whether resistance is based primarily on antixenosis (non-preference). Plant cultivars found to be promising through free-choice tests, should also be subjected to a non-choice test. The range of material tested for whitefly resistance is often too narrow to obtain a clear view of intraspecific variations (de Ponti et al., 1990).

In the case of non-availability of sufficiently resistant cultivars, the wild accessions should be screened and exploited as sources of resistance. This was done in the case of tomatoes against *Trialeurodes vaporariorum* (de Ponti et al., 1975) and against *B. tabaci* (Berlinger et al., 1984).

The success of any breeding programme for resistance to insects essentially depends on realistic testing methods to screen a very large number of plants reliably with minimum effort. Studies in this direction broadly fall into three categories. The first category comprises sampling whiteflies in the field at regular intervals to estimate differences in population growth (Butler et al., 1988), or in the glasshouse to study *T. vaporariorum* by several workers. These tests undertook preliminary screening of a wide variety of genotypes and samples by sweeping, sticky trap catches (Berlinger, 1980; Berlinger and de Ponti, 1981; Butler and Wilson, 1984) or suction of adult whiteflies by vacuum catchers (Butler and Henneberry, 1984).

The second category of tests takes into account antixenosis, measuring landing and settling of adults (Berlinger et al., 1983c).

Antibiosis falls in the third category of tests, whereby factors such as female longevity, maturation period, fecundity, developmental period and mortality are measured (Berlinger and de Ponti, 1981). In *B. tabaci* the developmental period from egg to adult does not seem to be an important factor since the period is very similar on various host plants. The most important factors are survival and ovipositional rates of the adults (Berlinger, 1986). There is apparently no correlation between developmental duration of *B. tabaci* and the number of progeny (Coudriet et al., 1985, 1986).

Mechanisms of Resistance

Proper understanding of the mechanisms of resistance is vitally important to set the course of a breeding programme in the right direction. Resistance may be based on morphological characteristics of the plant or on plant chemicals which are repellent or toxic to the insect.

The effect of morphological characteristics such as degree of hairiness and shape of cotton leaves on the population build up of *B. tabaci* has been assessed in Chapter 8. Hair density and leaf thickness correlated positively with the population of *B. tabaci* and a positive correlation was obtained between the adult population and gossypol glands on stem internodes (Butter and Vir, 1989). Ilyas et al. (1991) found hair density and hair length to be equally important characters that influence whitefly population. Glabrousness of the leaves and plant architecture were also found to play a crucial role in the resistance of cotton to *B. tabaci*. It appears that a combination of glabrousness, small size or okra-leaf shape and an open plant canopy can reduce susceptibility to whitefly by about 75% (de Ponti et al., 1990).

The significant resistance of *Lycopersicon hirsutum* and *L. hirsutum glabratum* accessions to *B. tabaci* (Kisha, 1981; Berlinger et al., 1983a) was found to be at least partially due to their glandular leaf hairs which exude 2-tridecanone, a naturally occurring chemical in wild tomato with wide insect toxicity (Williams et al., 1980). Although 2-tridecanone was lethal to *B. tabaci* when offered as a vapour, and a correlation was obtained between content of this chemical in various *L. hirsutum* f. *glabratum* accessions and resistance (Belinger et al., 1983a), it is not certain that 2-tridecanone is the sole reason for resistance (Berlinger, 1986). De Ponti et al. (1990) reported that the 2-tridecanone-based resistance of accession PI 134417 used by Kennedy and Yamamoto (1979) is only effective against *T. vaporariorum* if the glandular trichomes are physically broken. Since the whiteflies are not able to break the membrane of these trichomes, the prospect of this factor in whitefly control remains dubious. On the other hand, Channarayappa et al. (1992) reported *L. hirsutum* to be the least affected by tomato leaf curl virus due to the possession of type VI C trichome glands on the leaf surface. They found that whiteflies became entrapped in the exudate of these glands. The mortality rate of whiteflies on *L. hirsutum* was very high and no eggs or pupae were observed on the leaf surface. Their findings indicated that the ability of *Lycopersicon* species to support whitefly populations is less a function of trichome density than of trichome type.

Solanum pennellii, another related species that can be crossed with tomato, is almost completely resistant to *B. tabaci*. The resistance is solely due to the sticky exudation from glandular hairs covering the leaves and stems (Berlinger et al., 1983a). Its resistance is so complete that even virus transmission is prevented (Berlinger, 1986).

B. tabaci develops readily on many solanaceous plants which sometimes contain high levels of toxic materials. It appears from the literature that there is more evidence of the toxic effect of external leaf toxins than of internal ones.

Breeding for resistance on the basis of a single chemical factor may not be rewarding since it is likely to fade out due to adaptation of the target insect (Kogan, 1986). On the other hand, response to all possible resistance factors is reflected by bioassays, thereby providing scope for multifactorial resistance, which is generally more durable (de Ponti et al., 1990). A simple chemophysical test for resistance was used by Berlinger et al. (1983c), who showed acceptance of cotton by *B. tabaci* to be affected by the pH of leaf sap.

Factors Affecting Plant Resistance

Berlinger (1986) has listed various factors which are antagonistic to plant resistance. Climatic conditions have been found to alter the degree of resistance. A laboratory test revealed an accession of *L. hirsutum* f. *glabratum* to be remarkably more susceptible when grown under lower light intensity, independent of day length. In *S. pennellii* only low light intensity and a short-day photoperiod resulted in susceptibility to some accessions, while plants were relatively resistant at higher light regimes (Berlinger et al., 1983b). A preliminary study suggested soil or water salinity to have a negative effect on the resistance of *S. pennellii* to *B. tabaci*.

The use of nitrogenous fertilisers in cotton has been found to enhance infestation of the whitefly. This is apparently due to increase in fertility of the insect due to the higher nitrogen content of the leaves. Furthermore, the denser canopy offers a favourable microclimate and better shelter (Jackson et al., 1973).

Whitefly Resistance and Virus Spread

Although plant resistance to insect vectors is likely to alter their probing and feeding behaviour, settlement and population size, examples of significant reduction in virus spread are few. The inclusion of the viral factor brings forth an additional dimension and resultant complexity. The interaction no longer remains confined to the host plant and the whitefly. Two more intricate interactions, namely, that between the host plant and the virus, and that between the virus and the vector whitefly, enter the scene as does the influence of environment on this interlinked chain of relationships. The more important factors are virus-vector relationship, the relative importance of primary and secondary spread, and the type and level of resistance to the whitefly.

When the virus is brought in from outside sources by vector individuals, inoculation of the same to the disease-free plants remains the only part of the transmission cycle to be completed. Since the inoculation threshold period is generally not long enough to be deterred substantially by vector-resistance factors unless they are strongly repelled, very high percentages of infection have been reported for several seasonal crops within a few weeks after planting (Nitzany et al., 1964; Thresh, 1984). Such instances strongly indicate virus spread to be mainly achieved by heavy influx of viruliferous vectors. If the crop is also a preferred host, as is generally the case, the incoming vectors settle down and multiply, causing secondary spread. Resistance to vectors attains better scope for manifestation at this stage by curbing population build-up and consequent secondary spread of the virus.

Most of the viruses transmitted by *B. tabaci* belong to the geminivirus group and are persistent in nature. The persistent viruses require prolonged periods of feeding; the longer the feeding the better the chances of acquisition. Moreover, there is always a detectable latent period after acquisition for the vector to become infective. The host plant has to be acceptable to the whitefly for transmission of such virus within a crop. Due to persistence of the virus in the vector for several days or weeks, the adults dispersing to other crops may infect the latter if they are susceptible to the virus. It appears from the discussion so far that the antixenosis type of resistance is likely to be more effective in escaping viral infection, more so because of the relatively fewer number of whiteflies required to spread the virus.

Whitefly resistance has been used to curb virus spread in a number of crops. The incidence of African cassava mosaic was reduced by using cassava varieties resistant to *B. tabaci* (Bellotti and Kawano, 1980). Limited secondary spread of cowpea golden mosaic and lima bean golden mosaic in cowpea and lima bean, respectively was attributed to antixenosis to *B. tabaci.* Compared to field-susceptible genotypes, the field-resistant ones to viral infection harboured fewer *B. tabaci* (Vetten and Allen, 1983). Resistance to cotton leaf curl follows the same pattern (Tarr, 1951, cited by Jones, 1987). Kisha (1984) found a few tomato cultivars to have a lower incidence of tomato leaf curl than the more susceptible ones that supported larger populations of the whitefly. The relationship between population levels of *B. tabaci* and the incidence of viral diseases has been investigated by a number of workers. The examples include correlation of population densities of *B. tabaci* with the incidence of tobacco leaf curl (Pruthi and Samuel, 1942; Hill, 1968), yellow mosaic of green gram (Murugesan et al., 1977) and tomato leaf curl in Cyprus (Ioannou and Iordanau, 1985). In recent years, similar studies were conducted in India with regard to tomato leaf curl (Saikia and Muniyappa, 1989; Borad et al., 1992a, in press), tobacco leaf curl (Valand and Muniyappa, 1992) and okra yellow vein mosaic (Borad et al., 1992b, in press).

A good correlation between population density of *B. tabaci* and the incidence of tomato yellow leaf curl virus (TYLCV) is known to exist (Cohen et al., 1988). The injury level for virus transmission is rather low— approximately 10 whiteflies per trap/week (Berlinger and Dahan, unpublished; cited by de Ponti et al., 1990). The cultivated tomato is not sufficiently resistant to TYLCV but some wild *Lycopersicon* species are, especially *L. hirsutum, L. hirsutum glabratum* and *S. pennellii.* The infection rate of *S. pennellii* accessions and of tomato × *S. pennellii* is very low compared to tomato or to rather susceptible *L. hirsutum glabratum* accessions (Berlinger and Dahan, 1987).

Breeding for Improvement of Biological Control

Breeding for improvement of biological control of whiteflies is a fascinating approach that deserves more attention than it has received so far.

While chemical cues are required to locate the plant harbouring the potential prey, the searching efficiency of the parasitoid on the plant is influenced by morphological characteristics of the latter (Boethel and Eikenbary, 1986). Parasitism was reported to be enhanced on plants with higher levels of resistance (Sippell et al., 1987). Some work in this direction has been done for the control of the greenhouse whitefly, *Trialeurodes vaporariorum,* on cucumber by the parasitoid, *Encarsia formosa.* The failure of biological control of the whitefly on cucumber was attributed to the suitability of the plant for whitefly on the one hand, and the role of normal long hairs that seemed to hamper parasitoid movement on the other. Use of a glabrous mutant demonstrated a positive effect on the walking speed of the parasitoid. However, the speed was so fast that the parasitoid walked straight over the whitefly nymphs, not even noticing them. This experience led to the development of hybrids with half the number of hairs, based on the intermediate monogenic inheritance of glabrousness (Inggamer and de Ponti, 1983). Glasshouse experiments showed average parasitism to be significantly higher on the experimental hybrids. Based on these results, private breeding companies are now developing 'half-haired' hybrids (de Ponti et al., 1990).

Concluding Remarks

Breeding work for resistance to *B. tabaci* has been very limited and there are still some unsolved problems (Berlinger, 1986). Such a breeding programme requires many generations of selection and crossing before testing under normal cropping conditions. The long drawn-out nature of the exercise seems to explain the apparent lack of enthusiasm in this area of research. Another discouraging point is that in a multicomponent pest complex such as in cotton, the mechanism of resistance to one pest may make it vulnerable to another. Thus glabrous cotton is resistant to *B. tabaci* but susceptible to *Empoasca* spp., *Heliothis* spp., thrips, cotton aphid etc. On the other hand, high gossypol cotton is resistant to *Heliothis* spp. and *Spodoptera* spp. but susceptible to *B. tabaci* (Schuster, 1979). De Ponti et al. (1990) opined that the meagre progress in breeding insect-resistant varieties in general, compared to pathogen-resistant ones, has mainly been due to lack of mutual interest and co-operation between plant breeders and entomologists. In any case, screening methods can still be improved by developing reliable and quick testing methods which are more likely to be widely adopted.

While screening plants for whitefly resistance, care must be taken to provide the optimal environmental conditions for the whitefly. Choice of the right sources of resistance should be guided by due consideration of the effects of environmental conditions, such as light duration and intensity and plant nutrition on resistance (Berlinger, 1986).

In view of the growing limitations of chemical control, breeding offers sensible and safe control of insect pests. Host-plant resistance appears to be the best long-term solution to *B. tabaci* in cotton (Dowell, 1990).

In an integrated programme plant resistance should be the core since it influences other control methods. In view of the colossal losses resulting from viruses borne by *B. tabaci*, resistance breeding may offer the sole protection in various parts of the world, especially in tropical countries.

REFERENCES

Bellotti, A. and Kawano, K. (1980). Breeding approaches in cassava. In: *Breeding Plants Resistant to Insects* (F.G. Maxwell and P.R. Jennings, eds.). John Wiley & Sons, New York, pp. 313–355.

Berlinger, M.J. (1980). A yellow sticky trap for whiteflies: *Trialeurodes vaporariorum* and *Bemisia tabaci* (Aleurodidae). *Entomol. Experim. Appl.* 27: 98–102.

Berlinger, M.J. (1986). Host plant resistance to *Bemisia tabaci*. *Agric. Ecosys. Environ.* 17: 69–82.

Berlinger, M.J. and de Ponti, O.M.B. (1981). Methods of testing resistance to whiteflies in tomato and related species: a quick screening method. *Bull. IOBC/WPRS* 1981/4/1, pp. 115–118.

Berlinger, M.J. and Dahan, R. (1987). Breeding for resistance to virus transmission by whiteflies in tomatoes. *Insect Sci. Appl.* 8: 783–784.

Berlinger, M.J., Dahan, R. and Shevach-Urkin, E. (1983a). Breeding for resistance in tomato to the tobacco whitefly, *Bemisia tabaci*. *Phytoparasitica* 11: 132 (abstract).

Berlinger, M.J., Dahan, R. and Shevach-Urkin, E. (1983b). The effect of light on the resistance of wild species of Solanaceae to *Bemisia tabaci*. *Phytoparasitica* 11: 63 (abstract).

Berlinger, M.J., Magal, Z. and Benzioni, A. (1983c). The importance of pH in food selection by the tobacco whitefly, *Bemisia tabaci*. *Phytoparasitica* 11: 151–160.

Berlinger, M.J., Dahan, R. and Shevach-Urkin, E. (1984). Resistance to the tobacco whitefly, *Bemisia tabaci*, in tomato and related species: a quick screening method. *Bull. IOBC/WPRS* 1984/7/4, pp. 39–40.

Boethel, D.J. and Eikenbary, R.D. (eds.) (1986). *Interactions of Plant Resistance and Parasitoids and Predators of Insects*, Ellis Harwood Ltd., New York, 224 pp.

Borad, V.K., Puri, S.N., Brown, J.K. and Butler, G.D. (1992a). Seasonal monitoring of *Bemisia tabaci* and relationship to incidence of leaf curl disease in tomato. *J. Appl. Zool. Res.* 3 (2) (in press).

Borad, V.K., Puri, S.N., Brown, J.K. and Butler, G.D. (1992b). Seasonal monitoring of *Bemisia tabaci* and relationship to incidence of yellow vein mosaic disease of okra. *Pest Management and Economic Zoology* (in press).

Buddenhagen, I.W. and de Ponti, O.M.B. (1983). Crop improvement to minimize future losses to diseases and pests in the tropics. *FAO Plant Prot. Bull.* 31: 1–30.

Butler, G.D. and Henneberry, T.J. (1984). *Bemisia tabaci*: Effect of cotton leaf pubescence on abundance. *Southwestern Entomologist* 9: 91–94.

Butler, G.D. and Wilson, F.D. (1984). Activity of adult whitefly (Homoptera: Aleyrodidae) within plantings of different cotton strains and cultivars as determined by sticky-trap catches. *J. Econ. Ent.* 79: 1137–1140.

Butler, G.D., Rimon, D. and Henneberry, T.J. (1988). *Bemisia tabaci* (Homoptera: Aleyrodidae): populations on different cotton varieties and cotton stickiness in Israel. *Crop Protection* 7: 43–47.

Butter, N.S. and Vir, B.K. (1989). Morphological basis of resistance in cotton to the whitefly *Bemisia tabaci*. *Phytoparasitica* 17 (4): 251–261.

Channarayappa, Shivashankar, G., Muniyappa, V. and Frist, R.H. (1992). Resistance of *Lycopersicon* species to *Bemisia tabaci*, a tomato leaf curl virus vector. *Canadian J. Bot.* 70: 2184–2192.

Cock, M.J.W. (ed.) (1986) *Bemisia tabaci—A Literature Survey*. C.A.B. International Institute of Biological Control, U.K., 121 pp.

Cohen, S., Kern, J., Harpaz, I. and Ben-Joseph, R. (1988). Epidemiological studies of the tomato yellow leaf curl virus (TYLCV) in the Jordan Valley, Israel. *Phytoparasitica* **16** (3): 259–270.

Coudriet, D., Prabhaker, N., Kishaba, A.N. and Meyerdirk, D.E. (1985). Variation in developmental rate on different hosts and overwintering of the sweet-potato whitefly, *Bemisia tabaci* (Homoptera: Aleyrodidae). *Environ. Entomol.* **14**: 516–519.

Coudriet, D.L., Meyerdirk, D.E., Prabhaker, N. and Kishaba, A.N. (1986). Bionomics of sweet-potato whitefly (Homoptera: Aleyrodidae) on weed hosts in the Imperial Valley, California. *Environ. Entomol.* **15**: 1179–1183.

de Ponti, O.M.B., Pet, G. and Hogenboom, N.G. (1975). Resistance to the glasshouse whitefly (*Trialeurodes vaporariorum* Westw.) in tomato (*Lycopersicon esculentum*) and related species. *Euphytica* **24**: 645–649.

de Ponti, O.M.B., Romanow, L.R. and Berlinger, M.J. (1990). Whitefly-plant relationships: Plant resistance. In: *Whiteflies: Their Bionomics, Pest Status and Management* (D. Gerling, ed.) Intercept, Wimborne, England, pp. 91–106.

Dowell, R.V. (1990). Integrating biological control of whiteflies into crop management systems. In: *Whiteflies: Their Bionomics, Pest Status and Management* (D. Gerling, ed.) Intercept, Wimborne, England, pp. 315–335.

Hill, B.G. (1968). Occurrence of *Bemisia tabaci* (Genn.) in the field and its relation to the leaf curl disease of tobacco. *South African J. Agric. Sci.* **11** (3): 583–594.

Ilyas, M., Puri, S.N. and Rote, N.B. (1991). Effects of some morphological characters of leaf on incidence of cotton whitefly. *J. Maharashtra Agic. Univ.* **16** (3): 386–388.

Inggamer, H. and de Ponti, O.M.B. (1983). Intermediate inheritance of glabrousness in cucumber. *Cucurbit Genetics Co-operative Report* **6**: 24.

Ioannou, N. and Iordanau, N. (1985). Epidemiology of tomato yellow leaf curl virus in relation to the population density of its whitefly vector, *Bemisia tabaci* (Gennadius). *Tech. Bull., Agric. Res. Inst., Cyprus,* No. 71, 7 pp.

Jackson, J.E., Burhan, H.O. and Hassan, H.M. (1973). Effect of season, sowing date, nitrogenous fertilizer and insecticide spraying on the incidence of insect pests on cotton in the Sudan Gezira. *J. Agric. Sci.* **81**: 491–505.

Jones, A.T. (1987) Control of virus infection in crop plants through vector resistance: a review of achievements, prospects and problems. *Ann. Appl. Biol.* **111**: 745–772.

Kennedy, G.G. and Yamamoto, R.T. (1979). A toxic factor causing resistance in a wild tomato to the tobacco hornworm and some other insects. *Entomol. Experim. Appl.* **26**: 121–126.

Kennedy, G.G., Gould, F., de Ponti, O.M.B. and Stinner, R.E. (1987). Ecological, agricultural, genetic and commercial considerations in the development of insect-resistant germplasm. *Environ. Entom.* **16**: 327–338.

Kisha, J.S.A. (1984): Whitefly, *Bemisia tabaci*, infestations on tomato varieties and a wild *Lycopersicon* species. *Ann. Appl. Biol.* **104** (Supplement, Tests of Agrochemicals and Cultivars, 5): 124–125.

Kogan, M. (1986). Plant defense strategies and host plant resistance. In: *Ecological Theory and Integrated Pest Management* (M. Kogan, ed.). John Wiley & Sons, New York, pp. 83–134.

Kogan, M. and Ortman, E.E. (1978). Antixenosis—a new term proposed to replace Painter's "Nonpreference" modality of resistance. *E.S.A. Bull.* 24.

Murugesan, S., Chelliah, S. and Murugesan, M. (1977). Prediction of whitefly vector, *Bemisia tabaci* (Genn.) and yellow mosaic disease incidence in greengram. *Madras Agric. J.* **64**: 22–28.

Nitzany, F.E., Geisenberg, H. and Koch, B. (1964). Tests for the protection of cucumbers from a whitefly-borne virus. *Phytopathology* **54**: 1059–1061.

Painter, R.H. (1951). *Insect Resistance in Crop Plants*. The University Press of Kansas, Lawrence and London, 520 pp.

Pruthi, H.S. and Samuel, C.K. (1942). Entomological investigations on the leaf-curl disease of tobacco in northern India. V. Biology and population of the whitefly vector (*Bemisia tabaci* Gen.) in relation to the incidence of the disease. *Indian J. Agric. Sci.* **12**: 35–57.

Saikia, A.K. and Muniyappa, V. (1989). Epidemiology and control of tomato leaf curl virus in southern India. *Tropical Agriculture (Trinidad)* **66**: 350–354.

Schuster, M.F. (1979). Insect resistance in cotton. In: *Biology and Breeding for Resistance to Arthropods and Pathogens in Agricultural Plants* (M.K. Harris, ed.). Texas Agricultural Experimental Station, U.S.A., pp. 101–112.

Sippell, D.W., Bindra, O.S., and Khalifa, H. (1983). Resistance in cotton to whitefly (*Bemisia tabaci*). *10th Internat'l. Cong. Plant Protection 1983*. Volume 2. *Proc. Conf. Brighton, England, 20–25 November, 1983. Plant Protection for Human Welfare*, p. 841.

Sippell, D.W., Bindra, O.S. and Khalifa, H. (1987). Resistance to whitefly (*Bemisia tabaci*) in cotton (*Gossypium hirsutum*) in the Sudan. *Crop Protection* **6**: 171-178.

Thresh, J.M. (1984). Plant virus dispersal. In: *The Movement and Dispersal of Agriculturally Important Biotic Agents* (D.R. MacKenzie, C.S. Barfield, G.G. Kennedy, R.D. Berger and D.J. Toranto, eds.). Claitor's Publishing Division, Baton Rouge, Louisiana, pp. 51–106.

Valand, G.B. and Muniyappa, V. (1992). Epidemiology of tobacco leaf curl virus in India. *Ann. Appl. Biol.* **120**: 257–267.

Vetten, H.J. and Allen, D.J. (1983). Effect of environment and host on vector biology and incidence of two whitefly spread diseases of legumes in Nigeria. *Ann. Appl. Biol.* **102**: 219–227.

Williams, W.G., Kennedy, G.G., Yamamoto, R.T., Thacker, J.D. and Bordner, J. (1980). 2-Tridecanone: a naturally occurring insecticide from the wild tomato, *Lycopersicon hirsutum* f. *glabratum*. *Science* **207**: 188–189.

10

Natural Enemies

The natural enemies of *Bemisia tabaci* include predatory arthropods (Coleoptera, Neuroptera, Heteroptera, Diptera and Acarina) and parasitoids (Hymenoptera) besides a few records of entomophagous fungi.

Early studies on parasitism and parasitoid biology were done by Husain and Trehan (1933) and Samuel (1950) in India; Avidov (1956) in Israel; Gerling (1967) in California; Azab et al. (1969) in Egypt, and Gameel (1969) in the Sudan. Predators were studied by Teich (1966) and Elbadry (1967, 1968). Greathead and Bennett (1981) reviewed the possibilities of biological control of *B. tabaci*. They pointed out the inadequacy in knowledge of ecological aspects of *B. tabaci* and its natural enemies. However, studies during the next few years in Israel, led by Professor Gerling, considerably enhanced understanding of population ecology and the role of natural enemies there. Surveys by the Commonwealth Institute of Biological Control (CIBC) in Pakistan (CIBC, Pakistan Station, 1983) and by Gerling (1985) in East Africa, added to the knowledge of natural enemies. Lopez-Avila (1986) listed the natural enemies of *B. tabaci*, and Cock (1986) discussed the possibilities of classical biological control of the whitefly. Gerling (1986) reviewed the natural enemies and *B. tabaci* in the context of biological characteristics and potential control agents. He pointed out the lack of thorough knowledge of the parasitoid fauna of Central and South America and large parts of Central and East Asia, in spite of the wide distribution of *B. tabaci*. *Bemisia tabaci* has also figured in recent accounts of the natural enemies of whiteflies as a group (Gerling, 1990) and their use in biological control and pest management (Onillon, 1990; Dowell, 1990).

Besides the general treatments mentioned above, literature in this field shows numerous studies aimed at specific aspects of biology, physiology or ecology of the studied species as per interest and needs of the investigators. The presentation of the salient aspects of the diverse body of information here, is meant to provide an overview of the state of the art.

Predators

Unlike parasitoids, predators 'require the consumption of more than one individual in order to reach the adult stage' (Doutt, 1964). Since both adults and larvae of predators are mobile and their activity is often not restricted to the daytime, it is difficult to assess their role in curbing populations of a prey species.

The taxonomic composition of predator fauna of six relatively well-studied whitefly species including *B. tabaci*, was analysed by Gerling (1990). Mites were recorded only from *B. tabaci* and as many as 12 species were reported on the same whitefly. The curious association of mites with only one of the six species suggests intensive acarological studies on *B. tabaci* (Teich, 1966; Elbadry, 1968; Swirski et al., 1970 and references therein; Meyerdirk and Coudriet, 1985). The assumption holds ground due to the association of four species of mite predators with *Parabemisia myriceae*, established by Swirski et al. (1987), three of which also attack *B. tabaci*.

Great numbers of mites of the genera *Amblyseius* and *Typhlodromus* were sometimes found feeding on *B. tabaci* in one field. They fed readily on whiteflies in laboratory tests (Teich, 1966; Elbadry, 1968) but although *A. aleyrodes* survived periods of low whitefly populations, its high field populations did not coincide with those of its host.

Mites of the genera *Amblyseius, Euseius* and *Typhlodromus* prefer young whitefly eggs and also feed on the nymphs, especially the first two instars. The available data on the dietary requirements for larvae of different mites tends to suggest that whitefly eggs are most suitable for their development. The longest lifespan and highest total and daily oviposition were obtained for *E. (A.) hibisci* (Chant) when fed on eggs. Mites fed on first and second instars showed a decrease in these parameters in descending order.

The older records of insect predators are of Chrysopidae and Coccinellidae, which are polyphagous. The association of general predators such as *Chrysoperla* sp. and the coccinellids with *B. tabaci* may be fortuitous since definite information is lacking as to whether the whitefly is a preferred or incidental prey. While abundance of predators such as the lacewing, *Chrysoperla carnea,* is commonly encountered in large colonies of aphids, heavy infestations of *B. tabaci* are often devoid of predators (Gerling, 1986).

Besides immature stages, a few species of predators such as the coccinellid, *Clitostethus arcuatus* (Rossi) (Bathon and Pietrzik, 1986) and the empidid, *Drapetis* sp., also feed on whitefly adults (Susman, 1988); cited by Gerling, 1990).

Developmental duration of whitefly predators has been studied under varying conditions. The developmental duration of predatory mites is usually from one to two weeks. The mirid *Deraeocoris pallens* Reuter took 17 days in summer when fed on *B. tabaci* (Susman, 1988, cited by Gerling, 1990), having numerous generations per year. Kapadia and Puri (1991) studied the biology and predation efficacy of three heteropteran species in Maharashtra state of India in detail under laboratory conditions. The egg stage of *Deraeocoris* sp. lasted for 9 to 13 days with an average of 11.3 days. The total duration of six nymphal instars varied from 14–17 days with an average of 15.4 days. The total lifespan from nymph to adult ranged from 14–43 days with an average of 25.5 days. The nymphal stage of the other mirid, *Campylomma nicolasi* Reuter, varied from 10–13 days with an average of 11.4 days, having five instars. The average total lifespan was observed to be 20.6 days. The egg stage of the lygaeid *Geocoris ochropterus* ranged from 11–18 days with an average of 14.28 days. The total nymphal stage of five instars lasted 26–33 days, averaging 29.1 days. The average lifespan ranged from 45–68 days with an average of 57.3 days. *Deraeocoris* sp., *C. nicolasi* and *G. ochropterus* consumed on average 275.3, 128.8 and 482.5 nymphs of *B. tabaci* during their total lifespan (from nymph to adult) of 25.5, 20.6 and 57.3 days respectively. On the basis of consumption rate per day, *Deraeocoris* sp. proved to be a superior predator. Although these three predators figured in an earlier report from the same area by Kapadia and Puri (1989), only *Chrysoperla carnea* (Stephens) and *Serangium parcesetosum* (Sicard) were considered to be important predators. Thus laboratory experiments do not necessarily reflect the performance of a predator under natural conditions. This may be due to various factors, especially the lack of specific attractants and the wide host range of predators in general.

Parasitoids

Parasitoids are 'distinguished on the basis that the immature stages develop at the expense of a single individual which is termed as a host' (Doutt, 1964). All true records of parasitoids attacking *B. tabaci* belong to two genus groups, namely, *Encarsia* and *Eretmocerus,* under family Aphelinidae in superfamily Chalcidoidea. In spite of several contributions in recent years to the taxonomy of parasitoids, specific identification is still not available for many species, especially those belonging to the genera *Encarsia* and *Eretmocerus* . While *Eretmocerus* is clearly defined, the morphological characteristics for inclusion of parasitoids in the genus *Encarsia* are still controversial (Gerling, 1990). Gerling (1990) followed

Viggiani and Mazzone (1979) in grouping *Prospaltella, Trichaporus* and *Aleurodiphilus* (DeBach and Rose, 1981) with *Encarsia.*

Encarsia: The genus *Encarsia* contains about 150 species of parasitoids, the females of which develop in Diaspididae and Aleyrodidae (Viggiani and Mazzone, 1979).

Female-producing diploid eggs are hymenopteriform and laid in the body fluids of the host. The freely swimming first-instar larva as well as the second instar have no functional spiracles. The third-instar larva has open, functional spiracles. Following the feeding period, it voids its meconia and undergoes a prepupal phase before pupation.

Females develop as primary parasitoids while the males of *Encarsia* spp. are hyperparasitoids on mature female larvae or pupae of the same species, other *Encarsia* species, and other parasitoids within whiteflies and psyllids. The males may develop internally or externally on their hymenopterous hosts. Males of some species have also been reared as primary parasitoids of lepidopterous eggs (Gerling, 1967; Viggiani, 1984). Assessment of the potential of this genus as control agents is thus quite complicated (Williams, 1977).

Eretmocerus: All known species are solitary internal parasitoids of white-fly nymphs (Clausen, 1940). Eggs are deposited underneath the whitefly nymph. After hatching, the first-instar larva penetrates the host from the ventral surface. Unlike the pear-shaped first-instar larva, the second- and third-instar larvae are globular with recessed mouthparts. No meconia are cast at the end of larval development. Male development is slightly shorter than that of females (Foltyn and Gerling, 1985).

Gerling (1986) listed 18 species of parasitoids attacking *B. tabaci,* to show the kinds of research carried out on them. The list included 4 species of *Eretmocerus,* 13 species of *Encarsia* and *Pteroptrix bemisiae* Masi. Six aspects of study were categorised, namely, host, taxonomy, faunistic, field activity, life history, and searching and host recognition. Field and/or laboratory studies on all these aspects were found to have been done only on *Er. mundus* Mercet, *En. lutea* (Masi) and *En. formosa* Gahan. While work on the first two species was done with *B. tabaci,* studies on *En. formosa* were conducted with *Trialeurodes vaporariorum* as host. Lopez-Avila (1986) also noted the lack of adequate biological information on the parasitoids of *B. tabaci* except for *En. lutea* and *Er. mundus* and provided the information available on the same.

Parasitoid Bionomics: Studies on developmental duration, fecundity, longevity etc., have been limited to a small number of parasitoid species. Data on the same species by different workers are often quite variable, as evident from a brief survey of the literature.

Gameel (1969) reported that at 27–32°C, total development lasted 21–29 days for *En. lutea* and 28–32 days for *Er. mundus* in cage tests on cotton plants. Life was longest in *En. lutea* (14–30 days) in December, when 28–50 eggs were laid per female, and *Er. mundus* (32–38 days) in November, when 42–63 eggs were laid. Hafez et al. (1983) observed that the development period of *Er. mundus* in *B. tabaci* reared on sweet-potato was 13–14 days at 27–34°C and 65–75% RH. Tawfik et al. (1983) found *Er. mundus* females to lay about 15 eggs each at 18°C and 48 at 30°C. Complete development took 18 days at 30°C, 26 days at 19°C and 35 days at 12°C. While the proportion of females in the progeny of mated females was 81%, the same in the progeny of virgin females averaged only 36%. The females lived longer than the males. Laboratory and glass-house experiments in Jordan by Sharaf and Batta (1985) revealed a short-ening of the developmental period, the adult lifespan and preoviposition period, and an increase in fecundity of both *B. tabaci* and *Er. mundus* with an increase in temperature from 14 to 25°C. However, unfertilised eggs of *Er. mundus* resulted only in male progeny. The optimum ratio for controlling *B. tabaci* was found to be one female parasitoid per every third-instar nymph of whitefly.

Abdel-Fattah et al. (1987) studied the biology of *En. lutea,* using sweet-potato leaves as food for *B. tabaci.* At 15 and 28°C the egg and larval stages together lasted 25.6 and 8.8 days, respectively for males and 26 and 8.9 days for females. The pupal stage averaged 14.8 and 5.7 days for males and 16.1 and 6.2 days for females. The longest lifespans (6.3 days for males and 8.8 days for females) were noted in individuals fed with honey and water. Kapadia and Puri (1990) studied the development and relative proportions and emergence of *En. transvena* (Timberlake) and *Er. mundus,* the two most dominant parasitoids of *B. tabaci* on cotton at Parbhani in Maharashtra state, India. The developmental period from egg to adult emergence of *En. transvena* was shorter (12.89 ± 2.71 days) than *Er. mundus* (16.56 ± 2.69 days). The shortest and longest periods were 7 and 25 days for *En. transvena* and 12 and 28 days for *Er. mundus,* respectively. The adult emergence was high (78.18–94.50%) in humid months (August–September) and suppressed (42.33–66.0%) during cold months (November–January). The adult emergence was higher in *En. transvena* than *Er. mundus.* The seasonal average ratio of females and males in *En. transvena* was 6.24 : 1 and 1.6 : 1 in *Er. mundus.*

Subsequently, Kapadia and Puri (1991) showed that the average period of development of *En. transvena* on *B. tabaci* reared on cotton was con-siderably longer (18.68 ± 3.39 days) than that on brinjal (egg-plant) (12.31 ± 1.34 days). On the contrary, the development period of *Er. mundus* on

B. tabaci reared on cotton was shorter (15.91 ± 1.80 days) than that on brinjal (20.06 ± 1.70). These findings indicate the influence of the plant factor on parasitoid development via the whitefly host.

Besides ecological factors, the number of eggs laid and daily distribution are dependent on the rate of oogenesis and the number of ovarioles (Gerling, 1990).

Longevity of the synovigenic species is greatest for *Encarsia* and *Eretmocerus*. In laboratory experiments with honey-fed individuals, females lived longer than males, except for *En. lahorensis* (Viggiani and Mazzone, 1978). Unmated females had higher longevity than mated females. Exposure to hosts reduced longevity of ovipositing females of *En. deserti* (Gerling et al., 1987), while it increased in *En. formosa* (van Lenteren et al., 1987). The maximum longevity of *En. formosa* for 99 days was recorded at 15–16°C (Vet and van Lenteren, 1981) and 84 days for *En. deserti* (Gerling et al., 1987).

Bemisia tabaci is a thermophilic insect and its development slows down considerably in areas with a distinct winter season when suitable host plants become scarce. Long-lived parasitoid females which remain active during winter are in a position to exploit the available host individuals. Gerling (1983) recorded such winter parasitisation by *En. lutea* and *Er. mundus*.

The survival period during summer varies widely among species since it is the period of intensive activity—host searching and ovipositing. Gerling (1990) pointed out that instead of total longevities, the period when the females lay most of their egg complements ('effective longevities'), is a more meaningful parameter for understanding reproductive strategies. He tabulated the limited data available and showed that synovigenic whitefly parasitoids complete their effective longevities in less than 20 days at temperatures above 20°C. Probably also, 60% or more of the total fecundity materialised during the first 20 days of parasitoid life at 17°C (Vet and van Lenteren, 1981).

Host Feeding: Oogenesis is dependent on nutrition. The most common source for proteins are the body fluids of the hosts that the parasitoids acquire through host-feeding (Gerling, 1990). Jervis and Kidd (1986) pointed out the widespread occurrence of host-feeding by parasitic Hymenoptera to meet the requirements of proteinaceous nutrition. They classified this phenomenon as destructive and non-destructive on the basis of the impact of such feeding on the host, and as to whether oviposition was done (concurrent) or not (non-concurrent) on the hosts fed upon. The genera involved in host-feeding include *Encarsia* and *Eretmocerus*, and virtually fall entirely in the destructive, non-concurrent category.

Some species, such as virgin *En. transvena* and *En. deserti*, feed on unparasitised hosts (Gerling, 1983; Gerling et al., 1987); mated *En. deserti* feed mostly on second-instar nymphs of *B. tabaci* (Gerling et al., 1987). Contrary to these examples of feeding on host instars that are unsuitable or least suitable for oviposition, *En. lahorensis* both feeds and oviposits in the fourth instar of its host (Viggiani and Mazzone, 1978), and possibly some *Eretmocerus* species (Gerling, 1990).

Host Range: The authenticity of host range of each species depends on correct identification of the parasitoid and host involved. Unfortunately, specific determination of *Encarsia* and *Eretmocerus*, the two major genera of whitefly parasitoids, is uncertain (Gerling, 1990).

Lopez-Avila (1986) listed alternative hosts of parasitoids recorded from *B. tabaci*. Gerling (1986) noted that extensive oligophagy is typical of *B. tabaci* parasitoids. He remarked that of 11 species of parasitoids found in Pakistan, only 3 species of *Encarsia* had been reared from *B. tabaci* alone, the others being oligophagous. Gerling (1990) tabulated known host ranges of *Encarsia* species attacking *B. tabaci* and *T. vaporariorum* and showed that both species are attacked by parasitoids of local origin that do not occur in endemic ranges of these whiteflies. For example, although *B. tabaci* originated in eastern India, Pakistan and/or south-western Iran, in the Western Hemisphere it is parasitised by *En. deserti*, a species native of the south-western United States. All of the examined *Encarsia* species are apparently able to move on to new hosts with relative ease. Species of *Eretmocerus* seem to lack this flexibility and show a more restricted host range.

Host Instar Preference: When given no choice, both *Er. mundus* and *En. lutea* accepted all nymphal instars of *B. tabaci* for oviposition, except the late fourth-instar nymph (pupa).

Recently, some *Encarsia* species have been found to oviposit and develop in all instars of the host in no-choice experiments but such situations occur in nature only rarely. With a few exceptions, whitefly parasitoids parasitise hosts that are between second nymphal instar and pupal stage (Gerling, 1990). While *En. lutea* and *En. deserti* Gerling & Rivnay prefer the fourth instar of *B. tabaci* (Gerling and Foltyn, 1987; Gerling et al., 1987), *Er. mundus* prefers the second to third-instar nymphs (Foltyn and Gerling, 1985).

Parasitisation of nearly mature hosts would understandably require prompt interference with the host maturation and moulting processes. In species injecting their eggs into the hosts, this may be effected through the introduction of chemicals during oviposition. The injected chemicals allow for continuous survival and/or development of the host until the parasitoid undergoes the required development. They may also slow down development of the parasitoid when it is deposited in young hosts (Gerling, 1990). On the other hand, *Eretmocerus* species that oviposit externally, often prefer to attack earlier stages of the host since there is no scope to influence the host by introducing chemicals. Penetration into the host by the hatching parasitoid larva of *Eretmocerus* occurs only after the host reaches the third or fourth instar. Secondly, the first humoral contact between the host and the parasitoid larva probably induces arrestment of host development past the fourth nymphal stage (Gerling, 1966; Foltyn and Gerling, 1985).

The mode of penetration of *Eretmocerus* into nymphs of *B. tabaci* was recently studied by Gerling et al. (1990). Examination included scanning electron microscopy and light microscopy of stained and unstained whole mounts and sections. The *Eretmocerus* larva pierced the venter of its host shortly after hatching and subsequently entered the host through the same hole. The host reacted by forming a cellular capsule around the parasitoid larva. The capsule was incomplete with an opening opposite the penetration hole. The capsule remained intact during most of the second instar of the parasitoid. It then disintegrated but its remnants were still visible around the third-instar larva. The capsule did not prevent parasitoid development but apparently precluded contact of cellular elements of the host's blood with the developing parasitoid larva. *Eretmocerus* larval biology includes early contact with the host's internal medium that permits host regulation; delay in contact with the host's blood cells may preclude the need to confront host immunological systems.

Parasitoid Behaviour: Studies to determine long-distance attraction and arrestment have been few and mostly concerned with *En. formosa* and *T. vaporariorum*. In greenhouse tests, Ledieu (1976) found a significantly higher number of parasitoids on whitefly-infested or honeydew-contaminated plants than on clean plants. However, numerous observations so far have provided no evidence pointing to long-distance communication with semiochemicals in the *En. formosa–T. vaporariorum* system. In a recent study in Israel, Rapid, Shimron and Hafetz (cited by Gerling, 1990 as pers. comm.) compared attraction and arrestment of *En. deserti* and *Eretmocerus* sp. on clean cotton leaves with those infested by *B. tabaci*. There was no indication of long-distance attraction but a significant arrestment behaviour was noted on infested leaves.

With regard to the role of visual attraction, *En. formosa* and *En. opulenta* have been reported to be attracted to yellow. In contrast, Gerling and Horowitz (1984) rarely found parasitoids on the numerous yellow sticky traps placed in cotton fields for monitoring *B. tabaci*. The differences between these findings might be due to placement of traps vertically or horizontally and the parasitoid species caught.

Besides the innate attributes of a parasitoid, searching efficiency is influenced by the leaf surface characteristics. Rough leaves or those covered by dust or honeydew may affect parasitoid movement considerably. The influence of leaf structure on searching ability of *En. formosa* was studied by Li Zhao Hua et al. (1987). They found slower movement of the parasitoid and longer time taken to locate the host on very hairy cucumber leaves compared to leaves that were half as hairy.

Behaviour associated with host examination and oviposition has been best studied for the *En. formosa* and *T. vaporariorum* system. Van Lenteren et al. (1980) found that antennation and ovipositor probing were the two main means for detecting and ascertaining suitability of a host. Host suitability by *Encarsia* was determined either only through antennation or by ovipositor probing followed by antennation (van Lenteren et al., 1980; Gerling and Foltyn, 1987). In contrast to *En. lutea, Er. mundus* could almost always determine through antennation whether the host was already parasitised or not.

Host-Parasitoid Dynamics: Studies on host-parasitoid dynamics are few and have been mostly carried out in Egypt, Israel and Jordan with *En. lutea* and *Er. mundus* (Gerling, 1986). These studies show that both hosts and parasitoids overwinter as active individuals (Hafez et al., 1978; Sharaf, 1981; Gerling, 1984). Sharaf (1981) showed that parasitism on *Lantana camara* reached 40–50% between December and March and between May and August, and dropped to 30% or less during September and December. The percentage of parasitism did not fluctuate in harmony with fluctuation in whitefly populations. Parasitism on the same host in Egypt exceeded 90% from May to October during two successive years, coinciding with 'periods of higher populations of the whitefly' (Hafez et al., 1978). In an untreated cotton field in Israel, parasitism first reached high levels under low host populations but declined later in the season when host numbers rose. A decline in parasitism was encountered when the host population was high or low throughout the season (Gerling et al., 1980).

A different pattern of fluctuation was observed in Pakistan (CIBC, 1979–1981) where parasitism by *Eretmocerus mundus* in cotton fields was initially low, then later fluctuated in an apparently density-dependent manner. Studies on *B. tabaci*-parasitoid interactions in cotton fields in southern California, also showed a rise in late season parasitism, mainly by the local *En.* nr. *haldemani* and *En. deserti* (Gerling, 1967).

Kapadia and Puri (1989) studied host-parasitoid dynamics in cotton fields at Parbhani, Maharashtra, India, where *En. transvena* and *Er. mundus* were found to be the most predominant among six parasitoids. The highest parasitism of 54.61–63.04% was recorded in mid-September, followed by gradual decline as the season progressed. Parasitism was lowest (3.57–19.12%) during December. The average parasitism in September, October, November and December during the two seasons was 35.49, 32.50, 26.16 and 3.4%, respectively. The host-parasitoid ratio showed a negative relationship with parasitism. The maximum percentage of parasitism was obtained with the ratio 1.83 : 1 to 1.56 : 1. A similar trend was also reported by Lal (1981), who reported the highest parasitism (29.05%) of B. tabaci on cassava to occur with a host-parasitoid ratio at 2.40 : 1 and the lowest (6.81%) at a 24.00 : 1 ratio.

Fungi

So far, the pathogens reported to affect aleyroids have only been fungi. Investigations on the fungi of whiteflies are still a neglected field and information on B. tabaci in this regard is limited to a few examples.

The only notable record is that Paecilomyces farinosus caused 90% mortality of B. tabaci adults in the laboratory (Nene, 1973). The fungus also infected B. tabaci on cassava in India (Nair and Nambiar, 1984). Besides this fungus, Aschersonia aleyrodis (Berger, 1921), and P. fumosoroseus (Osborne, cited as pers. comm. by Fransen, 1990) are the two fungi recorded to infect B. tabaci.

Entomopathogenic fungi infect their hosts by penetration of the cuticle after germination of the conidiospore. The germ tube is formed and may penetrate directly into the cuticle or by means of an appressorium, and enzymes such as proteases, lipases and chitinases are produced (Fransen, 1990). According to Balakrishnan and Nene (1980), P. farinosus forms appressoria on the cuticle of B. tabaci nymphs.

Since B. tabaci causes severe damage in parts of the world where crops are grown under dry conditions, an epizootic by fungal pathogens is unlikely in such areas.

Possibilities of Biological Control

At the present state of knowledge, the use of predators to control B. tabaci does not appear promising. This is because of the difficulty in establishing the direct role of predators in natural control of whiteflies. Even under greenhouse conditions none of the predator species in the families Anthocoridae, Coccinellidae, Chrysopidae, Hemerobudae and most Miridae (Kajita, 1982, 1984) is able to maintain T. vaporariorum numbers below damaging levels. Some rare examples of satisfactory whitefly control through predators do not include B. tabaci.

Gerling (1990) provided directions for future research on the predators of whiteflies to build up a basis for their utilisation in biological control. Besides determination of the full predator complex for each whitefly species, his suggestions include studies on the life history and detailed morphology of each species; prey-finding cues; feeding ranges on prey and vegetative matter to determine their basic biological requirements; determination of the function response curve and fecundity changes with availability of prey.

The major limitation for the use of fungi in whitefly control is their requirement for high humidity. That is why they are hardly of any value against *B. tabaci*, which is prevalent on crops generally grown under relatively dry conditions. Fungal control of whiteflies is worth trying under greenhouse conditions where humidity is usually high and manipulable. Since fungi are generally insensitive to most insecticides, they can be used with or shortly after chemical treatments.

Compared to the arthropod predators and fungi, studies on the hymenopterous parasitoids have been extensive and deserve serious consideration for biological control of whiteflies in general, including *B. tabaci*.

While considering possibilities for biological control of *B. tabaci*, Greathead and Bennett (1981) pointed out the limitations due to incomplete knowledge of the whitefly ecology and its natural enemies. Cock (1986) felt that in spite of some efforts in this direction during the previous five years, little was known of the role of natural enemies, except on cotton in restricted areas, and even less of the status of *B. tabaci* and its natural enemies in the Oriental region. He furnished the information available locality-wise, pointing out that most of it consisted of spot samples of frequency of parasitism in relation to different host plants. The localities covered were California (USA), eastern Africa, Sudan, Egypt, Israel, Pakistan, India and Java. He summarised the more important parasitoids of *B. tabaci* in different localities as given in Table 10.1.

Table 10.1. The more important parasitoids of *B. tabaci*

Locality	Parasitoids
California, USA	*Eretmocerus haldemani*
East Africa	*Encarsia sublutea**
	Er. mundus
Sudan and Eastern Mediterranean	*En. lutea*
	Er. mundus
Pakistan	*Encarisia* sp. 'C'
	Encarsia sp. 'E'
	Er. aligarhensis
	Er. mundus
Northern India	*Pteropteryx bemisiae*

* Also present in Pakistan but is not important.

It must be pointed out in this connection that the parasitoid fauna attacking *B. tabaci* in India is much more diverse than the three species (*En. smithi, Er. masii* and *P. bemisiae*) recorded by Samuel (1950) in northern India and cited by Cock (1986). Besides *Er. mundus*, six species of *Encarsia* have been recorded from Parbhani, in western India (Kapadia and Puri, 1990, 1991). *Encarsia transvena* and *Er. mundus* were found to be the most predominant of the six species. This underscores the importance of more and more studies on the natural enemies in various agroclimatic regions for a meaningful approach to utilisation of promising species by introducing them into areas where they do not occur.

Most of the parasitoids of *B. tabaci* are oligophagous and can be divided into two groups according to the season of occurrence. Species such as *Er. mundus* and *En. lutea* occur early in the season and may cause over 70% parasitisation on low populations of *B. tabaci* in the early summer (Gerling, 1986). The late ones include *Er. californicus* and *En. deserti*, which may be more efficient later in the season.

The introduction of natural enemies into new areas might involve a number of complex problems and would require an understanding of the chain of interactions existing between the climate, the host plant, the whitefly and latter's natural enemies. The establishment and dispersal of natural enemies depend on a series of parameters, some of which depend on natural enemies and others exclusively on human involvement. Parameters related to natural enemies include ecological, ethological, trophic and physiological relations with the host. The establishment of natural enemies depends to a great extent on correct timing of release. Human-related parameters include cropping practices and the use of pesticides for crop protection.

In some cases native parasitoids adapt themselves to newly established whiteflies. Examples include *En. deserti* attacking *B. tabaci* in the south-eastern USA.

Greathead and Bennett (1981) indicated the studies needed for developing the potential for classical biological control of *B. tabaci*, which were fully endorsed by Cock (1986). The suggested lines of work included development of life tables from different regions; comparative studies on cotton and other crops, as well as weeds to assess their roles in harbouring whiteflies and their parasitoids; search for additional effective enemies on cotton and other major hosts of whiteflies in climatically suitable areas in Asia; determination of the factors leading to host and host-plant preference of suitable natural enemies; colonisation and post-colonisation monitoring of any introduction. They advocated minimisation of pesticide application to create an environment in which natural enemies could thrive.

Gerling (1990) concluded his discussion on predator and parasitoids of whiteflies with basic directions for parasitoid research on different aspects, covering taxonomy and specificity; immature development; developmental strategies; behaviour; population dynamics and modelling, and whitefly defenses. The behavioural studies have yielded success at the basic as well as applied levels. The link between mating behaviour and taxonomic specificity may open avenues for separation of species that are hard to differentiate on the basis of morphological characters (Viggiani and Battaglia, 1983). Information on host-associated behaviour has led to successful utilisation of *En. formosa* in biological control of greenhouse whiteflies in Europe (van Lenteren and Woets, 1988).

Gerling (1990) pointed out the deficiency in knowledge of the presence and mechanism of long-distance attraction to the host, which is an integral part of parasitoid biology.

Onillon (1990) stressed the importance of acclimatisation as a valuable tool for biological control and suggested the application of genetic engineering techniques for developing strains of natural enemies that are resistant to humidity and temperature extremes and pesticides. Dowell (1990) observed that the use of insect growth regulators for control of *B. tabaci* and other pests of cotton should improve the effectiveness of existing natural enemies. He also felt that developing pesticide-resistant predators and parasitoids of *B. tabaci* should be possible in view of the successful integrated pesticide-resistant predatory mite into almond orchards (Hoy, 1982) and development of pesticide resistant chrysopids (Grafton-Cardwell and Hoy, 1986).

In spite of a fairly large number of parasitoids and predators, *B. tabaci* continues to cause heavy losses to cotton, a crop that is almost entirely dependent on chemical control in many areas. Effective biological control under such conditions is not conceivable unless integrated with a pest-management programme, by judicious blending with selective insecticides and their application by carefully selected methods.

Lastly, it is worthwhile noting that adequate experimental background for parameter estimation and appropriate analysis to detect density-dependent processes would be necessary to assess the role of natural enemies (see Chapter 7). A general assessment of the role of whitefly natural enemies may be premature at this stage (Baumgärtner and Yano, 1990). Fortunately, the growing notoriety of *B. tabaci* has led to a positive thrust in research efforts to detect and utilise the natural enemies on a global scale. Most noteworthy are the current efforts by the American institutions towards worldwide exploration and testing of the parasitoids and other natural enemies. The current state of knowledge of the various parasitoid species regarding their taxonomy, biology, success in biological control of *B. tabaci* and rearing was very recently tabulated (Anon., 1992). Hopefully, such serious efforts will help in harnessing the regulatory role of natural enemies in the coming years. Success will largely depend on satisfactory solution of the current debate on the possible existence of two or more different but morphologically very similar species, so far considered as *B. tabaci*. Very recently, Perring et al. (1993) on the basis of genomic and behavioural studies, have provided evidence that the whitefly types A and B, long classified as biotypes of *B. tabaci*, are distinct species. Their findings, still subject to scrutiny for unequivocal acceptance, have significant implications, especially from the standpoint of biological control. This is understandable since different species are likely to vary in the predators and parasitoids they attract. Once the issue is resolved, this would greatly help in locating areas suitable for survey of natural enemies, their detection and utilisation.

REFERENCES

Abdel-Fattah, M.I., Hendi, A., Kolaib, M.O. and Elsaid, A. (1987). Studies on *Prospaltella lutea* Masi, a primary parasite of the cotton whitefly, *Bemisia tabaci* (Genn.) in Egypt (Hymenoptera: Aphelinidae). *Bull. Soc. Entomol. d'Egypte* 65: 119–129.

Anonymous (1992). Natural enemies. *Bemisia Newsletter* no. 6, December, 1992, pp. 6–8.

Avidov, Z. (1956). Bionomics of the tobacco whitefly (*Bemisia tabaci* Genn.) in Israel. *Ktavim* (English edition) 7 (1): 25–41.

Azab, A.K., Megahed, M.M. and El-Mirsawi, H.D. (1969). Parasitism of *Bemisia tabaci* (Genn.) in the U.A.R. (Hemiptera-Homoptera: Aleyrodidae). *Bull. Soc. Entomol. d'Egypte* 53: 439–441.

Balakrishnan, S. and Nene, Y.L. (1980). A note on the mode of penetration of the fungus *Paecilomyces farinosus* (Dickson ex Fries) Brown and Smith into the whitefly *Bemisia tabaci* Gennadius. *Science and Culture* 46: 231–232.

Bathon, H. and Pietrzik, J. (1986). Zur Nahrungsaufnahme des Bogen-Marienkaefers *Clitostethus arcuatus* (Rossi) (Col.: Coccinellidae), einem Vertilger des Kohlmottenlaus, *Aleurodes proletella* Linne. (Hom., Aleurodidae). *J. Appl. Ent.* 102: 321–326.

Baumgärtner, J. and Yano, E. (1990). Whitefly population dynamics and modelling. In: *Whiteflies: Their Bionomics, Pest Status and Management* (D. Gerling, ed.). Intercept, Wimborne, England, pp. 123–146.

Berger, E.W. (1921). Natural enemies of scale insects and whiteflies in Florida. *Quart. Bull. Florida Station Plant Board* 5: 141–154.

CIBC Pakistan Station (1983). Studies on potential biological control agents of whiteflies in Pakistan. March 1979–February 1982. Unpublished Report. Rawalpandi, Pakistan, 88 pp.

Clausen, C.P. (1940). *Entomophagous Insects*. McGraw-Hill Book Co. Inc., New York, 688 pp.

Cock, M.J.W. (1986). Possibilities for classical biological control. In: *Bemisia tabaci—A Literature Survey* (M.J.W. Cock, ed.). C.A.B. International Institute of Biological Control, U.K., pp. 63–72.

DeBach, P. and Rose, M. (1981). A new genus and species of Aphelinidae with some synonymies, a rediagnosis of *Aspidiotiphacus* and a key to pentamerous and heteromerous Prospatellinae (Hymenoptera, Chalcidoidea, Aphelinidae). *Proc. Entomol. Soc. Washington* 83: 658–674.

Doutt, R.L. (1964). Biological characteristics of entomophagus adults. In: *Biological Control of Insect Pests and Weeds* (P. DeBach, ed.). Reinhold Publ. Corp., New York., pp. 145–167.

Dowell, R.V. (1990). Integrating biological control of whiteflies into crop management systems. In: *Whiteflies: Their Bionomics, Pest Status and Management* (D. Gerling, ed.). Intercept, Wimborne, England, pp. 315–335.

Elbadry, En. A. (1967). Three new species of Phytoseiid mites preying on the cotton whitefly, *Bemisia tabaci* in the Sudan (Acarina: Phytoseiidae). *Entomologist* 100: 106–111.

Elbadry, En. A. (1968). Biological studies on *Emblyseius aleyrodis*, a predator of the cotton whitefly (Acarina: Phytoseiidae). *Entomophaga* 13: 323–329.

Foltyn, S. and Gerling, D. (1985). The parasitoids of the aleyrodid *Bemisia tabaci* in Israel. Development, host preference and discrimination of the aphelinid *Eretmocerus mundus*. *Entomol. Experim. Appl.* 38: 255–260.

Fransen, J.J. (1990). Natural enemies of whiteflies: Fungi. In: *Whiteflies: Their Bionomics, Pest Status and Management* (D. Gerling, ed.). Intercept, Wimborne, England, pp. 187–210.

Gameel, O.I. (1969). Studies on whitefly parasites *Encarsia lutea* Masi and *Eretmoserus mundus* Mercet (Hymenoptera: Aphelinidae). *Rev. Zool. Botan. Africaines* 79: 65–77.

Gerling, D. (1966). Studies with whitefly parasites of southern California. II. *Eretmocerus californicus* Howard (Hym.: Aphelinidae). *Canadian Entomol.* 98: 1316–1329.

Gerling, D. (1967). Bionomics of the whitefly-parasite complex associated with cotton in southern California (Homoptera, Aleurodidae; Hymenoptera: Aphelinidae). *Ann. Entomol. Soc. Amer.* 60: 1306–1321.

Gerling, D. (1983). Observations of the biologies and interrelationships of parasites attacking the greenhouse whitefly *Trialeurodes vaporariorum* (Westw.) in Hawaii. *Proc. Hawaiian Entomol. Soc.* 24: 217–226.

Gerling, D. (1984). The overwintering mode of *Bemisia tabaci* and its parasites in Israel. *Phytoparasitica* 12: 109–119.

Gerling, D. (1985). Parasitoids attacking *Bemisia tabaci* (Homoptera: Aleyrodidae) in eastern Africa. *Entomophaga* 30: 163–165.

Gerling, D. (1986). Natural enemies of *Bemisia tabaci*, biological characteristics and potential as biological control agents: a review. *Agric. Ecosys. Environ.* 17: 99–110.

Gerling, D. (1990). Natural enemies of whiteflies: Predators and parasitoids. In: *Whiteflies: Their Bionomics, Pest Status and Management* (D. Gerling, ed.) Intercept, Wimborne, England, pp. 147–185.

Gerling, D. and Horowitz, A.R. (1984). Yellow traps for evaluating the population levels and dispersal patterns of *Bemisia tabaci* (Gennadius) (Homoptera: Aleyrodidae). *Ann. Ent. Soc. Amer.* 77: 753–759.

Gerling. D. and Foltyn, S. (1987). Development and host preference of *Encarsia lutea* (Masi) and interspecific host discrimination with *Eretmocerus mundus* (Mercet) (Hymenoptera, Aphelinidae) parasitoids of *Bemisia tabaci* (Gennadius), (Homoptera, Aleyrodidae). *J. Appl. Ent.* 103: 425–433.

Gerling, D., Motro, U. and Horowitz, A.R. (1980). Dynamics of *Bemisia tabaci* (Gennadius) (Homoptera: Aleurodidae) attacking cotton in the coastal plain of Israel. *Bull. Ent. Res.* **70**: 213–219.

Gerling, D., Spivak, Y. and Vinson, S.V. (1987). Life history and host discrimination of *Encarsia deserti* (Hymenoptera: Aphelinidae), a parasitoid of *Bemisia tabaci* (Homoptera: Aleyrodidae). *Ann. Entomol. Soc. Amer.* **80**: 224–229.

Gerling, D., Orion, T. and Delaria, Y. (1990). *Eretmocerus* penetration and immature development: a novel approach to overcome host immunity. *Arch. Insect Biochem. Physiol.* **13**: 247–253.

Grafton-Cardwell, E.E. and Hoy, M.A. (1986). Genetic improvement of common green lacewing, *Chrysoperla carnea* (Neuroptera: Chrysopidae): Selection for carbaryl resistance. *Environ. Entomol.* **15**: 1130–1136.

Greathead, D.J. and Bennett, F.D. (1981). Possibilities for the use of biotic agents in the control of the whitefly, *Bemisia tabaci. CIBC Biocontrol News and Information* **2**: 1–7.

Hafez, M., Tawfik, M.F.S., Awadallah, K.T. and Sarhan, A.A. (1978). Natural enemies of the cotton whitefly, *Bemisia tabaci* (Genn.), in the world and in Egypt. *Bull. Soc. Entmol. d'Egypte* **62**: 9–13.

Hafez, M. Tawfik, M.F.S., Awadallah, K.T. and Sarhan, A.A. (1983). Studies on *Eretmocerus mundus* Mercet, a parasite of the cotton whitefly, *Bemisia tabaci* (Genn.), in Egypt (Hymenoptera: Aphelinidae). *Bull. Soc. Entomol. d'Egypte* **62**: 15–22.

Hoy, M.A. (1982). Aerial dispersal and field efficacy of a genetically improved strain of the spider mite predator *Metaseiulus occidentalis. Entomol. Experim. Appl.* **32**: 205–212.

Husain, M.A. and Trehan, K.N. (1933). Observations on the life-history, bionomics and control of the whitefly of cotton (*Bemisia gossypiperda* M & L). *Indian J. Agric. Sci.* **3**: 701–753.

Jervis, M.A. and Kidd, N.A.C. (1986). Host-feeding strategies in hymenopteran parasitoids. *Biol. Rev. Cambridge Phil. Soc.* **61**: 395–434.

Kajita, H. (1982). Predation by adult *Orius sauteri* Poppius (Hemiptera: Anthocoridae) on the greenhouse whitefly *Trialeurodes vaporariorum* (Westwood) (Homoptera: Aleyrodidae). *Appl. Entomol. Zool.* **17**: 424–425.

Kajita, H. (1984). Predation of the greenhouse whitefly, *Trialeurodes vaporariorum* (Westwood) (Homoptera: Aleyrodidae), by *Campylomma* sp. (Hemiptera, Miridae). *Appl. Entomol. Zool.* **19**: 67–74.

Kapadia, M.N. and Puri, S.N. (1989). Seasonal incidence of natural enemies of *Bemisia tabaci* (Gennadius) on cotton. *Indian J. Ecol.* **16** (2): 164–168.

Kapadia, M.N. and Puri, S.N. (1990). Development, relative proportions and emergence of *Encarsia transvena* (Timberlake) and *Eretmocerus mundus* Mercet, important parasitoids of *Bemisia tabaci* (Gennadius). *Entomon* **15**: 235–239.

Kapadia, M.N. and Puri, S.N. (1991). Biology and comparative predation efficacy of three heteropteran species recorded as predators of *Bemisia tabaci* in Maharashtra. *Entomophaga* **36** (4): 555–559.

Lal, S.S. (1981). An ecological study of the whitefly, *Bemisia tabaci* (Genn.), population on cassava, *Manihot esculenta* Crantz. *Pestology* **5** (1): 11–17.

Ledieu, M. (1976). Dispersal of the parasite *Encarsia formosa* as influenced by its host *Trialeurodes vaporariorum. IOBC/WPRS Bull.* **76**: 121–124.

Li Zhao Hua, Lammes, F., van Lenteren, J.C., Huisman, P.W.T., van Vianen, A. and de Ponti, O.M.B. (1987). The parasite-host relationship between *Encarsia formosoa* Gahan (Hymenoptera, Aphelinidae) and *Trialeurodes vaporariorum* (Westwood) (Homoptera, Aleyrodidae). XXV. Influence of leaf structure on the searching activity of *Encarsia formosa. J. Appl. Ent.* **104**: 297–304.

Lopez-Avila, A. (1986). Natural enemies. In: *Bemisia tabaci—A Literature Survey* (M.J.W. Cock, ed.). C.A.B. International Institute of Biological Control, U.K., pp. 27–35.

Meyerdirk, D.E. and Coudriet, I. (1985). Predation and developmental studies of *Euseius hibisci* (Chant) (Acarina: Phytoseiidae) feeding on *Bemisia tabaci* (Gennadius) (Homoptera: Aleyrodidae). *Environ. Entomol.* **14**: 24–27.

Nair, R.G. and Nambiar, T.A. (1984). Annual Progress Report 1983, Central Tuber Crops Research Institute, Trivandrum, India, 140 pp.

Nene, Y.L. (1973). Note on a fungus parasite of *Bemisia tabaci* Genn., a vector of several plant viruses. *Indian J. Agric. Sci.* **43**: 514–516.

Onillon, J.C. (1990). The use of natural enemies for the biological control of whiteflies. In: *Whiteflies: Their Bionomics, Pest Status and Management* (D. Gerling, ed.). Intercept, Wimborne, England, pp. 287–313.

Perring, T.M., Cooper, A.D., Rodriguez, R.J., Farrar, C.A. and Bellows, T.S. (1993). Identification of whitefly species by genomic and behavioural studies. *Science* **259**: 74–77.

Samuel, C.K. (1950). Parasites and parasitism of the whitefly, *Bemisia tabaci* (Gen.), vector of tobacco leaf-curl in northern India. *Indian J. Ent.* **12**: 248–250.

Sharaf, N.S. (1981). Parasitization of the tobacco whitefly *Bemisia tabaci* Genn. (Hom., Aleyrodidae) on *Lantana camara* L. in the Jordan Valley. *Zeitschrift für Angewandte Entomologie* **91**: 263–270.

Sharaf, N.S. and Batta, Y. (1985). Effect of some factors on the relationship between the whitefly *Bemisia tabaci* Genn. (Homopt., Aleyrodidae) and parasitoid *Eretmocerus mundus* Mercet (Hymenopt., Aphelinidae). *Zeitschrift für Angewandte Entomologie* **99**: 267–276.

Swirski, E., Amitai, S. and Dorzia, N. (1970). Laboratory studies on the feeding habits, post embryonic survival and oviposition of the predaceous mites *Amblyseius chilensis* Dosse and *Amblyseius hibisci* Chant (Acarina: Phytoseiidae) on various kinds of food substances. *Entomophaga* **15**: 93–106.

Swirski, E., Blumberg, D., Wysoki, M. and Izhar, Y. (1987). Biological control of the Japanese bayberry whitefly, *Parabemisia myricae* (Kuwana) (Homoptera: Aleyrodidae), in Israel. *Israel J. Entomol.* **21**: 11–18.

Tawfik, M.F.S., Awadallah, K.T., Hafez, M. and Sarhan, A.A. (1983). Biology of the aphelinid parasite *Eretmocerus mundus* Mercet. *Bull. Soc. Entomol. d'Egypte* **62**: 33–48.

Teich, T. (1966). Mites of the family Phytoseiidae as predators of the tobacco whitefly *Bemisia tabaci*. *Israel J. Agric. Res.* **16**: 141–142.

van Lenteren, J.C. and Woets, J. (1988). Biological and integrated pest control in greenhouses. *Ann. Rev. Ent.* **33**: 239–270.

van Lenteren, J.C., Nell, H.W. and Sevenster van der Lelie, L.A. (1980). The parasite-host relationship between *Encarsia formosa* (Hymenoptera, Aphelinidae) and *Trialeurodes vaporariorum* (Homoptera: Aleyrodidae). IV. Oviposition behaviour of the parasite, with aspects of host selection, host discrimination and host-feeding. *Zeitschrift für Angewandte Entomologie* **89**: 442–454.

van Lenteren, J.C., van Vianen, A., Gast, H.F. and Kortenhoff, A. (1987). The parasite-host relationship between *Encarsia formosa* (Hym.: Aphelinidae) and *Trialeurodes vaporariorum* (Hym.: Aleyrodidae). XIV. Food effects on oogenesis, oviposition, life-span and fecundity of *Encarsia formosa* and other hymenopterous parasites. *J. Appl. Ent.* **103**: 69–84.

Vet, L.M. and van Lenteren, J.C. (1981). The parasite-host relationship between *Encarsia formosa* Gah. (Hymenoptera: Aphelinidae) and *Trialeurodes vaporariorum* (Westw.) (Homoptera: Aleyrodidade). X. A comparison of three *Encarsia* spp. and one *Eretmocerus* sp. to estimate their potentialities in controlling whitefly on tomatoes in greenhouses with a low temperature regime. *J. Appl. Ent.* **91**: 327–348.

Viggiani, G. (1984). Bionomics of the Aphelinidae. *Ann. Rev. Ent.* **29**: 257–276.

Viggiani, G. and Mazzone, P. (1978). Morfologia biologia e utilizazione de *Prospaltella lahorensis* How. (Hym.: Aphelinidae), parassita esotico introdotto in Italia per la lotta biologica al *Dialeurodes citri* Ashm. *Boll. Lab. Entomol. Agraria "Filippo Silvestri" Portici* **35**: 99–160.

Viggiani, G. and Mazzone, P. (1979). Contributialla conoscenza morfobiologica delle specie del complesso *Encarsia* Foerster-*Prospaltella* Ashmead (Hym.: Aphelinidae). 1. Un commento sull'attuale stato, con proposte sinonimiche e descrizione de *Encarsia silvestri* n. sp. parasita di *Bemisia citricola* Gom.-Men. (Hom. Aleyrodidae). *Boll. Lab. Entomol. Agraria "Filippo Silvestri" Portici* **36**: 42–50.

Viggiani, G. and Battaglia, D. (1983). Courtship and mating behaviour in a few Aphelinidae (Hym.: Chalcidiae). *Bull. Lab. Entomol. Agraria "Filippo Silvestri" Portici* **40**: 89–96.

Williams, J.R. (1977). Some features of sex-linked hyperparsitism in Aphelinidae (Hymenoptera). *Entomophaga* **22**: 345–350.

11

Chemical Control

Introduction

Insecticides used for satisfactory control of B. tabaci and, for that matter insects in general, have changed consistently over the years with the introduction of an ever-increasing number of chemicals, matching the growing notoriety of the whitefly as a pest and virus vector. From the early period of whitefly control with resin-soda (Thomas, 1932) and fish oil-resin soap sprays (Husain et al., 1939; Pruthi, 1946), chemical control has come a long way. The advent of DDT after the Second World War ushered in a revolution in the sphere of insect control. That DDT was not a panacea for solving insect pest problems was realised within a few years and paved the way for an array of synthetic chemicals to be formulated and introduced subsequently. Chemical control has since been dominated by synthetic organic compounds. A brief survey of the range of products used against the whitefly will give some idea of the trend of chemical control over the years.

While organochlorines such as DDT, BHC, endrin etc. have long fallen out of favour, the value of endosulfan has been greatly enhanced as a behaviour modifier. It will be discussed in due course in this chapter.

The organophosphorus (OP) compounds outnumber those of other broad insecticide groups and have been the most widely used. The large number of OPs include azinophos-methyl, chlorfenvinphos, chlorpyrifos, demeton-s-methyl, dichlorvos, dichrotophos, dimethoate, fenthion, fenitrothion, formothion, malathion, methidathion, monocrotophos, omethoate, parathion, penthoate, phosalone, phorate, phosphamidon, pirimiphos-methyl, profenofos, quinalphos, thiometon, tetrachlorvinphos, triazophos and vamidothion. Some of these compounds are absorbed and transported systemically to different parts of the plant. They are mostly used as sprays and relatively few as granules.

Apart from dimethoate, much attention has been given to monocrotophos on cotton, chillis and green gram (Matthews, 1986).

The carbamate insecticides are derivatives of carbamic acids and include carbaryl, carbofuran (phenyl carbamates) and aldicarb (oxime carbamate). Aldicarb appears to be the most effective and widely used carbamate against the whitefly.

The synthetic pyrethroids are powerful contact insecticides with a quick knock-down effect, a highly deserved quality to inactivate vector individuals within the period required for virus transmission. However, the broad spectrum insecticides that include cypermethrin, deltamethrin, fenvalerate, flucythrinate and permethrin are highly active against the non-target beneficial insects. The general surge of whitefly populations in the wake of widespread use of pyrethroids on cotton, has been experienced in many countries.

In recent years, mixtures of pyrethroid and OP compound have generally been found to have a strong synergistic effect, prolonging the effective period of whitefly control.

Besides the above, compounds with specific activity against the whitefly such as the OP-carbamate mecabram and amitraz, an amidine, have been used on cotton.

Mineral oils have been used against the whitefly on cotton and more often on the vegetable and legume crops to curb field spread of viral diseases (Nene, 1973; Butter and Rataul, 1973; Singh et al., 1973; Sastry et al., 1978; Rao et al., 1990). They have been found particularly effective when used in combination with synthetic organic compounds (Mote, 1978; Sharaf and Allawi, 1981; Ishaaya et al., 1986; Vadodaria and Vyas, 1987).

In recent years oils of plant origin, such as neem seed oil (Coudriet et al., 1985; Phadke et al., 1989; Flint and Parks, 1989; Rao et al., 1990; Puri et al., 1991; Butler et al., 1991); cotton seed oil (Butler et al., 1988; Broza et al., 1988, 1989; Butler et al., 1989, 1991; Puri et al., 1991); soybean oil (Butler et al., 1988); and castor oil (Puri et al., 1991; Butler et al., 1991), have been tested and the results are generally encouraging. Butler and Henneberry (1990) listed eight plant-derived oils used for pest control as well as a liquid detergent. Use of laundry detergent powder in India gave excellent kill of the immature stages of *B. tabaci* in addition to initial reduction of adults (Butler et al., 1991; Puri et al., 1991). Since these materials are safe to handle, economical and readily available in developing countries, they are likely to be widely used in the near future.

The current emphasis is on chemicals that induce behavioural change by repellency or irritation, and the use of insect growth regulators (IGRs) to disrupt growth and development of the whitefly. Buprofezin, an IGR, has already shown great promise, as will be evident from the concluding part of this chapter.

It appears from the extensive literature on chemical control of the whitefly that the choice of chemicals has largely been dictated by the availability and cost factors. Different methods, frequencies of application and spray volumes have been used, the dosages being quoted in terms of active ingredients or spray concentrations used. The insecticidal schedule that proves effecitve to curb whitefly population and incidence of any virus is often so different from that claimed to have been achieved through another, that generalisation of information is often very difficult. An attempt has been made here to extract the essentials from the findings of numerous trials with a large number of chemicals, using diverse formulations, dosages and application methods to control *B. tabaci* as a pest and vector on different crops under various agricultrual conditions. The object is to project the progress of chemical control over the years, the current trends and the future prospects.

Changes in field culture to intensify crop production and consequent changes in ecosystem, resulted in excessive use of a wide spectrum of synthetic organic insecticides to maintain high yield and quality. It exerted a strong selection pressure on whitefly populations, leading to the development of resistance and population upsurge. Resistance development is thus a major limitation of insecticidal control and this aspect will be dealt with separately a little later.

The bulk of the literature concerning chemical control of *B. tabaci* is related to the cotton crop, which is infested by a number of injurious pests other than the whitefly. In fact, the awesome stature of the whitefly as a cotton pest in various parts of the world seems to have been attained through human involvement. So much attention to control this pest on cotton is due to the great commercial importance of the crop and its impact on the national economy of countries such as the Sudan. Unlike other crops in general, chemical control on cotton has been primarily aimed at curbing the manifestation of the whitefly as a pest, rather than as a vector. Hence control studies on cotton are discussed first.

Insecticide Usage for Cotton

Discussions on insecticidal control on cotton should start with the experience gained in the Sudan, where *B. tabaci* was a secondary pest until the late 1970s. A mixture of DDT and dimethoate had been used since 1964 to control the bollworm, *Heliothis armigera*, and the jassid, *Empoasca lybica*. By 1974, DDT and dimethoate together accounted for more than 95% of the seasonal consumption of insecticides for cotton pest control. A small but quickly growing amount of other chemicals, such as monocrotophos, also appeared on the scene from 1972, joining the selection process. Resistance must have reached a level by the mid-1970s that enabled the whitefly to survive treatments with dimethoate and other organophosphorus (OP) compounds rather well. Added to this, the sublethal DDT residues provided a strong stimulus to whitefly fertility, enhancing egg production and frequency of generation cycles. *Bemisia tabaci* thus attained the stature of a primary pest of cotton in the Sudan, relegating the bollworm to a secondary role. The final outcome was the tremendous flare-up of whitefly populations in the 1980-81 season. Agricultrual practices and the socioeconomic factors also seem to have contributed to this development. After withdrawal of DDT and monocrotophos for cotton pest control in the Sudan, the whitefly pressure dropped considerably (Dittrich et al., 1986).

However, monocrotophos and dimethoate proved effective in India on cotton (Singh and Singh, 1982) and other crops as well. Another OP, triazophos, has been reported from India to be effective on cotton (Rao et al., 1990; Puri, 1991).

The advent of synthetic pyrethroids and their indiscriminate use to control cotton pests aggravated whitefly problems in several cotton growing belts in India and elsewhere. Wangboonkong (1981) reported from Thailand that even potent formulations such as cypermethrin and deltamethrin were less effective against the cotton whitefly because of alleged resistance. Johnson et al. (1982) found conventional insecticides to be completely ineffective against the cotton whitefly since these chemicals usually did not affect the nymphal and pupal stages due to their protective waxy covering. These authors emphasised that whitefly populations had been on the increase ever since the introduction of pyrethroids for cotton pest control in the USA. But the quick knock-down effect of pyrethroids has been utilised by mixing them with OP compounds, such combinations giving a much better performance than the individual chemicals (Table 11.1). In Israel, the OP-carbamate, mecabram, gave very good performance against nymphs and adults at 1.0 to 1.5 a.i./ha, being superior to pirimiphos methyl and pyrethroids, which led to a secondary poulation increase in the next generation (Koren et al., 1983). A similar phenomenon was reported from India, following treatment with phosalone (Satpute and Subramaniam, 1983). David and Jesudasan (1986) reported acceleration of *B. tabaci* on cotton treated repeatedly with cypermethrin, deltamethrin and phosalone. One reason suggested for the resurgence of the whitefly in India in recent years is the frequent use of pyrethroid insecticides for the key pests of cotton, such as bollworm and pink bollworm (Reddy et al., 1989). Rote et al. (1992) offered an interesting explanation for the increased number of whitefly and nymphs on cotton plants following application of synthetic pyrethroids. They considered the enhancement of whitefly number to be partially due to the indirect effects of the treatments on the plants rather than reduced populations of natural enemies that curb a whitefly population build-up. Cotton plants treated with synthetic pyrethroids exhibited reduced height and numbers of leaves per plant but increased leaf nitrogen content. The shorter developmental duration and higher fecundity of the whitefly were attributed to the increased leaf nitrogen.

The growing difficulties in curbing the whitefly menace by the available OPs and other insecticides led to the development and testing of new chemicals. Biological and physical assessments were made to determine the optimum spray characteristics of amitraz, an amidine, to control *B. tabaci* on cotton in the Sudan (Heijne and Peregrine, 1984). Subsequent experiments in the Sudan and Turkey showed that the dosage of amitraz had to be raised to 500 g a.i./ha to achieve 90% control against 50% control achieved through 50 g a.i./ha. Mixture with endosulfan appreciably improved adult control (Peregrine and Lemon, 1986).

Amongst the carbamates, aldicarb has proved to be highly effective. The systemic granular formulation must have access to the root system; this requires proper timing of irrigation and application at the appropriate sites of the soil for ready uptake by the plants at early and later stages of growth. In their economic analysis of cotton insect control in the Sudan Gezira, Carlson and Mohamed (1986) showed increase in yield by 13.8% due to use of aldicarb at field rates. Sixty per cent of the increased yield was claimed to be derived from control of *B. tabaci* and 40% due to suppression of other pests and plant growth improvement.

Amongst the modern pyrethroids, cyhalothrin has been most extensively tested in Central America (Morton et al., 1986) and reportedly controlled *B. tabaci* and suppressed transmission of the leaf crumple virus.

In recent years the trend has been to apply mixtures of insecticides to enhace efficacy. For example, a combination of cypermethrin and monocrotophos or methidathion (Ishaaya et al., 1987), and that of cypermethrin and DEF, a defoliant of cotton (Horowitz et al., 1988), showed pronounced synergistic effects (Table 11.1).

The value of oils in affecting the transmission of viruses led to their use on various virus-prone crops, such as legumes, tomato and okra (Tables 11.2, 11.3). For whitefly control of cotton, a mixture of 1% virol, a California type petroleum oil, and 0.005% fenpropathrin gave much higher mortality than either of the two alone. The LD 50 of the combination was about 5-fold lower than when fenpropathrin was applied alone (Ishaaya et al., 1986). Sprays of 2% mineral oil proved effective against *B. tabaci* on cotton (Rao et al., 1990). In recent years several plant-derived oils have been tested against *B. tabaci*, which include neem oil, cotton-seed oil and castor oil.

Table 11.1 Some examples of the use of insecticide mixtures against B. tabaci

Chemicals	Results	Reference
Diflubenzuron, an insect growth regulators and profenofos @ 0.4 kg a.i./ha	Gave best control of all stages of the pest	Khalil et al. (1979)
Mixture of pyrethroids, such as cypermethrin and deltamethrin, with OPs, such as dimethoate and triazophos	Increased cotton yield up to 30.1% in the Central African Republic	Cauquil (1981)
1 : 1 mixture of dimethoate (0.06%) and endosulfan	Provided good control of okra yellow vein mosaic and increased the yield considerably	Sinha and Chakrabarti (1982)
Amitraz and endosulfan	Particularly effective in aerial application on cotton	Peregrine and Lemon (1986)
Deltamethrin at 18.5 g a.i./ha and monocrotophos at 0.03% a.i./ha	Very effective on cotton in Pakistan	Ahmed and Baig (1987)
Chlorfenvinphos in mixture with cypermethrin (400/40) and with endosulfan (400/970, 500/900)	Reduced whitefly populations on cotton in the Sudan when applied from the air without affecting parasitism by *Eretmocerus* spp.	Shires et al. (1987)
Cypermethrin with equal wt. of moncrotophos or acephate or 8 parts of methidathion and 1 part of pyrethroid	Cypermethrin toxicity under conditions prevailing in cotton fields in Israel was strongly synergised and effective period for whitefly control prolonged	Ishaaya et al. (1987)
Combination of DEF (S,S,S-tributyl phosphorotrithioate) a defoliant for cotton, and cypermethrin and permethrin	Combinations showed strong synergism. DEF almost completely restored sensitivity of reaction towards both pyrethroids	Horowitz et al. (1988)
Deltaphos (0.05% triazophos + 0.002% deltamethrin)	Gave effective control of the whitefly on cotton in India	Rao et al. (1990)

Neem oil is recommended for the control of *B. tabaci* in India and several manufactured formulations are available in the country. Coudriet et al. (1985) and Phadke et al. (1989) reported successful use of neem oil. Butler and Rao (1990) reported that 0.5% sprays of three commerical neem oil formulations, namely Neemguard, Neemark and Neempon to single brinjal leaves, resulted in 97% fewer eggs and 87% fewer immatures compared to those on untreated leaves (Butler and Rao, 1990).

The failure of the products during preliminary trials in India in 1989 seemed to be due to the formulations tested, none of which gave a stable emulsion when mixed with water. Furthermore, the 0.3–0.5% concentration of the spray solution, recommended by the manufacturers, appeared

Table 11.2. Chemical measures to curb tomato leaf curl disease

Treatments found effective	Reference
Mineral oils at 2%, 4 times at 12-day intervals. Leaf curl incidence two months after transplanting averaged 38.1–56.8% as compared to 74.4% in untreated plots.	Butter and Rataul (1973)
Four spray applications of mineral oil at 10-day intervals reduced virus spread by 90%.	Singh et al. (1973)
Of 13 insecticides tested, the best results obtained from 4 fortnightly sprays of dimethoate, methyl-parthion or oxydemetonmethyl, or from a single application phorate 10 G @ 15 kg a.i./ha at the time of planting.	Sastry and Singh (1974)
Four sprays of 0.02% dimethoate found more effective than 4 other OPs in reducing vector populations and disease incidence.	Rataul and Butter (1976)
Foliar sprays of 0.2% agricultural spray oil either alone or in combination with OPs significantly reduced disease incidence. The highest yield was obtained after treatment with mixture of 0.05% monocrotophos and 0.2% spray oil.	Mote (1978)
Mephospholan and aldicarb granules applied as side dressing 24 h before transplanting showed minimum disease incidence. Of 12 spray formulations, tetrachlorvinphos was found to be the most effective.	Saklani and Mathai (1978)
Soil application of granular insecticides and foliar sprays of a synthetic pyrethroid reduced the number of nymphs and adults but failed to reduce incidence of tomato leaf curl.	Kisha (1981)
Deltamethrin (0.02 kg a.i./ha), permethrin (0.10 kg a.i./ha) and fenvalerate (0.05 kg a.i./ha) gave effective control of *B. tabaci* and reduced disease incidence. Deltamethrin gave the highest yield and the maximum net profit.	Mishra (1986)

Table 11.3. Chemical measures to curb yellow mosaic disease of grain legumes

Crop	Treatment found effective	Reference
Soybean	Soil application of aldicarb @ 1 kg a.i./ha 2 weeks after germination, followed by another at the same rate 3 weeks later.	Singh et al. (1971)
Soybean	Carbofuran and aldicarb @ 2 kg a.i./ha most effective, the former giving maximum yield.	Rataul and Singh (1976)
Green gram/mung (*Vigna radiata*) and black gram/urd (*V. mungo*)	Two applications (a fortnight apart) of dichlorvos, monocrotophos and phosphamidon at 500, 375 and 250 ml toxicant/ha.	Agrawal et al. (1979)
Green gram	Aldicarb at 2 kg a.i./ha at time of sowing and again 4 weeks later proved to be most effective of 5 granular insecticides tested, decreasing whitefly population and reducing number of infected plants by 28.2–65.9% as compared with untreated plots. Yield increase ranged from 48.6 to 137.3% during field trials over 2 years.	Kooner and Singh (1980)

Contd...

Table 11.3 contd.

Crop	Treatment found effective	Reference
Green gram	Both aldicarb and disulfoton delayed and reduced disease incidence but yield due to aldicarb was much higher, being 1212 kg/ha compared to 887 and 550 kg/ha in disulfoton-treated and untreated plots, respectively.	Singh et al. (1980)
Soybean	Aldicarb @ 1.0 kg a.i./ha applied once in furrow at sowing and once more as a side dressing 3 weeks after germination was most effective.	Chaudhary et al. (1981)
Green gram	Three foliar applications of monoctotophos at 0.25 kg a.i./ha at 10-days intervals, beginning on the 15th day after sowing, reduced disease incidence and increased yield.	Murugesen and Chelliah (1981)
Green gram	Aldicarb @ 1.5 kg a.i./ha in the furrow before sowing or in combination with endosulfan sprays reduced virus-infected plants in trials over 2 years by 31–39 and 25–46%.	Yein and Singh (1982)
Green gram	Aldicarb, phorate or disulfoton granules @ 2 kg a.i./ha or a combination of disulfoton granules and paraffin oil most effective in controlling virus spread.	Sharma and Varma (1982)
Moth bean (*Vigna aconitifolia*)	Monocrotophos at 0.25 kg a.i./ha applied 3 times at 15-day intervals, starting on the 15th day after sowing recommended against the disease.	Satyavir (1983)
Moth bean	Dimethoate at 0.02% the most effective, reducing disease incidence and increasing yield.	Rathore and Agnihotri (1985)
Soybean	Aldicarb @ 2 kg a.i./ha in split treatments resulted in lowest incidence of the vector and disease incidence along with appreciable yield increase.	Kooner et al. (1986)
Soybean	Phorate 10 G superior to carbofuran 3 G in controlling disease incidence.	Thapliyal et al. (1987)
Green gram	Application of 0.03 and 0.05% dimethoate gave maximum reduction in disease incidence. Soil application of aldicarb @ 1.5 kg a.i./ha effective for about 1 month.	Sardana and Verma (1987)
Green gram	Phorate 2 G along with monocrophos (0.04%) and orchard oil was the most effective of the 10 insecticide treatments tested.	Vadodaria and Vyas (1987)
Green gram	Basal application of aldicarb @ 1.0 kg a.i./ha, combined with 0.07% endosulfan proved effective in reducing disease incidence.	Sundararaju and Rangarajan (1987)

to be too low. Later, use of neem-seed oil at 5% gave control equal to that achieved through 5% cotton-seed oil and 5% castor oil (Butler et al., 1991). Puri et al. (1991) also reported satisfactory control of *B. tabaci* by plant-derived oils and Nirma® soap solution, where hand-held spray equipment was routinely used to apply insecticides. In view of the phytotoxic effect, though nominal, on some cotton cultivars due to application of 5% cotton-seed oil and Nirma® soap solutions at 15 and 30 ml/l, the authors suggested caution while treating the crop under hot conditions.

Impact of Insecticidal Applications on Natural Enemies: Few studies provide information on the impact of insecticides on the natural enemies of *B. tabaci*. Several reports suggest whitefly outbreak to have occurred due to reduced parasitoid populations (Johnson et al., 1982; Eveleens, 1983; Hafez et al., 1983; Abdel-Rahman, 1986; Bellows and Arakawa, 1988). However, there is little experimental evidence to support this hypothesis (Kapadia et al., 1992). Watson et al. (1982) and Shires et al. (1983) noted that high levels of parasitism by *Eretmocerus* spp. and *Encarsia* spp. were not affected following applications of chlorfenvinphos. More recently, this important aspect was studied by Shires et al. (1987) in the Sudan. They found effective reduction of whitefly numbers through parasitism by *Eretmocerus* to be maintaned following aerial application of chlorfenvinphos at 500 g/ha and in mixture with cypermethrin (400/40) and endosulfan (400/970; 500/900). Amitraz is another insecticide having little or no harmful effect on predaceous Coleoptera, Neuroptera and Heteroptera (Peregrine and Lemon, 1986).

Besides the chemical nature of insecticides, other factors may determine the differential effect of the same chemical on the whitefly and its natural enemies. For example, data showed little difference between treated and untreated cotton fields in Israel. Gerling (1986) advanced two possible explanations for this. First, at the time of aerial application the crop canopy was already closed and insecticide could reach only the top 50 cm of plants. Thus, the host as well as the parasitoids on the undersurface of leaves below this level were not affected. Secondly, the tendency of whitefly adults to move upward to the top of the canopy, exposed them to the lethal effects of insecticidal treatment from above. The parasitoid adults, on other hand, which spend most of their time searching for immature whiteflies, were less affected.

Recently, a highly interesting observation has been reported from India that contradicts the general belief that the use of synthetic pyrethroids leads to whitefly outbreaks. According to this report, the maximum activity of natural enemies was noted in plots treated with cypermethrin (Puri, 1991). The report was followed by detailed information from Kapadia et al.

(1992), who found the incidence of whitefly parasitisation on cotton during two seasons not to be affected by application of cypermethrin 0.0075%, 0.016% fenvalerate alone or fenvalerate alternated with 0.04% monocrotophos at 15-day intervals.

Insecticidal Protection of Other Crops

Unlike cotton, insecticidal control of *B. tabaci* and other field crops has generally been aimed at curbing the spread of viral diseases rather than direct injury by the whitefly. Besides tomato, which has received adequate attention in various parts of the world, literature on whitefly control on the grain legumes is also quite extensive. The yellow mosaic disease is a major constraint to the cultivation of mung bean or green gram (*Vigna radiata*), black gram (*V. mungo*), soybean and other grain legumes in India and neighbouring countries. Among other crops, okra, chilli, cassava and tobacco have received some attention with regard to insecticidal protection.

Tomato in various countries in the Middle East and Africa is affected by tomato yellow leaf curl virus (TYLCV) that causes considerable losses. Cohen et al. (1974) combined the application of straw mulch after germination with azinophos-methyl treatments at 4-day intervals, starting 10 days after germination. The purpose of the yellow-coloured straw mulch is to attract the adult whiteflies to their doom during vulnerable stages of the crop, which contributes to the partial prevention of virus spread. Field tests of nine different OPs on tomato in Jordan showed azinophos-methyl, methidathion, methamidophos, parathion methyl and pirimiphos-methyl to be effective against *B. tabaci* but none of the chemicals could prevent spread of TYLCV (Sharaf and Allawi, 1980). Later, Sharaf and Allawi (1981) carried out greenhouse experiments to determine the effect of 13 insecticides and 2 mineral oils with regard to their speed of action in preventing transmission of TYLCV by the adult whiteflies. Although none of the insecticides were quick enough to immobilise insects before virus transmission, pirimiphos-methyl gave the quickest kill, preventing TYLCV-carrying whiteflies from infecting sprayed plants to a large extent. Tomato yields were highly increased, by 188–239%.

The leaf curl disease of tomato, caused by tomato leaf curl virus (TLCV), is widely prevalent in the Indian subcontinent and there have been a number of studies on chemical control (Table 11.2).

The importance of the yellow mosaic malady of the grain legumes in India is evident from the selected information given in Table 11.3. The yellow mosaic disease complex is known by different names, such as mung bean yellow mosaic, urd bean yellow mosaic, horse gram yellow mosaic etc., according to the crop affected. All these diseases are caused by the geminivirus group and serious studies are required to determine whether the diseases are caused by mung bean yellow mosaic virus (MYMV) and its strains or whether another virus or viruses are involved. Accordingly, they are referred to here as the MYMV complex.

The wide prevalence of yellow vein mosaic disease of bhendi (okra) caused by BYVMV is not reflected by the rather limited number of studies conducted for its control. Sastry and Singh (1973a, b) tried 10 different insecticides, including systemic ones, and found that four sprays each of 0.02% parathion, 0.02% oxydemetonmethyl or 0.05% dimethoate at 10-day intervals following seed germination, or one application of phorate 10 G at the rate of 15 kg/ha at the time of sowing, not only reduced vector population but also virus spread to a great extent. They found the yield to be doubled after spraying. In 3-year trials with virus-tolerant cv. Pusa Sawani, fortnightly treatments with a 1 : 1 mixture of 0.06% dimethoate and 0.07% endosulfan, combined with regular removal of infected plants up to 55 days from sowing, gave good control of the disease and increased the yield of okra seed nearly twofold (Sinha and Chakrabarti, 1982).

Khan and Mukhopadhyay (1985) showed that soil application of phorate 10 G at the rate of 15 kg/ha, followed by 4 foliar sprays of metasystox (demeton-S-methyl) 25 EC at 0.03% at 15-day intervals, reduced the incidence of BYVMV to 23.26% against 82.22% in control and enhanced yield to 59.45 q/ha against 23.8 q/ha in untreated plots.

The leaf curl of chilli is another common viral malady in the Indian subcontinent, requiring chemical control measures. Joshi and Dubey (1976) reported parathion at 0.06% and endrin at 0.1% to be quite effective. Control of *B. tabaci* on chilli either by soil application of carbofuran or disulfoton, or by 4 sprays of mineral oils at 10-day intervals curbed incidence of the leaf curl disease (Singh et al., 1979). Datar (1980) conducted tests for insecticidal control of chilli leaf curl and recommended 4 sprays of monocrotophos at 10-day intervals, beginning 2 weeks after transplantation.

Effective control of the whitefly on tobacco in India was achieved through spray applications of systemic insecticides, demeton-S-methyl (0.20 kg a.i./ha), dimethoate (0.18 kg a.i./ha), or thiometon (0.20 kg a.i./ha) once in nursery beds 35 days after germination and 3 times at 15-days intervals, starting on the 10th day after transplantation (Chavan, 1983). In Iraq, tobacco leaf curl disease could be controlled by roguing infected plants, covering healthy plants with cheese-cloth or the application of carbofuran to kill the vectors (Al-Ani et al., 1987).

On cassava, Mahto and Sinha (1978) evaluated insecticides against *B. tabaci* in relation to the mosaic disease and found 8 foliar sprays of

0.02% parathion, applied at 10-day intervals, starting one month after planting, to be the best treatment. However, field trials, also in India, for three seasons with carbofuran and disulfoton at 1 kg a.i./ha and sprays of dimethoate and demton-S-methyl and the foliar protectants carbaryl and fenitrothion at 0.1% showed no significant differences in B. tabaci populations and spread of the disease (Nair, 1981). In Kenya, Seif (1982) attempted to prevent spread of cassava mosaic by weekly sprays of dimethoate.

Factors Determining Efficacy of Insecticides

Various factors determine the effect of different chemicals on B. tabaci and are briefly discussed below.

(i) **Chemical Structure or Group:** Each chemical is more or less toxic to the whitefly, but the nature and extent depend on the instrinsic physicochemical and biological properties of the chemical structure or group of the compound.

According to the assessment by Sharaf (1986), carbamates seem to be the most effective, followed by organophosphates of the thiophosphoric acid prototypes (e.g., bromophos, demeton, methylparathion, mevinphos) and the synthetic pyrethroids (e.g., cypermethrin, fenpropathrin, fenvalerate). According to him, organophosphates of the dithiophosphate (e.g., azinophos-methyl, dimethoate, phorate) or the phosphoric acid prototypes (e.g., carbicorn, chlorfenvinphos, tetrachlorvinphos) are moderately effective, while cyclo compounds (e.g, BHC, endrin) and diphenyl compounds (e.g., amitraz, DDT) are the least effective. He specially mentioned that the substitution of oxygen with sulphur on the phosphorus atom (thiophosphoric acid prototypes) enhanced the effectiveness of the organophosphorus (OP) compound against whiteflies and the spread of viral disease transmitted by them, being better than the additon of two sulphur atoms in the original OP-structure (dithiophosphate prototypes).

Such gross generalisation on the basis of the number of the more or less successful results gives some idea about the overall performance of different groups of chemicals. It should not necessarily dictate the choice of a chemical as that depends on the mode of its action, coverage of the sites to reach the target and its persistence. A product that gives control of the whitefly or a viral disease on the crop may fail on another crop-virus combination. Prevention of virus spread would require a fast-acting insecticide to knock down the whitefly or to repel it. For this reason, an insecticide that gives high kill of the whitefly may not necessarily be effective in preventing virus spread.

(ii) **Formulation Properties:** Formulation of a pesticide is the dilution of the high concentration of the chemical as dust, wettable powder, emulsifiable concentrate, granules etc. The choice of the proper formulation of a chemical is based on several factors. The chemical must have access to the whitefly in a form that will be lethal to the pest without affecting the non-target organisms and creating pollution problems.

Insecticides have most often been applied as sprays but spraying has several disadvantages. Besides the cost of spraying equipment and the labour involved, there is risk of spray drift and undesirable toxic effect on beneficial natural enemies, such as bees, fishes and birds. These disadvantages can be overcome by application of systemic insecticides in granular form, provided the crop thus treated remains toxic enough to take care of the whitefly throughout the vulnerable period of growth. But granular formulation has not yet arrived at the stage of replacing spray applications.

In general, granules have been found to be more effective than emulsifiable concentrates, the latter being more effective than dusts (Sharaf, 1986). In fact, the use of insecticidal dusts does not merit consideration for whitefly control. Insecticidal schedules often include initial application of granular products, followed by spraying at different intervals as the crop grows.

(iii) **Time and Frequency of Application:** The success of any control schedule depends on the timing and frequency of insecticidal application, which have to be determined by careful field observations. Chemical application has to be effective and the cost must not outweigh the benefit derived.

If the objective is limited to prevent direct injury of the whitefly, chemical operation has to be started as soon as the population reaches the economic threshold, which is determined either by working out the average population per leaf or when the adult whiteflies per sticky trap reaches a certain level (Melamed-Madjar et al., 1982).

In most cases the objective is to curb the incidence of viral diseases, when the economic threshold is close to unity. Since plants, in general, are most vulnerable to viral infection and injury during the early stages of growth, they require protection right from seed germination. Systemic granular formulations, such as aldicarb, are ideal for initial protection. Sometimes granular formulations are repeated 3–4 weeks after germination to tide over the vulnerable period.

The number and frequency of applications depend on various factors that include persistence of the chemical and the way it acts, the crop, season of cultivation, the prevailing weather conditions and the general agronomic practices in the area. The information available suggests that the earlier a chemical is applied, the greater the effectiveness obtained. The lower the number of applications, the better for the economy and the environment.

(iv) **Method of Application:** The effectiveness of insecticides under field conditions is limited by the application technique. The spray droplets should not only reach the foliage at different levels, but also the under-surface of the leaves, the preferred habitat of the whitefly, especially the immature stages. Such uniform coverage is difficult to achieve, especially when aerial treatment is done over large areas and the formulations used are too volatile. Even spraying with knapsack sprayers using large spray volumes, gives poor coverage of the crop canopy unless the nozzles are directed up through the crop canopy for deposition of the chemical on the undersurface of the leaves. The spray deposits on the undersurface of leaves rarely exceed 40–50% of those on the upper side of top leaves and may be as low as 5% and even less for the bottom leaves, following ultralow volume (ULV) spray applied by aircraft (Uk and Courshee, 1982).

Bemisia tabaci is usually regarded as a mid- to late-season pest of cotton when the crop canopy covers up the interrow spaces, obstructing deposition of spray droplets on the middle and lower leaves. Sprays released from above the crop canopy give maximum coverage of the top leaves and the amount deposited on the leaves below decreases exponentially from top to botton. This foliage barrier is related to the leaf structure and leaf area index, the latter being the ratio of total leaf area per unit ground surface covered. This vexing problem cannot be satisfactorily overcome by ground or aerial application by manipulating spray volumes as long as the spray droplets are directed from above. Kearns (1962) sprayed a closed cotton canopy about 60 cm high with 0.1% DDT emulsion to the point of complete wetting. Deposits of DDT on top, middle and bottom leaves were found to be 13.1, 7.7 and 5.8 $\mu g/cm^2$, respectively. A similar trend in vertical distribution of spray deposits was encountered with ULV spraying by hand-held equipment or by aircraft (Uk and Courshee, 1982; Uk, 1987). Deposit reduction due to canopy depth has been found to be approximately 1% for every cm of plant height.

A hand-carried spinning disc sprayer for ULV and very low volume (VLV) sprays over the top of a cotton crop have been used in some countries, such as Gambia (King, 1978; Nyirenda, 1982). Uk et al. (1981) compared the same chemical (endosulfan + dimethoate) as low volume (LV) and ULV sprays. Both treatments gave 70% control of the adults 1–2 days after application but the ULV treatment gave 30% control 5–8 days after application against 10% with LV spray. Attique and Shakeel (1983) compared ULV with conventional spraying against cotton pests in Pakistan. Both spraying techniques were effective but LV aqueous sprays gave better control than ULV sprays with EC formulations of deltamethrin, cypermethrin and triazophos.

Heijne and Peregrine (1984) reported the effects of ULV spray on the activity of amitraz against *B. tabaci*. Smaller droplets (45 µm) improved leaf coverage due to higher droplet numbers and higher application volumes (30 l/ha) also gave improved leaf coverage. The smallest droplets and highest volumes gave the best initial control. The improved persistence obtained with larger droplets or higher volumes was considered to be due to greater localised deposits. However, the prospects of improved coverage by manipulating droplet size and electrostatic charge, as indicated by their study, are still remote due to economic constraints (Dittrich et al., 1990).

Field plot tests to control *B. tabaci* on tomato in the Sudan showed that insecticide sprays applied by the electrodynamic technique were generally more effective than those applied by a knapsack sprayer (Kisha, 1986).

On the whole, very little work has been done to develop improved application techniques, particularly with ground equipment. Hence Butler et al. (1991) have stressed the need for more attention to this neglected aspect. In many tropical countries hand-held sprayers are used due to availability of cheap labour and other considerations, such as small-scale cultivations and high costs of aerial spraying and ground application equipment. In such a situation there is adequate scope for manipulation of the hand-held application technique in order to achieve better coverage of the underside of the leaves, especially of the new ones at the very top which are curled with dense hairs.

While spraying plant-derived oils and soap solutions, Puri et al. (1991) compared the coverage of the undersurface of the leaves at the top, middle and lower levels of cotton plants that could be achieved through the use of knapsack, motorised mist blowers and foot-operated sprayers. The foot sprayer gave the best coverage of the middle leaves where older eggs and nymphs were located. Shortening the length of the spray wand for knapsack and foot-operated sprayers was found to afford more flexibility in moving the wand in and between cotton plants. Reduced nozzle orifice was suggested to obtain better coverage, in particular with soap solutions, to prevent excessive run-off.

Soil treatment with granular formulations may require some ground equipment, as in the Sudan. For instance, although aldicarb has been shown to be effective on cotton in the Sudan Gezira, its wider use has been questioned due to the toxicity of the active ingredient for mammals. Application has thus been closely supervised using tractor-mounted applicators to reduce the risk of ill effects on animals entering the treated fields (Matthews, 1986).

Aharonson et al. (1986) showed that in a drip-irrigated cotton field in Israel, incorporation of aldicarb granules into the soil 25 cm away from the plants during early treatment (mid-June) was effective, but a distance of 50 cm from the plant stems proved more effective for late treatment (mid-July).

(v) **Nature of Crop Canopy:** Some information in this regard is available for the cotton crop. One of the causes of increase in the whitefly population in the Sudan was the introduction of varieties with a closed dense canopy. More open varieties of cotton are needed even if electrostatically charged sprays have to be applied. A new okra-leaf cotton variety, planted on a small area, reportedly requires only four instead of the recommended seven treatments.

(vi) **Differences in Efficacy Against Different Stages of Whitefly:** Different stages of *B. tabaci* generally respond to the same insecticide differently. The data compiled by Sharaf (1986) show that under laboratory conditions, most of the insecticides tested were more effective against the first and second nymphal stages than the egg, and third and fourth nymphal instars (Table 11.4). He related the effectiveness as Ineffective, moderately effective and highly effective without quantification, apparently due to lack of uniformity of available data.

Saraf (1986), however, pointed out that these responses were not confirmed under field conditions. Most of the chemicals tested were ineffective against immature stages but more or less effective against the adults.

Rao et al. (1990) reported the results of laboratory tests with some synthetic organic compounds against various developmental stages of *B. tabaci*.

Table 11.4. Effect of some chemicals on the different immature stages of *B. tabaci* under laboratory conditions (after Sharaf, 1986)

Chemical	Rating[+] of effectiveness against nymphal instar				
	Egg	Ist	2nd	3rd	4th (Pupa)
Azinophos-methyl	I	H	H	H	H
Dichlorvos	M	M	M	M	M
*Diflubenzuron	M	M	M	H	–
Methamidophos	I	H	H	H	H
Methyl parathion	H	H	H	H	H
Oxydemeton-methyl	I	H	H	I	I
Parathion	H	H	H	H	H
Phosphamidon	I	H	H	I	I
Pirimiphos-methyl	I	H	H	H	H
Triazophos	H	H	H	H	M
*Triflumuron	H	H	M	I	–

* Insect growth regulator
[+] I = Ineffective; M = Moderately effective; H = Highly effective.

Profenofos at 0.1% and fenpropathrin at 0.02% reduced egg hatch by 18 and 10%, respectively. Amitraz at 0.1%, triazophos at 0.1% and flucythrinate at 0.02% caused 25.2–28.7% mortality of the emerging nymphs. While amitraz at 0.05% caused 67.7% mortality of the late instar nymphs and adults, the corresponding mortality figure was 68% for fenpropathrin at 0.1%. Although this data does not allow comparison of stage-wise efficacy of the individual chemicals, the very modest performance of amitraz against the emerging nymphs compared to 67.7% mortality of the late-stage nymphs and pupae is quite interesting and differs significantly from the general trend in research results. It seems worthwhile to cite the findings of greenhouse tests by Prabhaker et al. (1989) with malathion, methyl parathion, monocrotophos, sulprofos, permethrin and neem seed extract against the various stages of insecticide resistant and susceptible populations. All the insecticides were most active against the first-instar nymphs, the lowest LC 50s ranging from 0.001–0.01 mg/ml for synthetic products and 1.44 mg/ml for neem seed extract. Toxicities decreased between successive stages. The LC 50 values were always higher for the egg and pupal stages. Adults of the resistant strain were the most tolerant, regardless of the insecticide tested, with LC 50 values ranging from 2.824 to 25.50 mg/ml. The first-instar nymphs were the least resistant to all the insecticides, the resistance ratio (RR) being a little more than twofold. The resistance increased to moderate levels in pupae (RR = 5.5–12.3-fold) and to high levels (RR = 46.3–108.6-fold) in adults. Neem seed extract was the least toxic to any of the stages but no resistance to neem was selected. Thus, even in the resistant population first-instar nymphs were the most vulnerable. The highest degree of resistance in the adults is a matter of great concern since they alone are responsible for virus spread.

Resistance of *Bemisia tabaci* to Insecticides

Factors leading to the spectacular rise of *B. tabaci* from a secondary to a primary pest of cotton in the Sudan Gezira, strongly point out the crucial role of high selection pressure in resistance (R) development. An analysis of the causes of this development was urgently needed that led Dittrich and Ernst (1983) to investigate the R status of the local races in the Sudan Gezira. Resistance to dimethoate and monocrotophos was found to be high (more than 200 ×), intermediate to dicrotophos and quinalphos (more than 60 ×), and low to profenofos, cypermethrin and oxamyl (less than 10 ×). Although no carbamate had been used against the local cotton pest complex, cross-R to carbofuran was found to be 190-fold. A subsequent study by Dittrich et al. (1985) showed a decrease in monocrotophos

R after its withdrawal in 1980 but further increase in dimethoate R, following its continued use.

It can thus be seen that R development is a continuously varying process and the R status of populations will understandably vary according to the extent of use of a chemical to which they have been subjected. An accurate picture of R development requires continuity of testing in the same location, uniformity in technique and operational aspects.

Prabhaker et al. (1985) conducted insecticide resistance tests on three separate field strains of B. tabaci from Coachella, Imperial and Palo Verde valleys, which had been subjected to different combinations of OPs and synthetic pyrethroids. Whiteflies from southern California and the Imperial Valley showed OP resistance, showing R values of 20 × and 54 × for sulprofos and parathion-methyl, respectively. Two strains had 12 and 29 × R towards permethrin, the latter from the Imperial Valley where the compound was widely used. Cross-R to DDT was also observed in all three strains.

Dittrich et al. (1990) cited the unpublished data of Ernst et al. (1987), reporting the R development revealed by monitoring work in three cotton-growing countries, with different backgrounds with regard to pesticide usage. Measurements were taken for over 7 years in the Sudan and over 3 years in both Turkey and Guatemala.

In the Sudan, mainly pyrethroids and endosulfan were used against the 'primary pests' with OPs such as dimethoate and chlorfenvinfos assisting to control sucking insects, including whiteflies. Specific whitefly control relied on foliar sprays of amitraz and aldicarb granules. The measurements indicated a general increase in OP resistance, mainly caused by continuous use of dimethoate. The early measurements did not show cross-R to be extended to pyrethroids, endosulfan and amitraz. However, increased R to pyrethroids became apparent over the years due to strong selection pressure but the R factor (RF-value = LC 50 field strain/LC 50 sensitive strain) for cypermethrin and deltamethrin decreased during the last two seasons, possibly due to reduced spray number during that period. The data up to 1987, the seventh year of study, showed little R to be induced by aldicarb and amitraz.

Data on the situation in Turkey from 1985 and 1987 showed the old OP resistance to dimethoate and monocrotophos and sensitivity to pyrethroids. Reintroduction of pyrethroids after an abstinence of 5 years resulted in a jump in R factors.

In Guatemala, R against OPs was beyond practical measurement and R against pyrethroids very high. Initially, the pyrethroids worked well under Central American conditions. Since parathion-methyl and pyrethroids are used to control boll weevils, bollworms and leafworms, a specific insecticide to control *B. tabaci* is lacking.

In view of the above experience, any practical approach to contain R, as pointed out by Dittrich et al. (1990), has to be based on:

(i)   Existing R situation in local whitefly populations.
(ii) Alternative insecticides which still work.
(iii) Integration of measures with control of the primary targets.

Alternation of various types of insecticides to prevent R has rarely been tested under practical conditions. The logical approach has been to control already resistant populations by using mixtures of chemically different compounds, one component of which is an inhibitor of the existing R mechanism in whiteflies. Strong synergy of the cotton defoliant, DEF (S,S,S-tributyl phosphorotrithioate), with cypermethrin and permethrin in a Californian field strain of *B. tabaci* was noted by Horowitz et al. (1988). The defoliant almost completely restored sensitivity of reaction towards both the pyrethroids. Prabhaker et al. (1988), also experimenting on synergists and whiteflies from the same area, concluded that R to OPs was partially caused by carboxyl-lesterases, glutathione-S-transferases and possibly to a lower extent, by mixed function oxidases. Pyrethroid R was reduced by both esterase and oxidase inhibitors. The prevailing R mechanism in the Sudanese *B. tabaci* was found to be increased esteretic activity and acetylcholinesterase insensitivity towards such inhibitors as carbofuran and monocrotophos (Dittrich et al., 1985).

Ishaaya and Ascher (1984) reported a strong synergistic effect of mixtures of monocrotophos and methidathion with cypermethrin on adult *B. tabaci*, both in the greenhouse and on field-planted cotton. While the respective amounts of OPs tested alone were ineffective, the mixtures with cypermethrin were highly effective, indicating the block of the prevailing R mechanism by the OP insecticides. The mechanism was subsequently identified to be an esterase which hydrolyses pyrethroids (Ishaaya et al., 1985). The esterase was very effectively inhibited in decreasing order, by monocrotophos, methidathion and methamidophos. However, in mice, monocrotophos and methidathion were much less effective than profenofos and methidathion were much less effective than profenofos and acephate, which were potent inhibitors. This finding indicates that the specificity of enzyme inhibitor combinations differs for insects and mammals.

Despite the encouraging results with a combination of insecticides, the effectiveness of such mixtures may be restricted as selection for a resistant population continues. In the absence of true synergists, the search should be directed towards non-insecticidal compounds to enjoy more lasting benefit of synergism or irritancy.

In the overall insecticidal schedule, applications need to be minimised to reduce selection of resistant populations. The number of applications of any pesticide should be related to the particular pest complex and the possibility of alternating effective chemicals between areas or regions should be explored (Matthews, 1986).

Prospects of Control by Behaviour Modification

Information accumulated over the years on the results of insecticidal measures against *B. tabaci,* clearly shows that the control approach limited to killing has severe limitations. In recent years there has been growing realisation of the need for relatively non-toxic chemicals, having the property to disrupt behaviour or normal development of the whitefly. Seeing great clouds of whiteflies flying away from an endosulfan-treated field, prompted Uk and Dittrich (1986) to investigate the chemically induced phenomenon. Field and laboratory experiments confirmed repellency of endosulfan and choice-chamber tests showed similar effects to be caused by chlordimeform. The behaviour modifying properties of chlordimeform and endosulfan were demonstrated in field studies on *B. tabaci* on cotton in the Sudan. Doses of 500–2500 g/ha chlordimeform and 960 g/endosulfan caused irritation and mass emigration of the adults from the treated cotton foliage without detectable direct mortality. They suggested the use of a behaviour modifier to avoid rapid selection for resistance which results from the use of conventional insecticides.

Irritation and repellency are known to have been caused by DDT and some pyrethroids to some insect pests, which calls for proper screening of synthetic chemicals to detect and exploit this property for whitefly control.

In recent years insect growth regulators, especially buprofezin, have been tested against *B. tabaci* and the results so far have been highly encouraging.

Khalil et al. (1979) reported diflubenzuron (Dimilin) to be effective against all stages of *B. tabaci.* Testing of two moult inhibitors, triflumuron and diflubenzuron, against immature stages showed the former to be more toxic. The third-instar nymphs were the most susceptible. Treatment of nymphs or pupae reduced adult emergence (Radwan et al., 1985).

The juvenile hormone, [2-(1-methyl–2 (4-phenoxy phenoxy) ethoxy pyridine] was found to be an ovicide for eggs of *B. tabaci* (Ascher and Eliyahu, 1988).

Wilson and Anema (1988) reported that two high-volume sprays of buprofezin at 7.5 g a.i./lit, provided long-term control of the whitefly on glasshouse crops in the U.K. and the Netherlands. Buprofezin was persistent under greenhouse conditions. Spray concentrations of 62.5 and 125 mg/litre resulted in 50% inhibition of egg hatch 4 and 7 days after application, respectively and suppression of more than 95% of progeny formation for up to 26 days after application. At concentrations of 125 and 250 mg/litre in the field, buprofezin decreased populations of *B. tabaci* by 90 and 80%, 35 and 50 days after application, respectively (Ishaaya et al., 1988).

Stenseth and Singh (1990) found buprofezin at 0.00625% to be active against *B. tabaci* on *Euphorbia pulcherrima* at temperatures from 15–27°C.

The biological and chemical persistence of buprofezin above and within cotton leaves, along with its vapour activity and translaminar effect against nymphs of *B. tabaci* were studied by de Cock et al. (1990). The 50% loss of foliar buprofezin varied from a short period (2.3 days) at 62.5 mg a.i./litre to a relatively long period (13 days) of 250 mg a.i./litre. At 250 mg a.i./litre, complete suppression of progeny formation was observed up to 14 days after treatment, the potency being reduced to 50% of its original value in 26 days for suppression of egg hatch and in 28 days for cumulative larval mortality. Buprofezin vapours emitted from leaves treated with 450 mg a.i./lit. resulted in 95.7 and 62.4% kill of the first-instar nymphs at a distance of 2 and 4 cm, respectively. Less than 4% of the initial deposit that penetrated the leaves sufficed to produce a moderate translaminar effect. These results strongly indicate that buprofezin acts by contact, inhalation or both.

Recent laboratory and field studies in Israel have demonstrated that buprofezin is highly effective against *B. tabaci* and that several other insect growth regulators are similarly effective against the noctuids, *Spodoptera* spp. and *Heliothis* spp., which are common important members of the cotton pest complex. Because of their low toxicity to parasitoids and mammals and their favourable persistence, these insecticides can be valuable components in integrated pest-management systems on cotton (Ishaaya, 1990).

REFERENCES

Abdel-Rahman, A.A. (1986). The potential of natural enemies of the cotton whitefly in Sudan Gezira. *Insect Sci. Appl.* **7**: 69–73.

Agrawal, H.S., Gupta, N.K., Prasad, V.K. and Vishwakarma, S. (1979). Chemical control of yellow mosaic of moong. *Pesticides* **13** (5): 44–47.

Aharonson, N., Magal, Z., Muszkat, L., Tepperman, D., Goren, E. and Tadmor, U. (1986). Application of aldicarb in a drip-irrigated cotton field for the control of the tobacco whitefly (*Bemisia tabaci*). *Phytoparasitica* **14**: 87–91.

Ahmed, R. and Baig, M.M.H. (1987). Observations on efficiency and economics of cotton pest control with deltamethrin alone and its combinations with monocrotophos and DDT. *Pakistan J. Sci. Indus. Res.* **30** (7): 517–519.

Al-Ani, R.A., Samir, S.H. and Jarjees, H.M. (1987). Identification and control of tobacco leaf curl virus. *Arab J. Plant Prot.* **5** (2): 70–73.

Ascher, K.R.S. and Eliyahu, M. (1988). The ovicidal properties of the juvenile hormone mimic Sumitomo S-31183 (SK-591) to insects. *Phytoparasitica* **16** (1): 15–21.

Attique, M.R. and Shakeel, M.A. (1983). Comparison of ULV with conventional spraying on cotton in Pakistan. *Crop Prot.* **2**: 231–234.

Bellows, T.S. and Arakawa, K. (1988). Dynamics of preimaginal populations of *Bemisia tabaci* (Homoptera: Aleyrodidae) and *Eretmocerus* sp. (Hymenoptera: Aphelinidae) in southern Californian cotton. *Environ. Entomol.* **17**: 483–487.

Broza, M., Butler, G.D. and Henneberry, T.J. (1988). Cottonseed oil for control of *Bemisia tabaci* on cotton. In: *Beltwide Cotton Producers' Research Conference*, New Orleans, Louisiana, National Cotton Council, Memphis, Tenn., p. 301.

Broza, M., Butler, G.D., Venetzian, A. and Shavit, A. (1989). *Bacillus thuringiensis* and cottonseed oil as control agents in an integrated pest management program for cotton in Israel. *Israel J. Entomol.* (cited by Butler et al., 1991).

Butler, G.D., Coudriet, D.L. and Henneberry, T.J. (1988). Toxicity and repellency of soybean and cottonseed oils to sweet-potato whitefly and the cotton aphid on cotton in the greenhouse. *Southwestern Entomologist* **13**: 81–86.

Butler, G.D., Coudriet, D.L. and Henneberry, T.J. (1989). Sweetpotato whitefly: host plant preference and repellent effect of plant-derived oils on cotton, squash, lettuce and cantaloupe. *Southwestern Entomologist* **14** (1): 9–16.

Butler, G.D. and Henneberry, T.J. (1990). Pest control on vegetables and cotton with household cooking oils and liquid detergents. *Southwestern Entomologist* **15**: 123–131.

Butler, G.D., Puri, S.N. and Henneberry, T.J. (1991). Plant derived oil and detergent solution as control agents for *Bemisia tabaci* and *Aphis gossypii* on cotton. *Southwestern Entomologist* **16** (4): 331–337.

Butler, G.D. and Rao, S.B.P. (1990). Cottonseed oil to combat white-fly. *Indian Textile J.* 1990: 20–25.

Butter, N.S. and Rataul, H.S. (1973). Control of tomato leafcurl virus (TLCV) in tomatoes by controlling the vector whitefly *Bemisia tabaci* Gen. by mineral-oil sprays. *Curr. Sci.* **42**: 864–865.

Carlson, G.A. and Mohamed, A. (1986). Economic analysis of cotton-insect control in the Sudan Gezira. *Crop Prot.* **5**: 348–354.

Cauquil, J. (1981). Utilisation de deux pyréthrinöides de synthese (deltamethrine et cypermethrine) pour la protection des cultures cotonnieres de Republique Centrafricaine. *Coton et Fibres Tropicales* **36**: 227–231.

Chaudhary, R.R.P., Bhattacharya, A.K. and Rathore, R.R.S. (1981). Use of systemic insecticides for the control of stemfly Melanagromyza sojae (Zehnt.) and whitefly Bemisia tabaci Genn. Indian J. Ent. **43**: 223–225.

Chavan, V.M. (1983). Efficacy of systemic insecticides for the control of Bemisia tabaci Genn., a vector of the leaf curl of cigar-wrapper tobacco. Indian J. Agric. Sci. **53**: 585–589.

Cohen, S., Melamed-Madjar, V. and Hameiri, J. (1974). Prevention of the spread of tomato yellow leaf curl virus transmitted by Bemisia tabaci (Gennadius) (Homoptera, Aleyrodidae) in Israel. Bull. Ent. Res. **64**: 193–197.

Coudriet, D.L., Prabhaker, N. and Meyerdirk, D.E. (1985). Sweetpotato whitefly (Homoptera: Aleyrodidae). Effects of neemseed extract on oviposition and immature stages. Environ. Entomol. **14**: 776–779.

Datar, V.V. (1980). Chemical control of chilli leaf curl complex in Maharashtra. Pesticides **14** (9): 19–20.

David, B.V. and Jesudasan, R.W.A. (1986). Status of the cotton whitefly Bemisia tabaci (Gennadius) excluding its vector biology. Pesticides **20**: 42–47.

de Cock, A., Ishaaya, I., Degheele, D. and Veierov, D. (1990). Vapor toxicity and concentration-dependent persistence of buprofezin applied to cotton foliage for controlling the sweet-potato whitefly (Homoptera: Aleyrodidae). J. Econ. Ent. **83** (4): 1254–1260.

Dittrich, V. and Ernst, G.H. (1983). The resistance pattern in whiteflies of Sudanese cotton. Mitteilungen der Deutschen Gesellschaft für Allgemeina und Angewandte Entomologie **4**: 96–97.

Dittrich, V., Hassan, S.O. and Ernst, G.H. (1985). Sudanese cotton and the whitefly: a case study of the emergence of a new primary pest. Crop Protection **4**: 161–176.

Dittrich, V., Hassan, S.O. and Ernst, G.H. (1986). Development of a new primary pest of cotton in the Sudan: Bemisia tabaci, the whitefly. Agric. Ecosys. Environ. **17**: 137–142.

Dittrich, V., Uk, S. and Ernst, G.H. (1990). Chemical control and insecticide resistance of whiteflies. In: Whiteflies: Their Bionomics, Pest Status and Management (D. Gerling, ed.) Intercept, Wimborne, England, pp. 263–285.

Eveleens, K.G. (1983). Cotton-insect control in the Sudan Gezira: analysis of a crisis. Crop Prot. **2**: 273–287.

Flint, H.M. and Parks, N.J. (1989). Effect of azadirachtin from the neem tree on immature sweetpotato whitefly Bemisia tabaci (Homoptera: Aleyrodidae) and other selected pest species on cotton. J. Agric. Entomol. **6** (4): 211–215.

Gerling, D. (1986). Natural enemies of Bemisia tabaci, biological characteristics and potential as biological control agents: a review. Agric. Ecosys. Environ. **17**: 99–110.

Hafez, M., Tawfik, M.F.S., Awadallah, K.T. and Sarhan, A.A. (1983). Imapct of the parasite Eretmocerus mundus Mercet on population of the cotton whitefly, Bemisia tabaci (Genn.), in Egypt. Bull. Soc. Entomol. d'Egypte **62**: 23–32.

Heijne, C.G. and Peregrine, D.J. (1984). The effects of ULV spray characteristics on the activity of amitraz against the cotton whitefly, Bemisia tabaci (Gennadius). Proc. 1984 British Crop Prot. Conf.—Pests and Diseases **3**: 975–979.

Horowitz, A.R., Toscano, N.C., Youngman, R.R. and Georghiou, G.P. (1988). Synergism of insecticides with DEF in sweetpotato whitefly (Homoptera: Aleyrodidae). J. Econ. Ent. **81**: 110–114.

Husain, M.A., Trehan, K.N. and Verma, P.N. (1939). Economics of field-scale spraying against the whitefly of cotton (Bemisia gossypiperda, M. & L.). Indian J. Agric. Sci. **9**: 109–126.

Ishaaya, I. (1990). Buprofezin and other insect growth regulators for controlling cotton pest. Pesticide Outlook **1** (2): 30–33.

Ishaaya, I. and Ascher, K.R.S. (1984). Synergized cypermethrin for controlling the whitefly, Bemisia tabaci, in cotton. Phytoparasitica **12**: 139–140.

Ishaaya, I., Austerweil, M. and Frankel, H. (1986). Effect of the petroleum oil Virol on toxicity and chemical residue of fenpropathrin applied against adults of Bemisia tabaci (Homoptera: Aleyrodidae) as high and low-volume sprays. J. Econ. Ent. 79 (3): 596–599.

Ishaaya, I., Mendelson, Z., Ascher, K.R.S. and Casida, J.E. (1985). Mixtures of synthetic pyrethroids and organophosphorus compounds for controlling the whitefly, Bemisia tabaci. Phytoparasitica 13: 76–77.

Ishaaya, I., Mendelson, Z., Ascher, K.R.S. and Casida, J.E. (1987). Cypermethrin synergism by pyrethroid esterase inhibitors in adults of the whitefly Bemisia tabaci. Pesticide Biochem. Physiol. 28 (2): 155–162.

Ishaaya, I., Mendelson, Z. and Melamed-Madjar, V. (1988). Effect of buprofrezin on embryogenesis and progeny formation of sweetpotato whitefly (Homoptera: Aleyrodidae). J. Econ. Ent. 81 (3): 781–784.

Johnson, M.W., Toscano, N.C., Reynolds, H.T., Sylvester, E.S., Kido, K. and Natwick, E.T. (1982). Whiteflies cause problems for southern California growers. Calif. Agric. 36: 24–26.

Joshi, R.D. and Dubey, L.N. (1976). Efficiency of certain insecticides in controlling leaf curl disease in chillies. Science and Culture 42 (5): 273–275.

Kapadia, M.N., Puri, S.N., Butler, G.D. and Henneberry, T.J. (1992). Whitefly, Bemisia tabaci Genn., and parasitoid populations in insecticide treated cotton. J. Appl. Zool. Res. 3 (1): 7–10.

Kearns, H.G.H. (1962). The Spraying of Cotton. Sudan Gezira Board Report 1962 (unpublished, cited by Dittrich et al., 1990).

Khalil, F.A., Watson, W.M. and Guirguis, M.W. (1979). Evaluation of demilin and its combinations with different insecticides against some cotton pests in Egypt. Bull. Entomol. Soc. Egypt (Economics) 11: 71–76.

Khan, M.A. and Mukhopadhyay, S. (1985). Effect of different pesticide combinations on the incidence of yellow vein mosaic disease of okra (Abelomoschus esculentus) and its whitefly vector, Bemisia tabaci Genn. Indian J. Virol. 1: 69–72.

King, W.J. (1978). Very-low-volume application of insecticides to cotton in the Gambia. Miscellaneous Rept. Ministry of Overseas Development 44, 15 pp.

Kisha, J.S.A. (1981). The effect of insecticides on Bemisia tabaci, tomato leaf curl virus disease incidence and yield of tomatoes in the Sudan. Ann. Appl. Biol. 99: 231–239.

Kisha, J.S.A. (1986). Comparison of electrodynamic spraying with use of a knapsack sprayer for control of whitefly on tomato in the Sudan Gezira. Ann. Appl. Biol. 108 (suppl.): 36–37.

Kooner, B.S. and Singh, H. (1980). Control of whitefly and the yellow-mosaic virus in green gram with granular insecticides. J. Res. Punjab Agric. Univ. 17: 268–271.

Kooner, B.S., Singh, H. and Sandhu, G.S. (1986). Control of yellow-mosaic virus in soybean by the soil application of granular systemic insecticides. Indian J. Ent. 48 (2): 125–129.

Koren, E., Marmelstein, M., Birathi, Y. and Rothchild, G. (1983). Mecarbam—an effective insecticide for control of the tobacco whitefly, Bemisia tabaci, in cotton. Phytoparasitica 11: 123.

Mahto, D.N. and Sinha, D.C. (1978). Evaluation of insecticides for the control of white fly, Bemisia tabaci Genn., in relation to the incidence of mosaic of cassava. Indian J. Ent. 40: 316–319.

Matthews, G.A. (1986). Overview of chemical control with special reference to cotton crops. In: Bemisia tabaci—A Literature Survey (M.J.W. Cock, ed.). C.A.B. International Institute of Biological Control, U.K., pp. 55–58.

Melamed-Madjar, V., Cohen, S., Tam, S. and Rosilio, D. (1982). A method for monitoring Bemisia tabaci and time spray applications against the pest in cotton fields in Israel. Phytoparasitica 10: 85–91.

Mishra, P.N. (1986). Studies on Bio-efficacy of some insecticides against the pest complex of tomato, *Lycopersicon esculentum* Mill., var. Pusa Ruby. *Madras Agric. J.* **71** (10): 673–676.

Morton, N., Byrone, J.E., Vigil, O., Rodrigues, R., Rodrigues, A. and Cabezas, G. (1986). A new insecticide for bollweevil control. *Proc. British Crop Prot. Conf. 1986. Pest and Diseases* **1**: 137–144.

Mote, U.N. (1978). Effect of a few insecticides along and in combination with agricultural spray oil on the control of whitefly (*Bemisia tabaci* Gennadius) population and incidence of leaf curl virus. *Indian J. Plant Prot.* **6** (1): 19–22.

Murugesen, S. and Chelliah, S. (1981). Efficacy of insecticides in the control of *Bemisia tabaci* (Genn.), a vector of the yellow-mosaic virus disease on greengram. *Indian J. Agric. Sci.* **51**: 583–584.

Nair, N.G. (1981). Relationship between cassava mosiac disease spread and whitefly (*Bemisia tabaci* Gen.) population under different insecticide treatments. *J. Root Crops* **7** (1/2): 15–19.

Nene, Y.L. (1973). Control of *Bemisia tabaci* Genn., a vector of several plant viruses. *Indian J. Agric. Sci.* **43**: 433–436.

Nyirenda, G.K.C. (1982). Daily application of ultra-low-volume (ULV) at low dosages to control insect pests of cotton in Malawi. *Crop Prot.* **1**: 213–220.

Peregrine, B.J. and Lemon, R.W. (1986). The value of amitraz for control of *Bemisia tabaci* on cotton. *Agric. Ecosys. Environ.* **17**: 129–135.

Phadke, A.D., Khandal, V.S. and Rahalkar, S.R. (1989). Effect of Neemark formulations on incidence of whiteflies and yield of cotton. *Pesticides* **22**: 36–37.

Prabhaker, N., Coudriet, D.L. and Meyerdirk, D.E. (1985). Insecticide resistance in the sweetpotato whitefly, *Bemisia tabaci* (Homoptera: Aleyrodidae). *J. Econ. Ent.* **78**: 748–752.

Prabhaker, N., Coudriet, D.L. and Toscano, N.C. (1988). Effect of synergists on organophosphate and permethrin resistance in sweetpotato whitefly (Homoptera: Aleyrodidae). *J. Econ. Ent.* **81**: 35–39.

Prabhaker, N., Toscano, N.C. and Coudriet, D.L. (1989). Susceptibility of the immature and adult stages of the sweetpotato whitefly (Homoptera: Aleyrodidae) to selected insecticides. *J. Econ. Ent.* **82** (4): 983–988.

Pruthi, H.S. (1946). Report of the Imperial Entomologist. *Abridged Science Reports, Agricultural Research Institute, New Delhi* 1941–44, pp. 64–71.

Puri, S.N. (1991). *Bemisia tabaci* (Gennadius) problem in Marathwada: some contributions in development of integrated management strategy. Dept. of Entomology, Marathwada Agricultural University, Parbhani, India, 13 pp.

Puri, S.N., Butler, G.D. and Henneberry, T.J. (1991). Plant-derived oils and soap solutions as control agents for the whitefly on cotton. *J. Appl. Zool. Res.* **2**: 1–5.

Radwan, H.S.A., Ammar, I.M.A., Eisa, A.A., Assal, O.M. and Omar, H.I.H. (1985). Development retardation and inhibitition of adult emergence in cotton whitefly *Bemisia tabaci* Genn. following immature stage treatments with two molt inhibitors. *Bull. Entomol. Soc. Egypt, Economic Series* no. 13, pp. 175–181.

Rao, N.V., Reddy, A.S. and Reddy, P.S. (1990). Relative efficacy of some new insecticides on insect pests of cotton. *Indian J. Plant Prot.* **18** (1): 53–58.

Rataul, H.S. and Butter, N.S. (1976). Control of tomato leaf curl virus in tomatoes (*Lycopersicon esculentum* Miller) by suppressing the vector population of *Bemisia tabaci* Genn. with insecticidal sprays. *J. Res. Punjab Agric. Univ.* **13**: 303–307.

Rataul, H.S. and Singh, L. (1976). Field studies on the control of soybean yellow-mosaic virus, tansmitted by whitefly *Bemisia tabaci* Genn. by using different granular systemic insecticides. *J. Res. Punjab Agric. Univ.* **13**: 298–302.

Rathore, G.S. and Agnihotri, J.P. (1985). Effect of insecticides on yellow mosaic of mothbean *Vigna aconitifolia* (Jacq.) (Marechel). *Indian J. Virol.* **1** (1): 92–94.

Reddy,.A.S., Rosaiah, B. and Bhaskara Rao, T. (1989). Seasonal occurrence of whitefly *Bemisia tabaci* (Genn.) on cotton and its control. *Andhra Agric. J.* **36**: 275–279.

Rote, N.B., Puri, S.N., Butler, G.D. and Henneberry, T.J. (1992). Whitefly population levels, fecundity and developmental period on cotton following insecticidal applications. *J. Appl. Zool. Res.* **3** (1): 1–6.

Saklani, U.D. and Mathai, P.J. (1978). Effect of insecticides on leaf curl incidence of tomato. *Pesticides* **12** (8): 17–20, 25.

Sardana, H.R. and Verma, S. (1987). Effect of fertilizers on the incidence of yellow mosaic disease of greengram, *Vigna radiata* Wilezeck. *Plant Prot. Bull. India* **39** (4): 3–6.

Sastry, K.S.M. and Singh, S.J. (1973a). Restriction of yellow vein mosaic virus spread in okra through the control of the whitefly vector, *Bemisia tabaci*. *Indian J. Mycol. Plant Pathol.* **3**: 76–80.

Sastry, K.S.M. and Singh, S.J. (1973b). Field evaluation of insecticides for the control of whitefly (*Bemisia tabaci*) in relation to the incidence of yellow vein mosaic of okra (*Abelomoschus esculentus*). *Indian Phytopath.* **26**: 129–138.

Sastry, K.S.M. and Singh, S.J. (1974). Control and spread of the tomato leaf curl virus by controlling the whitefly (*Bemisia tabaci* Gen.) population. *Indian J. Hortic.* **31**: 178–181.

Sastry, K.S.M., Singh S.J. and Sastry, K.S. (1978). Efficacy of krishi oil in relation to the control of whitefly population and the spread of tomato leaf curl virus (TLCV). *Pesticides* **12**: 28–29.

Satpute, U.S. and Subramaniam, T.R. (1983). A note on the secondary outbreak of whitefly (*Bemisia tabaci*) on cotton, with phosalone treatment. *Pestology* **7**: 4.

Satyavir (1983). Efficacy of some important insecticides in the control of *Bemisia tabaci* (Genn.), a vector of the yellow mosaic disease on mothbean. *Indian J. Plant Prot.* **11**: 31–33.

Seif, A.A. (1982). Effect of cassava mosaic virus on yield of cassava. *Plant Disease* **66**: 661–662.

Sharaf, N.S. (1986). Chemical control of *Bemisia tabaci*. *Agric., Ecosys. Environ.* **17**: 111–127.

Saraf, N.S. and Allawi, T.F. (1980). Studies on whiteflies on tomato in the Jordan Valley. III. Laboratory and field experiments on the control of whitefly (*Bemisia tabaci* Genn., Homoptera: Aleyrodidae) populations with organophosphorus insecticides and the incidence of the tomato yellow leaf curl virus. *Zeitschrift für Pflanzenkrankheiten und Pflanzenschutz* **87** (3): 176–184.

Sharaf, N.S. and Allawi, T.F. (1981). Control of *Bemisia tabaci* Genn., a vector of tomato yellow leaf curl virus disease in Jordan. *Zeitschrift für Pflanzenkrankheiten und Pflanzenschutz* **88**: 123–131.

Sharma, S.R. and Varma, A. (1982). Control of yellow mosaic of mungbean through insecticides and oil. *J. Ent. Res.* **6**: 130–136.

Shires, S.W., Murray, A. and Sadig, S. (1983). Stickiness in cotton: progress in solving the problem. *Shell Agric.* May, pp. 1–2.

Shires, S.W., Inglesfield, C. and Tipton, J.D. (1987). Effects of chlorfenvinphos on *Bemisia tabaci* Genn. and its parasites on cotton in the Sudan Gezira. *Crop Prot.* **6**: 109–116.

Singh, D. and Singh, R. (1982). Bio-efficacy of some systemic insecticides against jassid, thrips and whitefly attacking cotton. *Pesticides* **16**: 13–14.

Singh, H., Sandhu, G.S. and Mavi, G.S. (1971). Control of yellow mosaic virus in soybean, *Glycine max* (L.) Merrill, by the use of granular insecticides. *Indian J. Ent.* **33**: 272–278.

Singh, R.A., Gurha, S.N., Misra, D.P. and Gangal, L.L. (1980). Role of systemic insecticides in augmenting yields with reduced yellow mosaic virus incidence in mung bean. *Indian J. Plant Prot.* **8**: 167–169.

Singh, S.J., Sastry, K.S.M. and Sastry, K.S. (1973). Effect of oil spray on the control of tomato leafcurl virus in field. *Indian J. Agric. Sci.* **43**: 669–672.

Singh, S.J., Sastry, K.S. and Sastry, K.S.M. (1979). Efficiency of different insecticides and oil in the control of leaf curl virus disease of chillies. *Zeitschrift für Pflanzenkrankheiten und Pflanzenschutz* **86**: 253–256.

Sinha, S.N. and Chakrabarti, A.K. (1982). Studies on the control of yellow vein mosaic in okra seed crop. *Vegetable Science* **9** (1): 64–69.

Stenseth, C. and Singh, H.M. (1990). Buprofezin against the glasshouse whitefly and the cotton whitefly. *Buprofezin mot veksthusmellus og bomullsmellus. Gartneryrket* **80** (1): 18–19.

Sundraraju, D. and Rangarajan, A.V. (1987). Effect of insecticides in combination with fertilizers in controlling yellow mosaic disease and pod borer of green gram. *Pesticides* **21** (12): 20–21.

Thapliyal, P.N., Dubey, K.S. and Bhadula, H.K. (1987). Control of yellow mosaic of soybean with granular insecticides. *Indian Phytopath.* **40** (1): 110–111.

Thomas, R. (1932). Periodic failure of the Punjab-American cotton crop. *Agric. Livestock in India* **2** (3): 243–274.

Uk, S. (1987). Distribution patterns of aerially applied ULV sprays by aircraft over and within cotton canopy in the Sudan Gezira. *Crop Prot.* **6**: 43–48.

Uk, S. and Courshee, R.J. (1982). Distribution and likely effectiveness of spray deposits within a cotton canopy from the fine ultra-low volume spray applied by aircraft. *Pesticide Science* **13**: 529–536.

Uk, S. and Dittrich, V. (1986). The behaviour-modifying effect of chlordimeform and endosulfan on the adult whitefly *Bemisia tabaci* (Genn.) which attacks cotton in the Sudan. *Crop Prot.* **5**: 341–347.

Uk, S., Burden, R. and Wyatt, J. (1981). Agricultural Aviation Progress Report 111/81 (unpublished, cited by Dittrich et al., 1990).

Vadodaria, M.P. and Vyas, H.N. (1987). Control of whitefly *Bemisia tabaci* (Gennadius) and its impact on yellow mosaic virus (YMV) in green gram *Vigna radiata* (L.) Wilczck and the grain yield. *Indian J. Agric. Res.* **21** (1): 21–26.

Wangboonkong, S. (1981). Chemical control of cotton insect pests in Thailand. *Tropical Pest Management* **27**: 495–500.

Watson, J.S., Hopper, B.L. and Tipton, J.D. (1982). Whitefly and the problem of sticky cotton. *Span* **25** (2): 71–73, 90, 92, 94.

Wilson, D. and Anema, B.P. (1988). Development of buprofezin for control of whitefly *Trialeurodes vaporariorum* and *Bemisia tabaci* on glasshouse crops in the Netherlands and the U.K. In: *Brighton Crop Protection Conference, Pests and Diseases.* Surrey, U.K., British Crop Protection Council, no. 1, pp. 175–180.

Yein, B.R. and Singh, H. (1982). Effect of pesticides and fertilizers on the population of whitefly and incidence of yellow-mosaic virus in greengram. *Indian J. Agric. Sci.* **52**: 852–855.

12

Bemisia tabaci and Plant Diseases

The notoriety of *Bemisia tabaci* as a pest is obscured by its role as an efficient vector of a large number of important plant diseases, affecting various crops such as cassava, cotton, grain legumes, including cowpea, soybean and other beans, tobacco, tomato, chillis, okra, squash, melon, watermelon, lettuce and papaya, in the tropical and subtropical parts of the world. The prevalence and distribution of *B. tabaci*-transmitted viral maladies have increased during the past decade and the impact has often been devastating. Yield losses range from 20 to 100%, depending on the crop, season, vector prevalence and other factors (Brown and Bird, 1992). Many of the diseases have been considered viral in nature only by negative reasoning and the causes remain uncertain. *Bemisia tabaci* is incidentally the first whitefly species to be implicated as a vector of the cotton leaf curl disease in the Sudan (Kirkpatrick, 1930) and Nigeria (Golding, 1930).

A number of reviews of whitefly-transmitted diseases have been published during the last three decades (Varma, 1963; Costa, 1969, 1976; Bird and Maramorosch, 1978; Muniyappa, 1980; Bock, 1982; Francki et al., 1985; Duffus, 1987; Brown and Bird, 1992), which show the changes in our state of knowledge of the etiological aspect over the years. Some 70 or more diseases have been reported to be whitefly-borne (Duffus, 1987), affecting field crops, ornamentals and weeds. These diseases are mostly too inadequately described to be related to others and many reports of diseases involving different plant species may be manifestations of the same agent or its strains. Thus the total number of whitefly-borne diseases provides no clue to the number of viruses or disease agents involved. That is why no detailed list of diseases is provided here; the reader may consult Muniyappa (1980), Brunt (1986) and Duffus (1987) for such information.

The poor state of knowledge of the whitefly-borne diseases will be evident from the groupings of these diseases until recently. Costa (1976) grouped them as (a) mosaic diseases, (b) leaf curl diseases and (c) the yellowing diseases. Muniyappa (1980) categorised them in four groups:

(a) yellow mosaic diseases, (b) yellow vein mosaics, (c) leaf curl diseases and (d) mosaic and other types of diseases. Bird and Maramorosch (1978) used the term 'rugaceous diseases' to designate whitefly-borne diseases causing symptoms of malformations, leaf curl, enations and yellowing mosaic. The prolonged phase of groping in the dark was partially terminated with the detection of virus particles and characterisation on the basis of particle morphology, serology and biochemical properties. Whitefly-borne viruses of six or seven morphological classes have been demonstrated so far, namely, geminivirus, carla-like, clostero-like, poty-like, luteo-like and nepo- or como-like viruses (Duffus, 1987; Cohen, 1990). Of these, the geminivirus group is by far the most important, both in terms of number of diseases and their economic impact in various parts of the world (Bock, 1982; Duffus, 1987; Byrne et al., 1990; Brown and Bird, 1992). The distinctive morphology and fascinating molecular biology of geminiviruses have attracted intense attention from researchers in recent years, resulting in exciting progress in our knowledge, as will be evident from the discussion below.

Geminiviruses

The name 'geminivirus' was first coined by Harrison et al. (1977) to describe viruses having quasi-isometric particles found predominantly in pairs (from Latin *gemini*, meaning twin) and containing circular single-stranded DNA. Although the geminate morphology was first clearly depicted by Bock et al. (1974), the genomic nature was revealed three years later by Goodman (1977a), when particles of bean golden mosaic virus (BGMV) were shown to contain single-stranded DNA. Members of this group are mainly divided into three groups on the basis of vector specificity and whether infecting monocotyledonous or dicotyledonous hosts. They are:

(1) **Whitefly-transmitted Geminiviruses** (WTGs): Members of this category infect dicotyledonous hosts and all are transmitted by *B. tabaci*. Infection causes hypertrophy of the nucleoli and separation of nucleolar material into the granular fibrillar region with concomitant production of a characteristic fibrillar ring (Kim et al., 1978; Adejare and Coutts, 1982). Although these viruses are predominantly confined to phloem, some, such as the African cassava mosaic (ACMV), referred to as the cassava latent virus until recently, and tomato yellow mosaic virus (TomYMV) have been reported to occur in the cortex, mesophyll and epidermis (Sequeira and Harrison, 1982; Lastra and Gill, 1981). The phloem-restricted nature of the WTGs in general, low virus titres that are strongly influenced by light and temperature, and the extremely labile nature of some viruses seem

to account for the inordinate delay in discovery of the unique geminate particle morphology until 1974.

More and more diseases, whose etiologies remained obscure until recently, have been attributed to the geminiviruses (Table 12.1) and more are likely to follow in the near future.

The list given in Table 12.1 gives some idea about the reported association of geminate particles with various diseases; however, how many distinct viruses or their strains are involved is not known. The basic studies for characterising and identifying these viruses will be discussed shortly, followed by a brief account of the economically important geminivirus diseases transmitted by *B. tabaci*.

(2) Leafhopper-transmitted Geminiviruses Infecting Monocotyledonous Plants: Chloris striate mosaic virus (CSMV), maize streak virus (MSV) and wheat dwarf virus (WDV) are well studied members of this group. The host range of the viruses is limited to Gramineae only and all of these viruses proliferate in the nuclei of their hosts, producing a characteristic array of particles, and are rarely observed in the cytoplasm, mesophyll and guard cells (Markham et al., 1985).

(3) Leafhopper-transmitted Geminiviruses Infecting Dicotyledonous Plants: Beet curly top virus (BCTV) is the well-studied member of this group that also includes bean summer death virus (BSDV) and tobacco yellow dwarf virus (TobYDV). While BSDV and TobYDV are serologically closely related, no relationship has been observed with MSV or CSMV. Report of a weak serological relationship between BCTV and the whitefly-borne tomato golden mosaic virus (TGMV) (Stein et al., 1983), requires substantiation.

While the leafhopper-transmitted geminiviruses (affecting monocotyledonous and dicotyledonous plants) have monopartite genomes, the whitefly-borne geminiviruses were thought to have exclusively bipartite genomes until just recently. The reported monopartite nature of tomato yellow leaf curl virus (TYLCV) from Israel (Navot et al., 1991) and of TYLCV isolate from Sardinia (Kheyr-Pour et al., 1991) may necessitate establishment of yet another distinct geminivirus subgroup.

During the last ten years, our knowledge of the biological, biochemical and molecular nature of geminiviruses has increased considerably. The advent of recombinant DNA technology and subsequent development of techniques to produce transgenics by introducing cloned nucleic acids into plants, have provided insight into the genomic structure and gene function. Thus by 1983 the genome of a single geminivirus had been cloned and sequenced but no gene functions, with the exception of the capsid gene, had been ascribed, nor viral replication studied. Recent focus of intense investigation, matching the economic importance of

Table 12.1. Diseases caused by whitefly-transmitted geminiviruses

Name of disease	References
Abutilon mosaic	Abouzid and Jeske, 1986; Frischmuth et al., 1990
African cassava mosaic	Bock et al., 1978; Stanley and Gay, 1983
Bean calico mosaic	Brown and Bird, 1992
Bean dwarf mosaic	Brown and Bird, 1992
Bean golden mosaic	Galvez and Castaño, 1976; Goodman et al., 1977; Goodman, 1977a
Bhendi (okra) yellow vein mosaic	Handa (1991), Harrison et al., 1991
Chino del tomate	Brown and Nelson, 1988
Cotton leaf crumple	Brown and Nelson, 1984
Croton yellow vein mosaic	Harrison et al., 1991
Dolichos yellow mosaic	Harrison et al., 1991
Eggplant yellow mosaic	Honda et al., 1986
Eupatorium yellow vein mosaic	Inouye and Osaki, 1980; Bock, 1982
Euphorbia mosaic	Kim and Flores, 1979
Indian cassava mosaic	Malathi and Sreenivasan, 1983; Harrison et al., 1991
Jacquemontia mosaic	Brown and Bird, 1992
Jatropha mosaic	Kim et al., 1986
Macroptilium mosaic	Brown and Bird, 1992
Melon leafcurl	Duffus and Johns, 1985
*Mung bean yellow mosaic	Honda et al., 1983; Morinaga et al., 1990; Muniyappa et al., 1987; Harrison et al., 1991
*(Yellow mosaic of grain legumes including black gram, horse gram, pigeon-pea, soybean)	
Pepper mild tigre	Brown et al., 1989
Rhynchosia yellow mosaic	Brown and Bird, 1992
Serrano golden mosaic	Brown and Bird, 1992
Sida mosaic	Brown and Bird, 1992
Sinaloa tomato leaf curl	Brown and Bird, 1992
Soybean crinkle leaf	Iwaki et al., 1986
Squash leaf curl	Cohen et al., 1983
Squash leaf curl (Watermelon curly mottle strain)	Brown and Nelson, 1986; Brown and Bird, 1992
Texas pepper	Stenger et al., 1990
+Tobacco leaf curl	Osaki and Inouye, 1981; Honda et al., 1986; Harrison et al., 1991
+(Tomato leaf curl, papaya leaf curl, chilli leaf curl).	
Tomato golden mosaic	Maytis et al., 1975; Stein et al., 1983; Hamilton et al., 1984
Tomato mottle	Brown and Bird, 1992
Tomato yellow leaf curl	Czosnek et al., 1988; Navot et al., 1991
Tomato yellow mosaic (Potato yellow mosaic)	Lastra and Gill, 1981

* Closely related, possibly caused by the same virus or its strains
+ Closely related, possibly caused by the same virus or its strains

geminiviruses and their potential as vectors for the expression of foreign genes in plants, has led to genomic information for at least a dozen of these viruses (Lazarowitz, 1992). Gene functions for replication and systemic movement have been defined and viral origins for ssDNA and dsDNA replication have been mapped to small nucleotide regions. Fundamental differences in the genomic structure and organisation of the whitefly- and leafhopper-borne geminiviruses, as well as differences among those infecting dicotyledonous or monocotyledonous hosts, have been established.

In view of the great economic importance of the geminiviruses, a brief survey of the molecular biology of this fascinating group of plant viruses is felt necessary for proper understanding of the diseases and their management.

Molecular Biology of Geminiviruses

Genome Organisation: Goodman (1977a) demonstrated that the genome of bean golden mosaic virus (BGMV) contains ssDNA. A similar observation in respect of the African cassava mosaic (then termed the cassava latent virus) and maize streak viruses was reported by Harrison et al. (1977), who also showed the genome to be circular. Goodman (1977b) estimated the size of the genome to be $7.1–8.0 \times 10^5$ DA corresponding to 2265–2510 nucleotides. The relative small size of the genome and its analogy with other eukaryotic DNA viruses led to the suggestion that the geminivirus genome might be multipartite. The first experimental evidence of a divided genome in the geminivirus was furnished by Haber et al. (1981) for BGMV. Size estimates of the restriction enzyme digest of the BGMV genome indicated cumulative fragment sizes of twice that expected for a single DNA species. The obvious possibility of the occurrence of two distinct but related strains of the same virus was ruled out on the basis of infection kinetics of bean mesophyll protoplast with single-stranded DNA. Hamilton et al. (1982) showed the genome of the tomato golden mosaic virus (TGMV) to be bipartite on the basis of restriction enzyme digestion of virus-specific dsDNA. Nucleotide sequence analysis of ACMV (known then as the cassava latent virus or CLV) by Stanley and Gay (1983) showed the genome to contain two similar sized (2779 and 2724 nucleotides) but distinct circular DNA components. A more definitive proof of the bipartite nature of the ACMV genome was furnished by Stanley (1983) by cloning full-length copies of both components (designated A and B) in the M 13 vector, both of which were shown to be necessary for infectivity. Construction of infective clones of TGMV (Hamilton et al., 1983), BGMV (Morinaga et al., 1983) and squash leaf curl virus

(Lazarowitz and Lazdins, 1991) also revealed the bipartite nature of the genomes. The genome of mung bean yellow mosaic virus (both Thai and Indian isolates) also contains two DNA populations (Morinaga et al., 1990; Varma et al., 1992).

A bipartite genome seemed to be the unifying feature of whitefly-transmitted geminiviruses until Navot et al. (1991) showed that the tomato yellow leaf curl virus (TYLCV) from Israel contains a single genomic component. Through agroinoculation, these authors demonstrated that even a single genomic component has the capacity to cause systemic infection in tomato with severe disease symptoms and that whiteflies could transmit the disease from agroinoculated plants to uninfected test plants. A similar genome organisation of a TYLCV isolate from Sardinia was reported by Kheyr-Pour et al. (1991). Its cloned single DNA component was capable of producing typical symptoms of the disease and *B. tabaci* transmitted the disease from the agroinoculated plants to test tomatoes. These findings were in contrast with those by Rochester et al. (1990), who described a TYLCV isolate from Thailand with a bipartite genome.

The complete genome sequences of several whitefly-borne geminiviruses are now available, namely, ACMV (Stanley and Gay, 1983), TGMV (Hamilton et al., 1984), BGMV (Howarth et al., 1985), AbMV (Frischmuth et al., 1990), SqLCV (Lazarowitz and Lazdins, 1991) and TYLCV (Navot et al., 1991). Sequence comparison indicates a greater degree of homology between DNA-A (or DNA 1) than DNA-B (or DNA 2) of these viruses (Stanley, 1985; Lazarowitz, 1987, 1992). Roberts et al. (1984) showed that ACMV DNA-A can detect BGMV, TobLCV, TGMV and TYLCV although no homologies were detected using ACMV DNA-B. The higher degree of sequence conservation for DNA-A than DNA-B reflects a more rigid structural constraint on DNA-A encoded proteins.

The nucleotide sequence of DNA-A and DNA-B is very different except for a ~200 nucleotide intergenic common region (Stanley and Davies, 1985; Davies et al., 1987; Lazarowitz, 1987, 1992).

Sequence data and analysis of RNA transcripts suggest bidirectional transcription strategy for geminiviruses. DNA-A and DNA-B together encode six genes that are named according to the component (A or B) and location on the virion (rightward) or complementary (leftward) DNA strand. The gene AR 1 is the coat protein gene whereas AL 1 and AL 3 are involved in viral replication. Mutational analysis and expression of viral genes in transgenic plants have shown that the AL 1 protein is the only virus-encoded product required for the replication of DNA-A and its cognate B component (Brough et al., 1988; Elmer et al., 1988; Hanley-Bowdoin et al., 1990; Etessami et al., 1991). On the other hand, the AL 3 gene product increases the efficiency of viral DNA replication but is not essential. DNA-B encodes BR 1 and BL 1, the only genes contained in the B component (Elmer et al., 1988; Brough et al., 1988; Etessami et al., 1988). These two genes along with AL 2 are involved in movement of a virus in plants, the latter possibly playing an indirect role (Sunter and Bisaro, 1991).

Although six functional coding regions have been described, only one virus-specific product, i.e., the coat protein, has been well studied so far. The coat protein open reading frame is highly conserved, reflecting the strong immunogenic cross-reaction observed between whitefly-transmitted geminiviruses. The serological relatedness of whitefly-transmitted members and their common vector, *B. tabaci*, suggests that coat protein plays a crucial role in virus transmission (Roberts et al., 1984).

Although the genes responsible for systemic spread of the virus are thought to be confined to DNA-B, agroinoculation of ACMV DNA-A into *Nicotiana benthamiana* resulted in some systemic spread but no symptoms appeared (Klinkenberg and Stanley, 1990). DNA-A of TYLCV isolate from Thailand seemed even less dependent on DNA-B, as it was capable of both systemic spread and mild symptom production of agroinoculated tobacco and tomato (Rochester et al., 1990). Absence of DNA-B in TYLCV from Israel (Navot et al., 1991) and TYLCV isolate from Sardinia (Kheyr-Pour et al., 1991) and the ability of their DNA-A to complete the disease cycle, support the notion that DNA-B has no function in the interaction of a whitefly-transmitted geminivirus with its vector. A similar thought was expressed by Etessami et al. (1988) in respect of ACMV. Sequencing of the reported B component of TYLCV and genetic analysis should throw new light on the recognition between the A and B components and the partitioning of replication and movement functions in geminiviruses (Lazarowitz, 1992).

Replication: Geminivirus infection is associated with major cytopathological changes in the cell nucleus. Irregular aggregates or a paracrystalline array of virus particles are observed, and nuclei become hypertrophied and separate into granular bodies and a fibrillar structure (Francki et al., 1985; Stanley and Davies, 1985). Kim et al. (1978) showed that granular nuclear structures are largely ribonucleoprotein whereas fibrillar rings are thought to be deoxyribonucleoprotein. The appearance of virus particles in the nucleus coinciding with the development of fibrillar rings, has led to the suggestion that these structures may be sites for DNA relplication or virus assembly.

The replication events of geminiviruses can be divided into synthesis of complementary-sense DNA or, in other words, the conversion of virion ssDNA to a double-stranded form, proliferation of dsDNA and finally, production of virus-sense DNA from a double-strand intermediate. Recently, Saunders et al. (1991) for ACMV, and Stenger et al. (1991) for TGMV, showed that replication is consistent with a rolling circle mechanism. Following uncoating, the single-stranded DNA is converted into a transcriptionally active double-stranded form. The infectious nature of ssDNA from a purified virus was demonstrated earlier for BGMV (Goodman, 1977a, b), TGMV (Hamilton et al., 1981), MYMV (Ikegami et al., 1984), suggesting that synthesis of complementary sense DNA is entirely under the host-encoded enzymes. After the second strand synthesis is over, the gap in the complementary sense is sealed prior to synthesis of virus-sense DNA. As the host factor might be expected to recognise the similar feature of both the genomic components, it was suggested that a common region harbours the origin of replication (Stanley and Gay, 1983). Recently, two groups of workers have independently shown that the geminivirus-coded AL 1 protein is a sequence-specific DNA binding protein and the origin of replication is located within the ~90 nulceotide fragment that includes the conserved geminivirus potential stem loop structure and the ~60 nucleotide of 5' upstream sequence (Fontes et al., 1992; Lazarowitz et al., 1992).

To produce virus-sense DNA from a double-strand template, a nick is then introduced into the virus-sense strand. The 3' terminus of the nicked DNA acts as a primer for DNA synthesis displacing the original virus-sense strand as a template strand is copied, thereby producing concatomeric DNA. After a full round of replication, the nascent DNA is cleaved and relegated to produce a circular single strand and the double-strand template DNA. The circular ssDNA might enter into DNA replication to serve as a template for the generation of additional dsDNA or it might be sequestered for the purpose of encapsidation. Regulation of this process may be under the control of the coat protein (Saunders et al., 1991).

The double-stranded replicative form generated during the replication cycle interacts with the host factor(s) and converts into a transcriptionally active supercoiled DNA (Sc DNA). In analogy with ScDNA of the cauliflower mosaic virus (CaMV), a spherical virus with dsDNA, it may markedly affect host symptomatology.

Since the first demostration of the ssDNA genome of the tomato golden mosaic virus, significant advancement has been made in the molecular biology of geminiviruses. This knowledge has provided a conceptual framework for further research on viral replication and gene expression, as well as the interactions of viral proteins and components with those of the host cell, to gain insight into systemic movement and development of disease. Some progress has recently been achieved in defining sequence elements and domains in viral-encoded proteins that are potentially important in determining viral host range and symptom development in different host plants. Further studies to unveil the factors governing viral movement in the plant, hold potential for engineering resistant mechanisms against different viruses based on dominantly mutant viral-movement proteins in transgenic plants (Lazarowitz, 1992).

Because of the small DNA genome and their ability to multiply in high copy numbers, geminiviruses have attracted attention as an amplifiable vector for stable plant transformation and transient expression assay (Davies and Stanley, 1989; Hayes et al., 1988). This provides two distinct advantages. First, these viruses systematically infect plants, thereby obviating the need for the difficult and time-consuming step of regeneration from a transformed single cell. Secondly, they multiply as an autonomous entity in high copy numbers, which is why any gene cloned in a geminivirus vector will be highly amplified.

The boundaries of the geminivirus group are expanding rapidly with records of more and more diseases caused by its members. In view of the colossal losses caused by these disease in various parts of the world, development of genetically engineered plants providing resistance to geminiviruses, remains the most desirable goal in this field.

Geminivirus Diseases of Economic Importance

Whitefly-borne geminiviruses, transmitted exclusively by *B. tabaci*, affect numerous crops in the tropical and subtropical parts of the world. The more important diseases are briefly discussed here in alphabetical order.
African Cassava Mosaic: Caused by the well-worked-out African cassava mosaic virus (ACMV), earlier known as the cassava latent virus. The type strain of ACMV (ACMV-T), isolated in western Kenya, is serologically related to all other whitefly-transmitted geminiviruses. Isolates of ACMV from different parts of Africa and from India have been divided into three groups on the basis of serology and DNA hybridisation (Harrison et al., 1986). Group A includes strains from Angola, the Ivory Coast, Nigeria, Congo and western Kenya, and also defective strains that do not produce virus particles. Strains from coastal Kenya, Madagascar and Malawi comprise group B; group C strains are not more closely realted to other strains than are different whitefly-transmitted geminiviruses found in other hosts. The name Indian cassava mosaic virus (ICMV) is now used for group C strains from India and Sri Lanka (Fauquet and Fargette, 1990).

The most visible symptom is the leaf mosaic, more pronounced on young plants than old ones. Symptoms range from barely perceptible mosaic to plant stunting and extreme reduction of the leaf blades.

Yield losses due to ACMV, extremely difficult to estimate, have been reported from various countries as ranging from 20 to 95%. On the basis of available data, the total reduction of cassava yield in Africa in plants derived from diseased cuttings is at least 50%, or 50 million metric tons per year, and may be equivalent to $2 billion (U.S.) (Fauquet and Fargette, 1990). In view of the fact that cassava is the most important food crop grown in the African continent, the tremendous economic impact is quite clear.

Bean Golden Mosaic: When first reported from Sao Paulo, Brazil, BGMV was considered a minor disease. Now it is prevalent in the Americas and the Caribbean Basin (Brown and Bird, 1992) and has become an economically important disease in many countries (Bock, 1982).

Infected plants of *Phaseolus vulgaris* and other leguminous hosts show downward rolling of leaves which later develop golden mosaic symptoms. Infection with BGMV apparently reduces the number of pods, the number of seeds per pod and seed weight. Losses in yield vary from 40 to 100% depending on the age of the crop at the time of infection, varietal differences and possible strains of the virus (Bock, 1982). The prevalence of BGMV has been attributed at least in part to an increase in populations of *B. tabaci* due to expanding cultivation of soybean, which is not a host of the virus but supports large populations of the vector that emigrate to *P. vulgaris* and other beans as the soybean crops mature. It has also been suggested that tobacco, tomato and cotton plantings in El Salvador and Guatemala are largely responsible for enhancing populations of the whitefly (Bock, 1982).

Bhendi (Okra) Yellow Vein Mosaic (Fig. 12.1): Yellow vein mosaic disease of bhendi (*Abelomoschus esculentus*) was first reported from Bombay, India in the early 1920s and is very common in India, Sri Lanka and Bangladesh. It has posed a major constraint to the cultivation of this popular vegetable crop in many areas. Capoor and Varma described the disease in detail back in 1950.

The first detectable symptom is clearing of the small veins, followed by the same of the larger ones. Veins on the lower surface in the leaves show thickening. Leaves of severely diseased plants exhibit general chlorosis. Flowering in infected plants is sparse and few fruits form. Loss in yield may exceed 80% if the plants are infected within 4–5 weeks after germination.

Handa (1991) established bhendi yellow vein mosaic virus (BYVMV) to be a geminivirus. NASH tests, using heterologous probes of ICMV DNA-A, showed that it is possible to detect BYVMV-specific DNA sequences in crude DNA extracts prepared from infected tissues as well as from

Fig. 12.1. Leaf of bhendi (okra) showing symptoms of yellow vein mosaic.

Fig. 12.2. Trifoliate leaf of black gram, showing symptoms of MYMV.

Fig. 12.3. Yellow mosaic with leaf curling in Frenchbean due to MYMV infection.

Fig. 12.4. Tobacco plant showing symptoms of leaf curl.

viruliferous whiteflies. Harrison et al. (1991) also reported BYVMV to be caused by a geminivirus.

Chino del Tomate: The disease has been a serious problem to tomato cultivations in Mexico since 1970 and the causal virus is now known as Chino del tomate virus (CdTV), a geminivirus (Brown and Nelson, 1988). The virus has an apparently narrow host range within Asclepiadaceae, Leguminosae, Malvaceae and Solanaceae and includes economically important plants in Solanaceae (tomato, pepper) and Leguminosae (common bean, mung bean). It is similar in some respects to tomato golden mosaic virus (TGMV) but differs in host range and, unlike TGMV, CdTV is not mechanically transmissible. CdTV may be closely related to tomato yellow leaf curl virus prevalent in the Middle East and Africa (Brown and Nelson, 1988).

Cotton Leaf Crumple: This disease of cotton was reported by Dickson et al. (1954) from Coachella and south-eastern California in the United States. It has also been reported from India (Mali, 1977). The primary symptom is hypertrophy of the intervenal leaf tissue, along with shortening of veins in severe cases. A severe strain of the virus causes mosaic, puckering and downward cupping of the leaves and symmetrical ruffing of petals in some cotton varieties. The symptoms of leaf crumple disease are distinct from those of cotton leaf curl in Africa and crazytop in Arizona (Dickson et al., 1954).

Cotton leaf crumple virus (CLCV) also infects common bean, cheeseweed, *Malva parviflora*, and several other species of cultivated plants and weeds (Duffus and Flock, 1982; Brown and Nelson, 1984, 1987). Problems of CLCV are mostly associated with situations wherein cotton is ratooned (Byrne et al., 1990).

Mung Bean Yellow Mosaic (Figs 12.2; 12.3): The disease of mung bean (*Phaseolus aureus*) was first reported from New Delhi, India. The causal virus, mung bean yellow mosaic virus (MYMV), could be transmitted by *B. tabaci* and grafting but not by sap inoculation (Nariani, 1960). Subsequently, MYMV was found to occur widely in the Indian subcontinent, causing severe losses to grain legumes (Chenulu and Varma, 1988). It has a slightly broader range of hosts than BGMV, including several other *Phaseolus* spp. and soybean (Honda et al., 1983). Of the various hosts of MYMV, mung bean, black gram (*P. mungo*) and soybean are more seriously affected.

Initial symptoms of the disease on mung bean appear on the young leaves in the form of mild scattered yellow specks or spots. The next trifoliate leaf emerging from the growing apex shows irregular alternation of yellow and green patches. The green areas are sometimes raised, causing slight puckering and reduction in leaf size. Some of the apical leaves turn completely yellow. Infection leads to reduction in plant size and number of flowers. The pods are fewer and smaller, bearing small and mostly shrivelled seeds.

Infected back gram plants show more or less similar symptoms. Early infection may result in total crop failure.

Various isolates of MYMV from India, Bangladesh, Pakistan and Sri Lanka have similar transmission characteristics but the Thailand isolate differs from all of them in being readily sap transmissible (Honda et al., 1983).

Reduction in yield due to MYMV depends on the age of the crop at the time of infection and severity of disease. Estimation of losses due to the disease in farmer's fields is difficult as it varies from year to year and variety to variety. According to conservative estimates, the extent of loss due to MYMV in epidemic years is over $300 million (U.S.) in the three major crops, namely, black gram, mung bean and soybean (Varma et al., 1991).

Squash Leaf Curl: This whitefly-borne disease of cucurbits in California was first described as squash leaf curl disease by Flock and Mayhew (1981). The viral nature of the disease was described by Cohen et al. (1983), who showed it (SLCV) to be a geminivirus.

Severe stunting and leaf curl symptoms were induced by SLCV in all cultivars of *Cucurbita maxima, C. moschata* and *C. pepo* tested. Besides squashes, SLCV severely reduces yields in such crops as lettuce, cantaloupe and cucumber. The watermelon curly mottle strain of SLCV (Brown and Bird, 1992) infects watermelon.

Tobacco Leaf Curl (Fig. 12.4): The disease is caused by the tobacco leaf curl virus (TbLCV) which enjoys a wide distribution in the tropics and its range also includes the United States, Europe and Japan.

The leaves of affected plants develop curling, vein thickening, venal depressions and enations. The affected plants remain stunted. Several types of symptoms on tobacco caused by different isolates of the virus suggest the occurrence of strains of TbLCV.

The leaf curl malady is the most destructive disease of tobacco in India and causes substantial yield losses (Pal and Tandon, 1937; Pruthi and Samuel, 1942; Reddy and Nagarajan, 1982).The epidemiology of the tobacco leaf curl disease in India was recently studied by Valand and Muniyappa (1992). They found the incidence of the disease in ten tobacco-growing areas in India to range from 1.2% to 77%, with the highest in Andhra Pradesh, followed by 59% in Gujarat.

It appears from the literature that several leaf curl diseases of other crops such as chilli (*Capsicum annuum*), tomato and papaya are caused by TbLCV, but the molecular relationships of these diseases have yet to be worked out. The regular and widespread occurrence of these diseases and the losses caused, merit some discussion.

Chilli Leaf Curl: The most characteristic symptom is the abaxial curling of the leaf blade. Curling of leaves is accompained by puckering and blistering of intervenal areas and thickening and swelling of veins. As the disease progresses, clusters of small leaves are produced by axillary buds and the plant assumes a bushy appearance with stunted growth (Mishra et al., 1963).

The disease is quite common in different parts of India and is also a major disease of chilli in Sri Lanka. Shivanathan (1983) studied the epidemiology of the disease in Sri Lanka.

Papaya Leaf Curl: The disease was first reported by Thomas and Krishnaswami (1939) from Madras, India.

The characteristic symptoms are severe curling, crinkling and distortion of the leaves, which become leathery and brittle and the intervenal areas become rugose. Plant growth is arrested and neither flowers nor fruits are borne. Those fruits which had set before infection become rough and small in size.

Papaya leaf curl, also known as leaf crinkle, is very widespread in India.

Tomato Leaf Curl: This is the most important disease of tomato in India (Pruthi and Samuel, 1939; Sastry and Singh, 1973; Butter and Rataul, 1981; Muniyappa and Veeresh, 1984; Chenulu and Giri, 1985) and perhaps in many tropical countries (McClean, 1940; Yassin and Nour, 1965; Nour-Eldin et al., 1969; Yassin, 1978; Retuerma et al., 1977; Thanapase et al., 1983).

The main symptoms are vein-clearing, stunting and marked reduction in leaf size with mild or severe mosaic pattern or chlorosis with marginal curling of leaves. Severely affected plants show complete yellowing of intervenal areas and puckering of leaves. Occasionally the younger leaves resemble cork-screws. Production of numerous lateral branches imparts a bushy appearance to the affected plant. The disease induces complete or partial sterility.

Losses in tomato yield depend on severity and the stage of the crop at the time of infection. Early infection may result in losses of over 90%.

Tomato Yellow Leaf Curl: The disease was first described by Cohen and Harpaz (1964) from Israel, where it is the principal problem in tomatoes (Czosnek et al., 1988) and causes severe losses. The disease also occurs in the Mediterranean basin and East Africa.

Infected plants show chlorosis and curling of the leaves. The virus causes thickening of leaves and drying of plants.

The tomato yellow leaf curl virus (TYLCV) has a unique relationship with its vector, *B. tabaci*, and a very distinctive genomic organisation.

The unusual phenomenon in virus-vector relationship is that the vector cannot acquire a new virus unless transmission following previous acquisition has completely ceased. Cohen and Harpaz (1964) termed this phenomenon 'periodic acquisition'.

Another distinctive feature of TYLCV is the absence of DNA-B; it is the lone example among whitefly-transmitted geminiviruses. This aspect has already been discussed earlier in this chapter.

Besides the geminivirus diseases discussed so far, there are several others which occasionally create problems. The more important of these include tomato golden mosaic virus (TGMV), which has been well characterised and is prevalent in South America, and soybean crinkle leaf, which occurs widely in Thailand (Iwaki et al., 1983).

Diseases Caused by Other Viruses

Besides geminiviruses, *B. tabaci* transmits a few rod-shaped viruses as well. The diseases caused by them are briefly dealt with here.

Cowpea Mild Mottle: The disease was first recorded on cowpea in Ghana (Brunt and Kenten, 1973) and reported later in groundnut in India and Thailand. Cowpea mild mottle virus (CMMV) is a slightly flexuous rod-shaped particle, measuring 10–15 × 650–700 nm (Iwaki et al., 1982) and appears to be carlavirus.

Transmission characteristics show the virus to be non-circulative and non-persistent in nature with apparently no latent peiod (Muniyappa and Reddy, 1983). Since and symptoms of the disease are mild or not detectable, it is of no great concern.

Cucumber Vein Yellowing: The disease has been reported to infect cucumbers, cantaloupe and pumpkin in Israel (Cohen and Nitzany, 1960). The virus is unique in being a rod-shaped (740–800 × 15–18 nm) one with double-stranded DNA (Sela et al., 1980). Transmission by *B. tabaci* is semi-persistent in nature and the virus can also be transmitted mechanically; however, both methods proved inefficient (Sela et al., 1980).

Lettuce Infectious Yellows: The disease occurred pandemically for the first time in 1981 in the crop-growing desert areas of south-western United States, infecting virtually 100% of the lettuce plantings and other crops that could serve as host of the virus. Yields of lettuce, sugar-beet, cantaloupe and melons were severely affected.

The causal virus was described as lettuce infectious yellows virus (LIYV) by Duffus et al. (1986). The particles are long and flexuous, measuring 1800–2000 × 13–14 nm. The virus is transmitted by *B. tabaci* in a semi-persistent manner.

The virus is of considerable economic importance in the United States.
Sweet-potato Mild Mottle: This disease, reported from eastern Africa, is caused by the sweet-potato mild mottle virus (SPMMV). The virus resembles potyviruses in having 800–950 nm long filamentous particles with one protein of 3.7×10^4 molecular weight and single-stranded RNA (Hollings et al., 1976). It induces the formation of cytoplasmic pinwheel inclusions, characteristic of the potyviruses.

Milne (1988) divided the large group of potyviruses into four subgroups according to the vector group involved in transmission. The sole representative of the whitefly-transmitted subgroup is SPMMV. Although transmission of SPMMV by *B. tabaci* has not yet been defined in terms of persistence (Duffus, 1987), the characteristic pinwheel inclusions justify its inclusion in the potyvirus group.

Since most of the hosts of SPMMV are non-cultivated plants, the virus has not been reported to create much concern.
Tomato Necrotic Dwarf: Larsen et al. (1984) reported a new whitefly-transmitted virus, namely, tomato necrotic dwarf virus (TNDV), to affect tomato, pepper and other solanaceous crops and weeds. Infected plants show mosaic or ringspot symptoms. The virus is transmitted mechanically and by *B. tabaci* in a non-persistent manner. The virus has been shown to contain three distinct isometric components, about 30 nm in diameter. The sedimentation coefficient of the three types of particles was 57S, 117S and 138S. Molecular weights of the single-stranded RNA of the middle and botton components were 1.8×10^6 and 2.7×10^6 respectively. Both these components are required to initiate infection, as appeared from mechanical inoculation tests.

The virus apparently has close affinities with the comoviruses and nepoviruses; Duffus (1987) considered TNDV to be nepovirus-like.

Virus-Vector Relationships

Information on virus-vector relationships provides valuable clues to the epidemiology of vector-borne diseases and helps in devising control strategies. The criteria for distinguishing different types of relationships, namely, *non-persistent, semi-persistent* and *persistent*, were evolved during studies on aphid transmission. Besides these terms, based on duration of infectivity following acquisition of the virus, viruses are first broadly grouped as *circulative* and *non-circulative* on the basis of virus route in vectors. The transmission characteristics in different types of virus-vector relationships are given in Table 12.2.

The term 'circulative' refers to virus transmission wherein the virus is absorbed through the midgut wall to the haemolymph, translocated to the salivary glands and eventually inoculated into plants through the virus-laden saliva. The first and foremost test of a circulative virus is its passage through moulting of the vector, which means that the vector remains infective after moulting. A non-circulative virus, on the other hand, is lost by moulting since the cuticular lining of the foregut is shed like the stylets.

While the persistent viruses are logically deemed to be circulative, both non-persistent and semi-persistent viruses are non-circulative. Although these terms are not equally applicable to vector groups other than the aphids and are often difficult to determine experimentally, they are frequently used in the literature. Since all developmental stages of *B. tabaci* are sedentary except for the first-instar nymphs prior to settling down for feeding, it is difficult to determine whether the virus passes through moults. However, removal of pupae formed on diseased plants and tests with adults emerging from the same, have given evidence of transtadial passage of some viruses.

The aspects of virus-vector relationships commonly studied include the acquisition and inoculation threshold periods, latent period, the ability of single whiteflies to infect plants, the number of whitefly adults to cause maximum infection, and the period for which the vector remains infective.

Table 12.2. Transmission characteristics of different types of virus-vector relationships (Basu and Giri, 1993)

Test	Non-circulative		Circulative
	Non-persistent	Semi-persistent	Persistent
Preacquisition fasting	Enhances chances of acquisition	No such effect	No such effect
Superficial probing	-do-	No acquisition	No acquisition
Duration of acquisition access	Longer the access, *lesser* the chance of acquisition	Longer the access, *better* the chance of acquisition	Longer the access, *better* the chance of acquisition
Latent period	No detectable latent period	No detectable latent period	Always a latent period following acquisition to become infective
Effect of moulting	Vector no longer remains infective	Vector no longer remains infective	Transmission not affected
Injection of purified virus into haemolymph	Insect not rendered infective	Not rendered infective	Injected insect becomes infective
Retention of infectivity	Minutes or hours, rarely longer	Hours to days	Days to weeks, often lifelong

Studies on sex-wise differences in transmission ability and differences in transmission ability of whiteflies reared on different hosts are relatively few. The findings of numerous experiments with various virus-host combinations under different conditions, are diverse and extensive. The salient aspects are given here without unnecessary details.

The inoculation threshold is generally less than the acquisition threshold. Demonstration of the existence of a latent period is important since it provides evidence of the circulative nature of the virus. But the duration of the latent period as well as that of the period of virus retention arrived at through one experiment may vary in another since these depend on several factors, especially the ambient temperature. With regard to the number of whiteflies, batches of five or more invariably gave significantly higher percentages of transmission than did single whiteflies. The females retained infectivity for much longer periods and generally proved to be more efficient than the males with rare exceptions. For instance, Butter and Rataul (1978) found the transmission rate of tomato leaf curl virus (TLCV) for males to be 86% against 56% for females.

Of the various types of viruses transmitted by *B. tabaci*, only the geminiviruses are transmitted in a circulative-persistent manner. Unlike non-circulative viruses, there is always a detectable latent period after acquisition for the vector to become infective. Infectivity is retained much longer, at least for a few days and often for weeks. There is no evidence so far of multiplication of a geminivirus within the vector. This holds true also for the well-studied leafhopper-borne geminiviruses, namely, maize streak and beet curly top.

As already mentioned, a unique phenomenon in the virus-whitefly relationship, known as *periodic acquisition* (Cohen and Harpaz, 1964), was discovered during transmission studies of tomato yellow leaf curl virus (TYLCV) by *B. tabaci*. The vector was found to progressively lose infectivity and most insects became non-infective 10 days after completion of acquisition access. The progressive loss of infectivity could not be prevented by prolonged or repeated access to the infected source plant. What was unique was the observation that infectivity of such vector individuals could be restored *only when they ceased to transmit completely.* A similar phenomenon was reported by Verma et al. (1975) during transmission studies on tomato yellow mosaic virus by *B. tabaci* in India.

An antiviral factor was detected in the homogenates of whiteflies carrying TYCLV which was termed Periodic Acquisition Related Factor (PARF). Reduced transmission of the virus was demonstrated by feeding whiteflies on PARF through parafilm membrane before or after acquisition. Further, a new factor, PARF-a, which is proteinaceous in nature, suppressed inoculation of TYLCV by the whiteflies when injected into them (Cohen, 1967, 1969; Cohen and Marco, 1970).

There is still no evidence of any propagative whitefly-borne virus. Squash leaf curl virus (SLCV) antigen could be detected by ELISA in extracts of female *B. tabaci* previously fed for over 48 hours on a source plant (Cohen et al., 1989). The SLCV antigen detected by ELISA decreased rapidly with time after leaving the source following acquisition. This suggests that SLCV is non-propagative. The SLCV antigen was also found to accumulate in the haemolymph of the non-vector whitefly, *Trialeurodes abutilonea* (Haldeman). An interesting observation was the reduction in transmission efficiency of melon leaf curl virus (MLCV), a virus closely related to SLCV, when insects were first allowed to acquire SLCV. These findings strongly indicate the active role played by the accessory salivary galnd in determining and regulating virus transmission, apparently by virus coat protein-specific receptors on its membrane surface.

The role of the coat protein in determining vector specificity was clearly demonstrated by Briddon et al. (1990). They substituted the coat protein gene of the single component beet curly top virus (BCTV) into the A component of the bipartite African cassava mosaic virus (ACMV). This chimeric virus was found to be transmitted by *Circulifer tenellus* (Baker), the leafhopper vector of BCTV, whereas ACMV was not transmitted by this vector.

Navot et al. (1989) described a rapid and sensitive technique for detection of TYLCV in squashes of plants and in single whiteflies that fed on infected plants. Polston et al. (1990) detected SLCV in *B. tabaci* by using full-length cDNA clones of the SLCV genome in a nucleic acid spot hybridisation assay. Viral cDNA was detected more readily in individual whiteflies ground in buffer and spotted onto membranes than in whiteflies squashed onto membranes. Viral nucleic acid was detected in adult whiteflies for at least 120 hours after 12–24 h acquisition access periods on infected plants. Viral nucleic acid remained constant over the 120 h period, while the whitefly fed on a non-host plant.

All the whitefly-borne viruses outside the geminivirus group have been reported to be transmitted semi-persistently with only a couple of examples of non-persistent transmission. The transmission of cowpea mild mottle virus (CMMV) and tomato pale chlorosis disease virus (TPCDV) has been reported to be non-persistent in nature, though the transmission properties are not strictly like those of aphid-borne ones. For instance, starvation before acquisition feed had no influence on transmission of CMMV (Muniyappa and Reddy, 1983). Both the viruses can be acquired in 10–15 min and inoculated in healthy plants in 5–15 min. Acquisition access from

1/2 to 1 h enhanced transmission but longer acquisition access did not improve the rate. The vector retained CMMV for 1 h and TPCDV for 6 h.

Effect of Virus-Infected Host Plant on *B. tabaci*: The effect of virus infection on *B. tabaci* has rarely been investigated. Butter and Rataul (1977) reported the effect of TLCV on the whitefly. They found significant reduction in the fecundity and fertility of the viruliferous females but no effect on the lifespan of adults of either sex. Murugesan and Chelliah (1978) studied the biology of *B. tabaci* on healthy and diseased plants of green gram (*Vigna radiata*), affected by the yellow mosaic disease. The whitefly was found to prefer infected to healthy plants for oviposition. The total developmental period on healthy and infected plants was 24.7 and 21.3 days repectively. Cohen et al. (1983) noted apparent harmful effects of SLCV on *B. tabaci*. The lifespan of female whiteflies fed for 24 h on SLCV-infected plants was significantly shorter than that of females fed on the same virus source for only 4 h. The average lifespan of females was 19.5 days, following feeding on the source for 24 h, whereas those fed for 4 h lived for 25.4 days.

Costa et al. (1991) compared the life history traits of *B. tabaci* on six virus-infected plant species with that on healthy ones. The adult whiteflies used in the experiments were from a population of *B. tabaci* that had been reared continuously on pumpkin plants for more than five years. They were exposed to the six plant species infected with one of four whitefly-transmitted plant viruses. Oviposition and immature survival rates varied between healthy and virus-infected host plants. Pumpkin was the only host on which whitefly progeny survived better on plants infected with watermelon curly mottle strain of squash leaf curl virus (WCMoV/SLCV) than on healthy plants. A significantly lower mean proportion of offspring survived to adulthood on zucchini infected with WCMoV/SLCV, on tomato infected with chino del tomate virus, and on cotton infected with cotton leaf crumple virus, compared to whiteflies on healthy control plants. For other virus-infected-healthy combinations there were no significant differenes in survival rates. No correlation was found between levels of total free amino acids in healthy and virus-infected plants and rates of oviposition and survival.

REFERENCES

Abouzid, A. and Jeske, H. (1986). The purification and characterization of gemini particles from Abutilon mosaic virus infected Malvaceae. *J. Phytopath.* **115**: 344–353.

Adejare, G.O. and Coutts, R.H.A. (1982). The isolation and characterisation of the virus from Nigerian cassava plants affected with cassava mosaic disease and attempted transmission of the disease. *Phytopathologische Zeitschrift* **103**: 190–210.

Basu, A.N. and Giri, B.K. (1993). *The Essentials of Viruses, Vectors and Plant Diseases.* Wiley Eastern, New Delhi, 242 pp.

Bird, J. and Maramorosch, K. (1978). Viruses and virus-diseases associated with whiteflies. In: *Advances in Virus Reaearch* (M.A. Lauffer, F.B. Bang, K. Maramorosch and K.M. Smith, eds.). Academic Press, London, **22**: 55–110.

Bock, K.R. (1982). Geminivirus diseases in tropical crops. *Plant Diseases* **66** (3): 266–270.

Bock, K.R., Guthrie, E.J. and Meredith, G.C. (1978). Distribution, host range, properties and purification of cassava latent virus, a geminivirus. *Ann. Appl. Biol.* **90**: 361–367.

Bock, K.R., Guthrie, E.J. and Woods, R.D. (1974). Purification of maize streak virus and its relationship to viruses associated with streak disease of sugar cane and *Panicum maximum. Ann. Appl. Biol.* **77**: 289–296.

Briddon, R.W., Pinner, M.S., Stanley, J. and Markham, P.G. (1990). Geminivirus coat protein gene replacement alters insect specificity. *Virology* **177**: 85.

Brough, C.L., Hayes, R.J., Morgan, A.J., Coutts, R.H.A. and Buck, K.W. (1988). Effect of mutagenesis *in vitro* on the ability of cloned tomato golden mosaic virus DNA to infect *Nicotiana benthamiana* plants. *J. Gen. Virol.* **69**: 503–514.

Brown, J.K. and Nelson, M.R. (1984). Geminate particles associated with cotton leaf crumple disease in Arizona. *Phytopathology* **74**: 987–990.

Brown, J.K. and Nelson, M.R. (1986). Characterisation of watermelon curly mottle virus, a geminivirus distinct from squash leaf curl virus. *Ann. Appl. Biol.* **115** (2): 243–252.

Brown, J.K. and Nelson, M.R. (1987). Host range and vector relationships of cotton leaf crumple virus. *Plant Disease* **71**: 522–524.

Brown, J.K. and Nelson, M.R. (1988). Transmission, host range, and virus-vector relationships of chino del tomate virus, a whitefly-transmitted geminivirus from Sinaloa, Mexico. *Plant Disease* **72**: 866–869.

Brown, J.K. and Bird, J. (1992). Whitefly-transmitted geminiviruses and associated disorders in the Americas and the Caribbean Basin. *Plant Disease* **76** (3): 220–225.

Brown, J.K., Campodonico, O.P. and Nelson, M.R. (1989). A whitefly-transmitted geminivirus from peppers with tigre disease. *Plant Disease* **73**: 610.

Brunt, A.A. (1986). Transmission of Diseases. In: *Bemisia tabaci—A Literature Survey* (M.J.W. Cock, ed.). C.A.B. International Institute of Biological Control, U.K., pp. 43–49.

Brunt, A.A. and Kenten, R.H. (1973). Cowpea mild mottle, a newly recognised virus infecting cowpea (*Vigna unguiculata*) in Ghana. *Ann. Appl. Biol.* **74**: 67–74.

Butter, N.S. and Rataul, H.S. (1977). Effect of TLCV infection on *Bemisia tabaci. Entomon* **2** (2): 163–164.

Butter, N.S. and Rataul, H.S. (1978). The virus-vector relationship of the tomato leaf curl virus (TLCV) and its vector, *Bemisia tabaci* Gennadius (Hemiptera: Aleyrodidae). *Phytoparasitica* **5** (3): 173–186.

Butter, N.S. and Rataul, H.S. (1981). Control strategies in whitefly-borne viruses—a review. *Pestology* **5** (12): 7–14.

Byrne, D.N., Bellows, T.S. and Parrella, M.P. (1990). Whiteflies in agricultural systems. In: *Whiteflies: Their Bionomics, Pest Status and Management* (D. Gerling, ed.). Intercept, Wimborne, England, pp. 227–261.

Capoor, S.P. and Varma, P.M. (1950). Yellow vein-mosaic of *Hibiscus esculentus* L. *Indian J. Agric. Sci.* **20**: 217–230.

Chenulu, V.V. and Giri, B.K. (1985). Viral and mycoplasmal diseases of tomato and their management. In: *Perspectives in Plant Virology* (B.M. Gupta, H.N. Varma and K.M. Srivastava, eds.). Print House, Lucknow, India, pp. 45–74.

Chenulu, V.V. and Varma, A. (1988). Virus and virus-like diseases of pulse crops commonly grown in India. In: *Pulse Crops* (B. Baldev, S. Ramanujam and H.K. Jain, eds.). Oxford and IBH Publishing Co., New Delhi, pp. 339–370.

Cohen, S. (1967). The occurrence in the body of *Bemisia tabaci* of a factor apparently related to the phenomenon of 'periodic acquisition' of tomato yellow leaf curl virus. *Virology* **31**: 180–183.

Cohen, S. (1969). *In vivo* effects in whiteflies of a possible antiviral factor. *Virology* **37**: 448–454.

Cohen, S. (1990). Epidemiology of whitefly-transmitted viruses. In: *Whiteflies: Their Bionomics, Pest Status and Management* (D. Gerling, ed.). Intercept, Wimborne, England, pp. 211–225.

Cohen, S., Duffus, J.E., Larsen, R.C., Liu, H.Y. and Flock, R.A. (1983). Purification, serology, and vector relationships of squash leaf curl virus, a whitefly-transmitted geminivirus. *Phytopathology* **73**: 1669–1673.

Cohen, S., Duffus, J.E. and Liu, H.Y. (1989). Acquisition, interference, and retention of cucurbit leaf curl viruses. *Phytopathology* **79**: 109–113.

Cohen, S. and Harpaz, I. (1964). Periodic, rather than continual acquisition of a new tomato virus by its vector, the tobacco whitefly (*Bemisia tabaci* Gennadius). *Entomol. Experim. Appl.* **7**: 155–166.

Cohen, S. and Marco, S. (1970). Periodic occurrence of an anti-TMV factor in the body of whiteflies carrying the tomato yellow leaf curl virus (TYLCV). *Virology* **40**: 363–368.

Cohen, S. and Nitzany, F.E. (1960). A whitefly transmitted virus of cucurbits in Israel. *Phytopath. Mediterranea* **1**: 44–46.

Costa, A.S. (1969). White flies as virus vectors. In: *Viruses, Vectors and Vegetation* (K. Maramorosch, ed.). Interscience, New York, pp. 95–119.

Costa, A.S. (1976). Whitefly-transmitted plant diseases. *Ann. Rev. Phytopath.* **14**: 429–449.

Costa, H.S., Brown, J.K. and Byrne, D.N. (1991). Life history traits of the whitefly, *Bemisia tabaci* (Homoptera: Aleyrodidae) on six virus-infected or healthy plant species. *Environ. Entomol.* **20** (4): 1102–1107.

Czosnek, H., Ber, R., Navot, N., Zamir, D., Antignus, Y. and Cohen, S. (1988). Detection of tomato yellow leaf curl virus in lysates of plants and insects by hybridization and with a viral DNA probe. *Plant Disease* **72**: 949–951.

Davies, J.W. and Stanley, J. (1989). Geminiviruses, genes and vectors. *TIG* **5**: 77–81.

Davies, J.W., Stanley, J., Donson, J., Mullineaux, P.M. and Boulton, M.I. (1987). Structure and replication of geminivirus genomes. *J. Cell. Sci. Suppl.* **7**: 95–107.

Dickson, R.C., Johnson, M. McD. and Laird, E.F. (1954). Leaf crumple, a virus disease of cotton. *Phytopathology* **44**: 479–480.

Duffus, J.E. (1987). Whitefly transmission of plant viruses. In: *Current Topics in Vector Research* (K.F. Harris, ed.). Springer-Verlag, New York, **4**: 73–91.

Duffus, J.E. and Flock, R.A. (1982). Whitefly-transmitted disease complex of the desert southwest. *Calif. Agric.* **36**: 4–6.

Duffus, J.E. and Johns, M.R. (1985). Melon leaf curl virus—a new geminivirus with host and serological variations from squash leaf curl virus (abstract 274). *Phytopathology* **75**: 1312.

Duffus, J.E., Larsen, R.C. and Liu, H.Y. (1986). Lettuce infectious yellows virus—a new type of whitefly-transmitted virus. *Phytopathology* **76**: 97–100.

Elmer, J.S., Brand, L., Sunter, G., Gardiner, W., Bisaro, D.M. and Rogers, S.G. (1988). Genetic analysis of tomato golden mosaic virus. II. The conserved AL1 ORF product is essential for replication. *Nucleic Acids Research* 16: 7043–7060.

Estessami, P., Callis, R., Ellwood, S. and Stanley, J. (1988). Delimitation of essential genes of cassava latent virus DNA 2. *Nucleic Acids Research* 16: 4811–4829.

Etessami, P., Saunders, K., Watts, J. and Stanley, J. (1991). Mutational analysis of complementary sense genes of African cassava mosaic virus DNA A. *J. Gen. Virol.* 72: 1005–1012.

Fauquet, C. and Fargette, D. (1990). African cassava mosaic virus: etiology, epidemiology and control. *Plant Disease* 74 (6): 404–411.

Flock, R.A. and Mayhew, D.E. (1981). Squash leaf curl, a new disease of cucurbits in California. *Plant Disease* 65: 75–76.

Fontes, E.P.B., Luckow, V.A. and Hanley-Bowdoin, L. (1992). A geminivirus replication protein is a sequence specific DNA binding protein. *Plant Cell* 4: 597–608.

Francki, R.I.B., Milne, R.G. and Hatta, T. (1985). Geminivirus group. In: *Atlas of Plant Viruses.* CRC Press, Boca Raton, Florida, 1: 33–46.

Frischmuth, T., Zimmat, G. and Zeske, H. (1990). The nucleotide sequence of Abutilon mosaic virus reveals prokaryotic as well as eukaryotic features. *Virology* 178: 461–468.

Galvez, G.E. and Castaño, M. (1976). Purification of the whitefly-transmitted bean golden mosaic virus. *Turrialba* 26: 205–207.

Golding, F.D. (1930). A vector of leaf curl of cotton in southern Nigeria. *Empire Cotton Growing Review* 7: 120–126.

Goodman, R.M. (1977a). Single stranded DNA genome in a whitefly-transmitted plant virus. *Virology* 83: 171–179.

Goodman, R.M. (1977b). Infectious DNA from a whitefly-transmitted virus of *Phaseolus vulgaris. Nature* 266: 54–55.

Goodman, R.M., Bird, J. and Thongmeearkom, P. (1977). An unusual virus-like particle associated with golden yellow mosaic of beans. *Phytopathology* 67: 37–42.

Haber, S., Ikegami, M., Bajet, N.B. and Goodman, R.M. (1981). Evidence for a divided genome for bean golden mosaic virus, a geminivirus. *Nature* 289: 324–326.

Hamilton, W.D.O., Bisaro, D.M. and Buck, K.W. (1982). Identification of novel DNA forms in tomato golden mosaic virus infected tissues. Evidence for a two component viral genome. *Nucleic Acids Research* 10: 4901–4912.

Hamilton, W.D.O., Bisaro, D.M., Coutts, R.H.A. and Buck, K.W. (1983). Demonstration of the bipartite nature of the genome of a single-stranded DNA plant virus by infection with the cloned DNA components. *Nucleic Acids Research* 11: 7387–7396.

Hamilton, W.D.O., Sanders, R.C., Coutts, R.H.A. and Buck, K.W. (1981). Characterisation of tomato golden mosaic virus as a geminivirus. *FEMS Microbiol. Lett.* 11: 1263–1267.

Hamilton, W.D.O., Stein, V.E., Coutts, R.H.A. and Buck, K.W. (1984). Complete nucleotide sequence of the infectious cloned DNA components of tomato golden mosaic virus: Potential coding regions and regulatory sequences. *EMBO Journal* 3: 2197–2205.

Handa, A. (1991). Further studies on yellow vein mosaic of okra (*Abelomoschus esculentus* (L.) Moench. Ph.D. thesis, Indian Agric. Res. Inst., New Delhi, 102 pp.

Hanley-Bowdoin, L., Elmer, J.S. and Rogers, S.G. (1990). Expression of functional replication protein from tomato golden mosaic virus in transgenic tobacco plants. *Proc. Natl. Acad. Sci.,* U.S.A. 87: 1446–1450.

Harrison, B.D., Barker, H., Bock, K.R., Guthrie, E.J., Meredith G. and Atkinson, M. (1977). Plant viruses with circular single-stranded DNA. *Nature* 270: 760.

Harrison, B.D., Lennon, A.M., Massalski, P.R., Robinson, D.J. and Thomas, J.E. (1986). Geographical variation in African cassava mosaic virus. Proc. 10th Plant Virus Epidemiological Workshop, pp. 9–11.

Harrison, B.D., Muniyappa, V., Swanson, M.M., Roberts, I.M. and Robinson, D.J. (1991). Recognition and differentiation of seven whitefly-transmitted geminiviruses from India, and their relationships to African cassava mosiac and Thailand mung bean yellow mosaic viruses. *Ann. Appl. Biol.* 118 (2): 299–308.

Hayes, R.J., Petty, I.T.D., Coutts, R.H.A. and Buck, K.W. (1988). Gene amplification and expression in plants by a replicating geminiviurs vector. *Nature* 334: 179–182.

Hollings, M., Stone, O.M. and Bock, K.R. (1976). Sweet potato mild mottle virus. *CMI/AAB Descrip. Plant Viruses* 162, 4 pp.

Honda, Y., Iwaki, M., Saito, Y., Thongmeearkom, P., Kittisak, K. and Deema, N. (1983). Mechanical transmission, purification, and some properties of whitefly-borne mungbean yellow mosaic virus in Thailand. *Plant Disease* 67: 801–804.

Honda, Y., Kiratiya-Angul, K., Sriihongchai, W. and Kiratiya-Angul, S. (1986). Virus diseases of solanaceous plants transmitted by whitefly. In: *Plant Virus Diseases of Horticultural Crops in the Tropics and Subtropics*. Taipei, Taiwan, Food and Fertilizer Technology for the Asian and Pacific Region, pp. 51–59.

Howarth, A.J., Caton, J., Bossert, M. and Goodman, R.M. (1985). Nucleotide sequence of bean golden mosaic virus and a model for gene regulation in geminiviruses. *Proc Natl. Acad. Sci.*, U.S.A. 82: 3572–3576.

Ikegami, M., Morinaga, T. and Miura, K. (1984). Infectivity of virus-specific double stranded DNA from tissue infected by mungbean yellow mosaic virus. *Virus Research* 1: 507–512.

Inouye, T. and Osaki, T. (1980). The first record in the literature of a possible plant virus disease that appeared in Manyoshu, A Japanese classic anthology, as far back as the time of the 8th century. *Ann. Phytopath. Soc. Japan* 46: 49–50.

Iwaki, M., Thongmeearkom, P., Honda, Y. and Deema, N. (1983). Soybean crinkle leaf: a new whitefly-borne disease of soybean. *Plant Disease* 67: 546–548.

Iwaki, M., Thongmeearkom, P., Prommin, M., Honda, Y. and Hibi, T. (1982). Whitefly transmission and some properties of cowpea mild mottle virus on soybean in Thailand. *Plant Disease* 66: 365–368.

Iwaki, M., Thongmeearkom, P., Honda, Y., Sarindu, N., Deema, N. and Surin, P. (1986). Soybean crinkle leaf disease occurring on soybean in Thailand. *Tech. Bull. Trop. Agric. Res. Center*, no. 21, pp. 132–143.

Kheyr-Pour, A., Bendahmane, M., Matzeit, V., Accotto, G.P., Crespi, S. and Gronenborn, B. (1991). Tomato yellow leaf curl virus from Sardinia is a whitefly-transmitted monopartite geminivirus. *Nucleic Acids Research* 19: 6763–6769.

Kim, K.S., Bird, J., Rodriguez, R.L., Martin, E.M. and Escudero, J. (1986). Ultrastructural studies of *Jatropha gossypifolia* infected with jatropha mosaic virus, a whitefly-transmitted geminivirus. *Phytopathology* 76: 80–85.

Kim, K.S. and Flores, E.M. (1979). Nuclear changes associated with Euphoribia mosaic virus transmitted by the whitefly. *Phytopathology* 69: 980–984.

Kim, K.S., Shock, T.L. and Goodman, R. (1978). Infection of *Phaseolus vulgaris* by bean golden mosiac virus: Ultrastructural aspects. *Virology* 89: 22–23.

Kirkpatrick, T.W. (1930). Leaf curl in cotton. *Nature* 125: 85–97.

Klinkenberg, F.A. and Stanley, J. (1990). Encapsidation and spread of African cassava mosaic virus DNA A in the absence of DNA B when agroinoculated to *Nicotiana benthamiana*. *J. Gen. Virol.* 71: 1409–1412.

Larsen, R.C., Duffus, J.E. and Liu, H.Y. (1984). Tomato necrotic dwarf, new type of whitefly-transmitted virus-like disease agent. *Phytopathology* 75: 1324.

Lastra, R. and Gill, F. (1981). Ultrastructural host cell changes associated with tomato yellow mosaic virus. *Phytopathology* 71: 524–528.

Lazarowitz, S.G. (1987). The molecular characterization of geminiviruses. *Plant Molecular Biol. Rept.* 4: 177–192.

Lazarowitz, S.G. (1992). Geminiviruses: genome structure and gene function. *Crit. Rev. Plant Sci.* **11** (4): 327–349.

Lazarowitz, S.G. and Lazdins, I.B. (1991). Infectivity and complete nucleotide sequence of the cloned genomic components of a bipartite squash leaf curl geminivirus with broad host range phenotype. *Virology* **180**: 58–69.

Lazarowitz, S.G., Wu, L.C., Rogers, S.G. and Elmer, J.S. (1992). Sequence-specific interaction with the viral AL1 protein identifies a geminivirus DNA replication origin. *Plant Cell* **4**: 799.

Malathi, V.G. and Sreenivasan, M.S. (1983). Association of gemini particles with cassava mosaic disease in India. *J. Root Crops* **9**: 69–73.

Mali, V.R. (1977). Cotton leaf crumple virus disease—a new record for India. *Indian Phytopath.* **30**: 326–329.

Markham, P.G., Pinner, M.S., Boulton, M.I. and Plaskitt, K. (1985). John Innes Institute, U.K., Report for 1983–1984.

Maytis, J.C., Silva, D.M., Oliveira, A.R. and Costa, A.S. (1975). Purifico e' morfologia do virus do mosaico dourado do tomateiro. *Suma Phytopath.* **1**: 267–274.

McClean, A.P.D. (1940). Some leaf curl diseases in South Africa. *Sci. Bull. South African Dept. Agric.* **225**: 1–70.

Milne, R.G. (1988). Taxonomy of rod-shaped filamentous virus. In: *The Plant Viruses*, vol. 4 (*The Filamentous Plant Viruses*) (R.G. Milne, ed.). Plenum Press, New York-London, pp. 3–33.

Mishra, M.D. Raychaudhuri, S.P. and Jha, A. (1963). Virus causing leaf curl of chilli (*Capsicum annuum* L.). *Indian J. Microbiol.* **3**: 73–76.

Morinaga, T., Ikegami, M. and Miura, K. (1983). Infectivity of the cloned DNAs from multiple genome components of bean golden mosaic virus. *Proc. Japan Acad. B* **59**: 363–366.

Morinaga, T., Ikegami, M. and Miura, K. (1990). Physical mapping and molecular cloning of mungbean yellow mosaic virus DNA. *Intervirol.* **31**: 50–56.

Muniyappa, V. (1980). Whiteflies. In: *Vectors of Plant Pathogens* (K.F. Harris and K. Maramorosch, eds.) Academic Press, New York, pp. 39–85.

Muniyappa, V. and Reddy, D.V.R. (1983). Transmission of cowpea mild mottle virus by *Bemisia tabaci* in a non-presistent manner. *Plant Disease* **67**: 391–393.

Muniyappa, V. and Veeresh, G.K. (1984). Plant virus diseases transmitted by whiteflies in Karnataka. *Proc. Indian Acad. Sci. Animal Sciences* **93**: 397–406.

Muniyappa, V., Rajeshwari, R., Bharatan, N., Reddy, D.V.R. and Nolt, B.L. (1987). Isolation and characterization of a geminivirus causing yellow mosaic disease of horsegram (*Macrotyloma uniflorum* (Lam.) Verdc.) in India. *Phytopathologische Zeitschrift* **119**: 81–87.

Murugesan, S. and Chelliah, S. (1978). Effect of yellow mosaic infection of the host green gram on the biology of *Bemisia tabaci* (Genn.). *Entomon* **3** (1): 41–43.

Nariani, T.K. (1960). Yellow mosaic of mung (*Phaseolus aureus* L.). *Indian Phytopath.* **13**: 24–29.

Navot, N., Ber, R. and Czosnek, H. (1989). Rapid detection of tomato yellow leaf curl virus in squashes of plants and insect vectors. *Phytopathology* **79** (5): 562–568.

Navot, N., Pichersky, E., Zeidan, M., Zamir, D. and Czosnek, H. (1991). Tomato yellow leaf curl virus: a whitefly transmitted geminivirus with a single genomic component. *Virology* **185**: 151–161.

Nour-Eldin, F., Mazyad, H. and Hassan, M.S. (1969). Tomato leaf curl virus disease. *Agric. Res. Cairo* **47**: 49–54.

Osaki, T. and Inouye T. (1981). Tobacco leaf curl virus. Commonwealth Mycological Institute and the Association of Applied Biologists. *Description of Plant Viruses*, no. 232, 4 pp.

Pal, B.P. and Tandon, R.K. (1937). Types of tobacco leaf-curl in northern India. *Indian J. Agric. Sci.* **7**: 363–393.

Polston, J.E., Al-Musa, A., Perring, T.M. and Dodds, J.A. (1990). Association of the nucleic acid of squash leaf curl geminivirus with the whitefly *Bemisia tabaci*. *Phytopathology* **80** (9): 850–856.

Pruthi, H.S. and Samuel, C.K (1939). Entomological investigation on the leaf-curl disease of tobacco in northern India. III. The transmission of leaf-curl by whitefly, *Bemisia gossypiperda*, to tobacco, sunn-hemp and a new alternative host of the leaf-curl virus. *Indian J. Agric. Sci.* **9**: 223–275.

Pruthi, H.S. and Samuel, C.K. (1942). Entomological investigation on the leaf-curl disease of tobacco in northern India. V. Biology and population of the whitefly vector (*Bemisia tabaci* Gen.) in relation to the incidence of the disease. *Indian J. Agric. Sci.* **12**: 35–57.

Reddy, T.S.N. and Nagarajan, K. (1982). Leaf curl disease of tobacco. *Tobacco News* **5**: 5–6.

Retuerma M.L., Pableo, G.O. and Price, W.C. (1977). Preliminary study of the transmission of Philippine tomato leaf curl virus by *Bemisia tabaci*. *Phil. Phytopath.* **7**: 29–34.

Roberts, I.M., Robinson, D.J. and Harrison, B.D. (1984). Serological relationships and genome homologies among geminiviruses. *J. Gen. Virol.* **65**: 1723–1730.

Roohoster, D.E., Kositratana, W. and Beachy, R.N. (1990). Systemic movement and symptom production following agroinoculation with a single DNA of tomato yellow leaf curl geminivirus (Thailand). *Virology* **178**: 520–526.

Sastry, K.S.M. and Singh, S.J. (1973). Assessment of losses in tomato leaf-curl virus. *Indian J. Mycol. Plant Pathol.* **3**: 50–54.

Saunders, K., Lucy, A. and Stanley, J. (1991). DNA forms of the geminivirus, African cassava mosaic virus consistent with the rolling circle mechanism of replication. *Nucleic Acids Research* **19**: 2325–2330.

Sela, I., Assouline, I., Tanne, E., Cohen, S. and Marco, S. (1980). Isolation and characterization of a rod-shaped, whitefly-transmissible, DNA-containing plant virus. *Phytopathology* **70**: 226–228.

Sequeira, J.C. and Harrison, B.D. (1982). Serological studies on cassava latent virus. *Ann. Appl. Biol.* **101**: 33–42.

Shivanathan, P. (1983). The epidemiology of three diseases caused by whitefly-borne pathogens. In: *Plant Virus Epidemiology. The Spread and Control of Insect-borne Viruses* (R.T. Plumb and J.M. Thresh, eds.). Blackwell Scientific Publications, U.K., pp. 323–330.

Stanley, J. (1983). Infectivity of the cloned geminivirus genome requires sequences from both DNAs. *Nature* **305**: 643–645.

Stanley, J. (1985). The molecular biology of geminiviruses. *Advances Virus Research* **30**: 139–177.

Stanley, J. and Davies, J.W. (1985). Structure and function of the DNA genome gemini-viruses. In: *Molecular Plant Virology* (J.W. Davies, ed.). CRC Press, Boca Raton, Florida, pp. 191–218.

Stanley, J. and Gay, M.R. (1983). Nucleotide sequence of cassava latent virus DNA. *Nature* **301**: 260–262.

Stein, V.E., Coutts, R.H.A. and Buck, K.W. (1983). Serological studies on tomato golden mosaic virus, a geminivirus. *J. Gen. Virol.* **64**: 2493–2498.

Stenger, D.C., Duffus, J.E. and Villalon (1990). Biological and genomic properties of a geminivirus isolated from pepper. *Phytopathology* **80** (8): 704–709.

Stenger, D.C., Revington, G.N., Stevenson, M.C. and Bisaro, D.M. (1991). Replication release of geminivirus genomes from tandemly repeated copies: evidence for rolling-circle replication of a plant viral DNA. *Proc. Natl. Acad. Sci.*, USA **88**: 8029–8033.

Sunter, G. and Bisaro, D.M. (1991). Transactivation in a geminivirus: AL 2 gene product is needed for coat protein expression. *Virology* 180: 416–419.

Thanapase, W., Polpol, P., Sutabutra, T. and Alathaom, S. (1983). Causal agent and some important characters of tomato leaf curl disease. *Kasetsart J.* 17: 80–89.

Thomas, K.M. and Krishnaswami, C.S. (1939). Leaf crinkle—a transmissible disease of papaya. *Curr. Sci* 8: 316.

Valand, G.B. and Muniyappa, V. (1992). Epidemiology of tobacco leaf curl virus in India. *Ann. Appl. Biol.* 120: 257–267.

Varma, A., Dhar, A.K. and Mandal, B. (1991). MYMV—the virus, its vector and their control in India. Consultative Group Meeting for MYMV, July 2–6, AVRDC, Taiwan.

Varma, A., Dhar, A.K. and Malathi, V.G. (1992). Cloning and restriction analysis of mungbean yellow mosaic virus. In: *International Conference on Virology in the Tropics*. Lucknow, India, p. 114.

Varma, P.M. (1963). Transmission of plant viruses by whiteflies. *Bull. Natl. Inst. Sci. India* 24: 11–33.

Verma, H.N., Srivastava, K.M. and Mathur, A.K. (1975). A whitefly transmitted yellow mosaic disease of tomato from India. *Plant Disease Reporter* 59: 494–498.

Yassin, A.M. (1978). Whitefly-borne virus diseases of important crop plants in the Sudan. In: *Proc. Fourth Conf. Pest Control*. September 30–October 3, 1978. Acad. Sci. Tech. Natl. Res. Centre, Cairo, Egypt, pt. 1, pp. 107–114.

Yassin, A.M. and Nour, M.A. (1965). Tomato leaf curl disease in the Sudan and its relation to tobacco leaf curl. *Ann. Appl. Biol.* 56: 207–217.

13

Epidemiology of Whitefly-borne Viruses and Approaches to Control

Although viral diseases transmitted by *B. tabaci* cause huge losses in tropical and subtropical parts of the world, detailed information on the epidemiology is available for only a few viruses (Bock, 1983; Muniyappa, 1983; Shivanathan, 1983; Cohen et al., 1988; Fauquet and Fargette, 1990; Valand and Muniyappa, 1992).

The natural spread of a vector-borne virus requires three basic components, namely, the virus itself, the host and the vector, While the host plant is the common victim of the vector and virus, the virus is the common beneficiary, exploiting the host plant as well as the vector. The vector is the linking agent and virus transmission is just incidental, occurring during its quest for food. Involvement of the vector is thus indirect but causes much more damage to the plant than that caused by its feeding. The relationships between host and virus, host and vector, and between virus and vector are subject to the influence of environmental conditions as well as human interference whereby the ecosystem is changed to improve agriculture. The incidence or prevalence of a disease is thus the net effect of these intricate relationships. Most of these aspects have featured in some earlier chapters. Here I have attempted to co-ordinate the diverse information and to project the various factors that need consideration.

Virus-Host Related Aspects

Sources of Viral Inoculum: The first and foremost point to consider is the source of the virus. The planting material itself may serve as the primary source as is the case of African cassava mosaic virus (ACMV). The major emphasis to control this extremely important disease is on the use of healthy cuttings. In annual crops, infected crop, plants and weeds are sources for whitefly-borne viruses in general.

Initial infection often originates from infected plants of some closely related crops in other fields. Mature crops commonly serve as sources for neighbouring young crops. When different growth stages of a crop are readily available in the same locality, the virus moves to younger crops through vectors. Overlapping of tomato crops in Cyprus was reported to aggravate the incidence of tomato yellow leaf curl virus (TYLCV).

Unrelated crops may sometimes play the role of virus sources. For instance, *Cajanus cajan* has been reported as a source of mung bean yellow mosaic virus (MYMV), which may help it to overwinter in northern India (Nene, 1972). *Althaea rosea* has been recorded as a source of yellow vein mosaic virus of bhendi (okra).

Weeds play a very vital role in the ecology of plant viruses (Duffus, 1971). In northern India weeds such as *Eclipta alba* and *Xanthium strumarium* have been found to be naturally infected with mung bean yellow mosaic virus (MYMV) and might serve as reservoirs of the virus (Nene, 1972). Wild okra (*Abelomoschus manihotus*) is a source of yellow vein mosaic of bhendi in India. A number of weeds, namely, *Malva parviflora*, *Physalis wrightii* and *Chenopodium murale* seem to play a major role in incidence of lettuce infectious yellows virus (LIYV) in the south-western USA. In the Jordan valley the annual weed *Malva parviflora* and the perennial weed *Cynanchum acutum* were found to be the natural hosts of TYLCV. Although *C. acutum* is not a preferred host of *B. tabaci*, the whitefly feeds on it long enough to acquire TYLCV. The important role of *C. acutum* as a source of the virus and epidemiology of the disease was established by marking whiteflies with fluorescent dust while feeding on the weed along the banks of the Jordan river and their subsequent trapping in the main tomato-growing area 7 km away. During the cold winter months (December–February), only the subterranean parts of the weed survive. The plants start growing again in the spring until August–September, thus providing inoculum to the whiteflies which overwinter and multiply mainly on plants immune to TYLCV (Cohen et al., 1988).

Susceptibility of Plants to Infection: The major host factors which can influence plant susceptibility to virus infection include inherent genetic traits and plant age at the time of infection.

Since cultivars of the same plant species differ in susceptibility to a virus, detection of the existing sources of resistance and their development through breeding have understandably been the major thrust in management of virus problems. Breeding for resistance against viral maladies has been a routine practice with various crop cultivar-virus combinations, as is evident from the extensive literature pertaining to this objective. Unfortunately, the lack of uniformity regarding varieties or selections of a crop, the experimental methods and differences in the local conditions, do not permit a comparative assessment of the results.

Whitefly resistance has been used to curb virus spread in various crops (see Chapter 9).

Breeding for resistance requires profound knowledge of the viruses concerned, their variability and the appropriate methods of sceening for evaluation of resistance. It calls for much better understanding of the whitefly-borne viruses, of which very little was known until recent years.

Generally, the younger the plant, the more susceptible it is to virus infection. Lower metabolic activity in mature plants must be an important factor to affect the extent and rapidity of virus multiplication.

When crops are grown in regions far away from their natural home, they may invite new viral problems. Cassava, the most important food crop grown in the African continent, suffers severe losses due to the disease caused by ACMV. But ACMV does not occur in South America, where the crop originated.

Availability of Viral Inoculum: The role of infected plants to serve virus sources depends on virus concentration and leaves of the same plant may vary in this regard.

The transmission rate of TYLCV by *B. tabaci* was 42% when the whiteflies were allowed to acquire it from young leaves of *Datura stramonium,* against 23% by those acquiring the virus from the older leaves, positioned third from the top (Cohen, 1965). The finding of Czosnek et al. (1988) that the highest concentration of TYLCV viral genomic DNA is located in the shoot apex, lends support to the results obtained by Cohen (1965).

Despite symptoms of ACMV, virus particles cannot be detected in cassava leaves older than the seventh from the apex and only the five youngest leaves of each shoot are susceptible to virus inoculation (Fauquet and Fargette, 1990). ELISA tests revealed a significantly higher viral titre in young leaves of squash plants infected with squash leaf curl virus (SLCV), compared to older leaves (third from the top) of the same plant. Moreover, virus content in young leaves of older plants (2–3 months after inoculation) was found to be significantly higher than that in young leaves of young plants which had been inoculated 15–20 days earlier at the first true leaf stage. Similarly, higher virus content was found in whiteflies fed on young leaves of old plants. However, the chances of acquiring SLCV from either kind of source were found to be the same (Cohen et al., 1989).

Unlike the above examples, titres of LIYV in different parts of several host plants were generally higher in the older leaves. However, virus recovery by whiteflies from the young leaves was relatively high. The whiteflies could recover virus only from the young leaves of *Chenopodium murale*, in spite of a very high antigen titre in all the leaves. The extreme case was virus acquisition by whiteflies only from the young leaves of melons, although no virus could be detected in such leaves by ELISA (Cohen et al., 1988).

Resistance or tolerance of a plant to infection does not necessarily reflect its potentiality as a source of the virus. For instance, cultivars tolerant to TYLCV serve as a source of the virus just as well as the susceptible one (Pilowsky and Cohen, unpublished; cited by Cohen, 1990).

Vector-Host Related Aspects

The factors involved in vector-host plant relationships are quite complex because of the intricate behavioural responses of the whitefly to slight differences in environmental cues and stimuli, especially the plant-induced ones. The natural spread of vector-borne plant diseases depends on vector dispersal and host selection; these are therefore crucial factors in disease epidemiology.

Vector Movement: The spread of diseases in time and space is related to the movements of the adult whiteflies. Temperature and wind are the major environmental factors that affect activity of aerial vectors. Rains and inclement weather are detrimental to flight. Movement of *B. tabaci* among crops and weed-hosts is determined by wind. The whitefly has limited ability to direct its flight. The flight speed of *B. tabaci* has been calculated to be about 0.2 m/s but the whitefly individuals can control their flight only when wind speed is low, such as occurs within the plant canopy (Fauquet and Fargette, 1990). Byrne and Houck (1989) could distinguish a migratory morph and a trivial-flying morph on the basis of alary characteristics. Although the migrators may be poor fliers, they have been demonstrated to disperse up to 7 km, as mentioned earlier.

Wind direction and speed understandably play a major role in the pattern of distribution of *B. tabaci* and the diseases transmitted by the whitefly. Crop fields located downwind in relation to a virus source are thus more vulnerable to infection.

Host location/Host Selection: Studies so far suggest that visual cue is the only factor in host location by *B. tabaci* from a distance. The whitefly seems to be attracted either to the short (blue/UV) or the longer wavelengths (especially yellow) but not to both at the same time. Mound (1962) speculated that the short wavelengths induced migratory behaviour while the longer wavelengths might facilitate host location. He found no reaction of *B. tabaci* to odour of the plant or to conspecific individuals.

Host selection after landing depends on various factors, namely, leaf age and nutritional status, leaf hairiness or glabrousness, leaf shape and nature of the foliage. These aspects have already been discussed in Chapter 8.

The establishment of vector populations and spread of disease are influenced by crop density. For instance, the incidence of ACMV is lowest in plots of cassava with high density, whereas infection progresses fastest in low density crop stands (Fauquet and Fargette, 1990).

Population Dynamics: A positive correlation between population size and spread of viruses has been reported by a number of workers. The viruses include cucumber vein yellowing virus in Israel (Nitzany et al., 1964), SLCV and LIYV in California (Duffus and Flock, 1982), TYLCV in the Middle East and Africa (Makkouk and Laterrot, 1983; Defranc et al., 1985; Ioannau, 1987; Cohen et al., 1988), yellow mosaic of horse gram in India (Muniyappa, 1983), lima bean golden mosaic and cowpea golden mosaic in Nigeria (Vetten and Allen, 1983), tomato yellow mosaic virus in Venezuela (Anzola and Lastra, 1985), leaf curl of tomato in southern India (Saikia and Muniyappa, 1989) and eastern India (Verma et al., 1989), ACMV in the Ivory Coast (Fauquet and Fargette, 1990), tobacco leaf curl virus (TbLCV) in India (Pruthi and Samuel, 1942; Valand and Muniyappa, 1992).

Climatic conditions, especially temperature, strongly influence the incidence and activity of whiteflies (see Chapters 5 and 7). The prevailing weather conditions seem to determine the timing, direction and extent of vector dispersal; vector behaviour and transmission efficiency; rate of disease development; rate of growth of vector populations and their survival. Interruption of crops in areas with pronounced summer and/or winter seasons makes it obligatory for the whiteflies to find suitable shelters for tiding over the unfavourable period. In warm arid climates, summer is the most critical period for vector survival. Showers during the dry season promote new plant growth that attract vectors. Such plants not only serve as reservoirs of the vector but also as the source of viral inoculum unless they are immune to the virus concerned. Year-round cropping systems of susceptible host plants have greatly aggravated disease losses in many areas.

Since *B. tabaci* is a thermophilic insect, its developmental rate and activities are curbed during the cold season, the degrees of which depend on the intensity of winter conditions.

The main overwintering hosts of the whitefly in one area may vary widely from those in another due to differences in agroclimatic conditions.

This calls for careful field studies to determine the potential hosts which may serve as reservoirs of the vector and the virus involved.

Virus-Vector Relationship

The type of virus-vector relationship gives some idea about the possible distances of spread of a disease and also helps in determining the appropriate control measures. Non-persistent viruses usually cannot spread far from the source since the vectors remain infective for very limited periods. Vectors can retain semi-persistent viruses usually for a day or two and sometimes a little longer, which allows a greater distance of spread than non-persistent viruses. In persistent transmission such as that of geminiviruses, the vector usually remains infective for many days and sometimes for life. Understandably, persistent viruses may be spread for longer periods and over long distances, depending on environmental conditions. Since the transmission threshold of circulative viruses is considerably longer than that of non-circulative ones, in particular the non-persistent viruses, insecticidal measures are more effective in preventing spread of persistently borne viruses. The success of such insecticidal treatments depends, however, on the amount of primary and secondary spread. In case the viral inoculum is brought from outside sources by virus-carrying whiteflies, infection of the crop would only require inoculation of the virus. The inoculation period is often not long enough to be prevented by insecticidal treatments unless the vectors are strongly repelled or knocked out before they indulge in feeding (see Chapter 11). On the other hand, insecticidal treatments are likely to be more or less effective in curbing secondary spread since the vectors need to live long enough to acquire the virus and become infective after hours or days of a latent period.

Virus-Vector-Host-Environment Interactions

An epidemic develops over a period of time and the onset, progress and final incidence depend on diverse factors, namely, the initial levels of inoculum, distance from the source, size of the vector population, crop cultivars, planting date, spacing and density of plants, field size, general cropping pattern of the area, previous cropping history and weather. This calls for thorough understanding of the ecological mechanisms regulating vector and virus population dynamics and behavioural changes in the vector. Such knowledge transcends the conventional boundaries of entomology, virology, plant pathology, plant physiology and other disciplines, such as meteorology and ethology. Epidemiology requires special knowledge in mathematics, statistics and computer science to integrate the extensive and diverse data and to correlate it in quantitative terms. The aim of epidemiological studies is to ascertain the underlying mechanisms determining the onset and course of epidemics and to predict whether control measures have to be taken and, if so, when. Understanding the chain of ecological components leading to an epidemic, helps in determining the weakest point to attack. This point may differ with the host-virus-crop combinations in different agroecosystems. Unfortunately, detailed information on the epidemiological cycle is available for just a few whitefly-borne viruses (Cohen, 1990).

Distance from the source of the virus is important since virus sources in and around plants lead to early onset of the disease. The plants are then more vulnerable and there is plenty of time for further spread within the crop. Weeds and cultivated hosts very often grow in proximity to one another, making it easy for the whitefly to move from one to the other as demanded by the situation. Removal of virus sources resulted in successful control of cotton leaf curl in the Sudan, tobacco leaf curl in Java and TYLCV in Cyprus (Bos, 1981; Muniyappa, 1980; Ioannau, 1987). Studies on the epidemiology of TYLCV in the Jordan valley, mentioned earlier in this chapter, revealed the vital role of C. acutum a perennial weed, in serving as a host bridge for the virus between seasons. This finding led Cohen et al. (1988) to conclude that eradication of the weed in June–July, before the beginning of B. tabaci migration, might limit the spread of TYLCV into tomato fields.

Next to the presence of virus sources, the single most important factor which can influence the amount of virus spread in a season is the number of vectors available and their activity. Quantitative estimation of whitefly populations may be made by counting them on a fixed number of plants or leaves. The aerial populations are determined by trapping adults. Sampling techniques have been detailed in Chapter 6.

It appears that the amount of virus spread depends not only on vector numbers, but perhaps more on vector activity. Vector activity is very difficult to measure as it includes feeding, dispersal and host selection. If the host of a virus is also a preferred host of B. tabaci, then the latter is most likely to settle down for feeding and colonisation, as is the known habit of the whitefly. The option for an assured shelter instead of exploratory movements in search of a suitable host is expected to limit virus spread. On the other hand, vector density in a crop can influence vector activity by imposing stress factors on the host due to overcrowding and consequent dispersal in large numbers. In such cases, where the breeding host serves also as a virus host, the crop itself may serve as the major inoculum source.

A connection between vector population and virus spread has been reported by various workers. While weeds undoubtedly play an important role in maintaining whitefly populations and disease inoculum, cultivated plants are often more important (Byrne et al., 1990). Large-scale migration from crops such as cotton, legumes and cucurbits is a seasonal feature in various agroecosytems. In the south-western United States, large populations of migrating whiteflies leave cotton in early autumn, when the first lettuce crops are growing in the field. The migrating populations may acquire LIYV by feeding on plants infected with the virus, which has an extensive host range, before entering the lettuce plantings. The incidence of LIYV in lettuce has been correlated with the number of whiteflies moving transiently through the crop (Bellows and Arakawa, 1986). The breeding hosts that give rise to large populations of the whitefly and influence disease spread vary from place to place. In Central America the soybean crop has reportedly created problems for the beans by harbouring large populations of *B. tabaci*, thereby enhancing the spread of bean golden mosaic virus (BGMV). Measures against the whiteflies before they start leaving the breeding hosts in large numbers are likely to reduce virus spread. Meyerdirk et al. (1986) advocated termination of cotton by late August by a defoliant and the use of an adulticide to break the cotton-lettuce chain, thereby preventing huge losses through viral diseases.

The aim of epidemiological studies is to arrive at the stage of forecasting in order to be forearmed, which definitely would be economically beneficial. The initial approach should be to identify the important parameters influencing disease incidence. If the more important parameters are found to be influenced by one common factor or the key variable, then the chances of accuracy of the predictions are greatly enhanced. In tropics and subtropics, for instance, the dry season rainfall is the single key factor which has considerable impact on survival of virus and vector between cropping seasons. The more severe incidence of the cotton leaf curl disease in the southern areas of Sudan was found to be related to higher rainfall during the pre-crop dry season compared to that in the north. The explanation offered was that rains during the hot months of April and May facilitate survival of cotton stumps from the previous year's crop; their regenerated growths served as initial foci of the virus. The correlation between pre-season rainfall and leaf curl incidence proved useful in giving warning ten weeks before sowing to enable removal of such volunteer sources before planting (Thresh, 1986).

Development of a local forecasting system is extremely difficult. As mentioned previously, a large number of physical and biotic variables are involved in the epidemiology of a vector-borne disease. Different sets of factors may lead to great differences in the onset, progress and final incidence of a disease at different sites. In most of the countries where whitefly-borne diseases of field crops are rampant, farming is largely done by small and marginal farmers. The fragmentary nature of cultivation adds to the diversity and makes the exercise all the more difficult.

Approaches to Curb Diseases

No strategy for control of whitefly-borne geminiviruses has proved effective in practice (Brown and Bird, 1992). The use of insecticides and oils to affect virus transmission by whiteflies has yielded more or less satisfactory results in a limited number of cases (see Chapter 11). Cultural control measures to reduce disease incidence include sanitation, mixed cropping, use of reflective surfaces by way of mulches, physical barriers and cultivation of resistant varieties.

Removal of the remnants of the previous crop, 'volunteer' plants and weeds, should be a routine practice before planting as they may harbour viruses and vectors. Removal of weeds, however, may not necessarily reduce virus incidence when the weeds harbour natural enemies of the vector or serve as a barrier to virus spread. Furthermore, if the crops around harbour vector populations, weeds will have little or no impact. In the south-western United States, lettuce, carrots, broccoli, tomato and alfalfa may serve as overwintering hosts. Under such circumstances, as Meyerdirk et al. (1986) pointed out, an area-wise weeding programme may not be an effective method in terms of the cost-benefit ratio. They felt that use of some of the weed hosts instead as sites for release of introduced natural enemies of the whitefly, would perhaps yield long-term benefits.

When crop plants serve as the main source of virus inoculum, delaying or omitting a crop may reduce disease incidence in certain cropping systems. In Cyprus, the incidence and rate of spread of TYLCV were maximum in crops transplanted during summer and early autumn, whereas crops transplanted in winter and early spring (December–March) escaped infection (Ioannou and Iordanou, 1985).

Bemisia tabaci is strongly attracted to yellow plastic or straw mulches. In hot, dry climates, whiteflies attracted to such mulches probably stay there long enough to be killed by reflected heat. Mulching of tomatoes and cucumber fields with sawdust, straw or yellow polyethylene sheets markedly reduced the incidence of TYLCV and cucumber vein-yellowing virus and populations of the whitefly vector (Nitzany et al., 1964; Cohen and Melamed-Madjar, 1978). Mulching treatments have limitations, however, since the control effect has been found to last for only 20–30 days due to fading of the mulches and progressive shading with developing foliage.

Nevertheless, during that period the mulches are more effective than insecticides (Cohen, 1982). In West Bengal, India, the incidence of yellow mosaic disease of bhendi (okra) was 24.3% in plots with yellow polyethylene mulch against 58.6% in control (Khan and Mukhopadhyay, 1985).

While discussing the cultural control of whitefly-borne viruses, Cohen and Berlinger (1986) concluded that the use of physical barriers such as row covers could be the best method to control spread. However, success depends on the quality of the covering material which must allow passage of air and light and at the same time be durable enough to last for several months.

Planting trap crops may reduce vector populations and disease incidence in certain cropping systems. Selection of the crop to be used as a bait depends on various factors, such as the crop to be protected, the virus involved, the season of cultivation and local agronomic parctices. Spraying the trap or barrier crops with insecticides makes them doubly effective. In Jordan, intercropping tomatoes with cucumber resulted in considerable lowering of the incidence of TYLCV. Cucumber is known to be a preferred host for whiteflies and immune to TYLCV. Insecticides were applied when adult whitefly populations reached high levels, usually two weeks after planting of cucumber and the second one before tomato planting (Sharaf, 1986). Cucumber proved to be the best trap crop to reduce the incidence of TYLCV in the plastic house. When *B. tabaci* fed on them for 10 days before moving to tomatoes, TYLCV infection was reduced by 48% (Al-Hitty and Sharif, 1987). The incidence of TYLCV in plastic houses in Iraq on tomato planted with capsicum was reduced by 10–26% during the first three months of tomato transplanting (El-Serwiy et al., 1987).

The prospect of minimising disease incidence by manipulation of the planting date on the basis of vector abundance, has been explored by various workers. Patel and Patel (1966) reported that the incidence of leaf curl disease in Gujarat, India was least on the tobacco crop transplanted on 15th August compared to that transplanted on 30th August and 15th September. In Egypt, *B. tabaci* was reported to attack tomato during April–October, with an infestation peak in August–October. Early tomatoes sown in February were seldom infected, whereas those sown from April onwards became increasingly severely infected with tomato leaf curl virus (Shaheen, 1983). In southern India the worst effect of the yellow mosaic disease of horse gram can be avoided by sowing the crop from July to October, when populations of *B. tabaci* are most affected by high rainfall and relative humidity and relatively low temperatures (Muniyappa, 1983). However, raising a crop outside its normal growing season generally affects the yield and may affect the quality too. At the same time, an unseasonal crop is likely to fetch higher returns, especially if it is a vegetable.

The use of resistant cultivars is the most desirable means for avoiding severe crop losses due to disease epidemics, especially in tropical conditions where viruses often spread very rapidly. However, sources of resistance are not always available and it takes a long time to introduce the resistant trait through breeding. In spite of these difficulties, screening to find resistant varieties has been a general routine for a large number of crops, including cassava, food legumes and vegetables. No attempt has been made to provide the findings of numerous screening tests here, nor is it felt necessary in view of the lack of uniformity in the varieties tested under diverse conditions. The fact remains that such an exercise often leads to detection of the relatively resistant varieties, which may at least reduce the rate of disease spread. One limitation of a resistant variety is the appearance of new strains, although this phenomenon is less common for viruses than for fungi. That is why care has to be taken to avoid the grave consequences of cultivating a variety or varieties that possess the same resistant genes without break, either in space or time. Another practical difficulty is to convince the farmers, who are generally reluctant to accept resistant cultivars unless they meet the local needs and perferences.

Besides disease resistance, resistance to B. tabaci has been used to minimise virus incidence in various crops, such as varieties of cassava against ACMV. In Nigeria, genotypes of cowpea and lima bean that showed field resistance to golden mosaic, supported fewer B. tabaci than field-susceptible ones (Vetten and Allen, 1983). Resistance to cotton leaf curl in Africa reportedly follows the same pattern (Jones, 1987).

Transferring genes for disease resistance through conventional breeding practices or protoplast fusion involves a long-drawn out process of selection and back-crossing, the breeder having little control over the number and type of genes transferred. Remarkable progress in recent years in the field of biotechnology holds the prospects for artificial insertion of resistant genes into traditional cultivars which are suitable in other respects. The geminiviruses may be exploited to produce such transgenic plants because any gene cloned in a geminivirus vector, is due to be highly amplified (see Chapter 12).

It is clear from the foregoing discussion that an understanding of the ecological background of disease outbreak is necessary for devising suitable management practices. Single measures may not be effective in all crop systems in all seasons. This is particularly true for plant resistance and insecticides, both of which tend to lose their protective value over time, especially when they serve as the sole means of control. A combination of methods with different modes of action, such as mulches and oils, or mulches and insecticides, is likely to be more effective than one or the other alone. Such combinations would minimise selection of a new vector biotype (Maelzer, 1986).

An integrated management programme for a vector-borne disease should have plant resistance as the core due to its influence on the success of other control measures. Other methods that may be usefully added to enhance control are: (i) manipulation of planting date; (ii) minimising introduction of inoculum in the crop by a mulch, a trap crop or an interplant crop, and (iii) minimising virus spread within the crop by an oil or a 'soft' insecticide to take care of the vector without affecting its natural enemies (Maelzer, 1986). In Sao Paulo, Brazil an effective combination of measures for integrated control of tomato golden mosaic virus was worked out. The best result in terms of tomato yield and effect on beneficial arthropod predators, was achieved through planting the best tomato cultivar with a 20-m wide band of grain sorghum around the crop, and soil application of carbamate insecticide. This combination proved superior to either sorghum bands or insecticides used alone (Gravena et al., 1984). However, such ecologically balanced measures have to be adopted by the entire farming community in the area if the desired impact is to be achieved. Various socioeconomic constraints, such as small holdings, limited choice of cultivars and general lack of resources, may prevent wide adoption of such integrated measures. Research can provide direction but the collaboration of extension services and personnel is essential for effective implementation of a programme.

REFERENCES

Al-Hitty, A. and Sharif, H.L. (1987). Studies on host preference of *Bemisia tabaci* (Genn.) on some crops and effects of using host on the trap spread of tomato yellow leaf curl virus to tomato in a plastic house. *Arab J. Plant Prot.* **5**: 19–23.

Anzola, D. and Lastra, R. (1985). Whitefly population and its impact on the incidence of tomato yellow mosaic virus in Venezuela. *Phytopathologische Zeitschrift* **112** (4): 363–366.

Bellows, T.S. and Arakawa, K. (1986). Modelling the relationship between transient vector densities and plant disease incidence with special reference to *Bemisia tabaci* (Homoptera: Aleyrodidae) and lettuce infectious virus yellows. *J. Econ. Ent.* **79**: 1235–1239.

Bock, K.R. (1983). Epidemiology of cassava mosaic virus in Kenya. In: *Plant Virus Epidemiology* (R.T. Plumb and J.M. Thresh, eds.). Blackwell Scientific Publications, Oxford, U.K., pp. 337–347.

Bos, L. (1981). Wild plants in the ecology of virus diseases. In: *Plant Diseases and Vectors: Ecology and Epidemiology* (K. Maramorosch and K.F. Harris, eds.). Academic Press, New York, pp. 1–33.

Brown, J.K. and Bird, J. (1992). Whitefly-transmitted geminivirus and associated disorders in the Americas and the Caribbean Basin. *Plant Disease* 76 (3): 220–225.

Byrne, D.N. and Houck, M.A. (1989). Morphometric identification of wing polymorphism in *Bemisia tabaci* (Gennadius) (Homoptera: Aleyrodidae). *Ann. Entomol. Soc. Amer.* 83: 487–493.

Byrne, D.N., Bellows, T.S. and Parrella, M.P. (1990). Whiteflies in agricultural systems., In: *Whiteflies: Their Bionomics, Pest Status and Management* (D. Gerling, ed.). Intercept, Wimborne, England, pp. 227–261.

Cohen, S. (1965). Investigations on plant virus tranmitted by the tobacco whitefly (*Bemisia tabaci* Gennadius) in Israel. Ph.D. thesis, Faculty of Agriculture, Hebrew University of Jerusalem, Rehovot, Israel, 79 pp.

Cohen, S. (1982). Control of whitefly vectors of viruses by colour mulches. In: *Pathogens, Vectors and Plant Diseases: Approaches to Control* (K.F. Harris and K. Maramorosch, eds.). Academic Press, New York, pp. 45–56.

Cohen, S. (1990). Epidemiology of whitefly-transmitted viruses. In: *Whiteflies: Their Bionomics, Pest Status and Management* (D. Gerling, ed.). Intercept, Wimborne, England, pp. 211–225.

Cohen, S. and Melamed-Madjar, V. (1978). Prevention by soil mulching of the spread of tomato yellow leaf curl virus transmitted by *Bemisia tabci* (Gennadius) (Homoptera: Aleyrodidae) in Israel. *Bull. Ent. Res.* 68: 465–470.

Cohen, S. and Berlinger, M.J. (1986). Transmission and cultural control of whitefly-borne viruses. *Agric. Ecosyst. Environ.* 17: 89–97.

Cohen, S., Duffus, J.E. and Berlinger, M.J. (1988). Epidemiological studies of whitefly-transmitted viruses in California and Israel. Final Report. BARD project no. I-589-83, ARO, Bet Dagan, Israel, 91 pp.

Cohen, S., Duffus, J.E. and Liu, H.Y. (1989). Acquisition, interference and retention of cucurbit leaf curl viruses. *Phytopathology* 79: 109–113.

Czosnek, H., Ber, R., Navot, N., Zamir, D., Antignus, Y. and Cohen, S. (1988). Detection of tomato yellow leaf curl virus in lysates of plants and insects by hybridization with a viral DNA probe. *Plant Disease* 72: 949–951.

Defranc, Q., D'Hondt, M. and Russo, M. (1985). Tomato yellow leaf curl in Senegal. *Phytopathologische Zeitschrift* 112: 153–160.

Duffus, J.E. (1971). Role of weeds in the incidence of virus diseases. *Ann. Rev. Phytopath.* 9: 319–340.

Duffus, J.E. and Flock, R.A. (1982). Whitefly-transmitted disease complex of the desert southwest. *Calif. Agric.* 36: 4–6.

El-Serwiy, S.A., Ali, A.A. and Razoki, I.A. (1987). Effect of intercropping of some host plants with tomato on population density of tobacco whitefly, *Bemisia tabaci* (Genn.), and the incidence of tomato yellow leaf curl virus (TYLCV) in plastic houses. *J. Agric. Water Resources Res., Plant Prod.* 61 (2): 81–89.

Fauquet, C. and Fargette, D. (1990). African cassava mosaic virus etiology, epidemiology and control. *Plant Disease* 74 (6): 404–411.

Gravena, S., Churata-Masca, M.G.C., Arai, J. and Raga, A. (1984). Manejo integrado da mosca branca *Bemisa tabaci* (Gennadius, 1889) em cultivares de tomateiro de crescimentio determinado visando reducão de virose de mosaico durado. *Anais da Sociedade Entomológica de Brasil* **13** (1): 35–45.

Ioannau, N. (1987). Cultural management of tomato yellow leaf curl disease in Cyprus. *Plant Pathol.* **36**: 367–373.

Ioannau, N. and Iordanau, N. (1985). Epidemiology of tomato yellow leaf curl virus in relation to the population density of its whitefly vector, *Bemisia tabaci* (Gennadius). *Tech. Bull. Agric. Res. Inst. Cyprus* no. 71, 7 pp.

Jones, A.T. (1987). Control of virus infection in crop plants through vector resistance: a review of achievements, prospects and problems. *Ann. Appl. Biol.* **111**: 745–772.

Khan, M.A. and Mukhopadhyay, S. (1985). Studies on the effect of some alternative control methods on the incidence of yellow vein mosaic virus disease of okra (*Abelomoschus esculentus*). *Indian J. Virol.* **1**: 69–72.

Maelzer, D.A. (1986). Integrated control of insect vectors. In: *Plant Virus Epidemics. Monitoring, Modelling and Predicting Outbreaks* (G.D. Maclean, R.G. Garret and W.G. Ruesink, eds.). Academic Press, New York, pp. 484–512.

Makkouk, K.M. and Laterrot, H. (1983). Epidemiology and control of tomato yellow leaf curl virus. In: *Plant Virus Epidemiology* (R.T. Plumb and J.M. Thresh, eds.). Blackwell Scientific Publications, Oxford, U.K., pp. 315–321.

Meyerdirk, D.E., Coudriet, D.L. and Prabhaker, N. (1986). Population dynamics and control strategy for *Bemisia tabaci* in the Imperial Valley, California. *Agric. Ecosys. Environ.* **17**: 61–68.

Mound, L.A. (1962). Studies on the olfaction and colour sensitivity of *Bemisia tabaci* (Genn.) (Homoptera: Aleyrodidae). *Entomol. Experim. Appl.* **5**: 99–104.

Muniyappa, V. (1980). Whiteflies. In: *Vectors of Plant Pathogens* (K.F. Harris and K. Maramorosch, eds.). Academic Press, New York, pp. 39–85.

Muniyappa, V. (1983). Epidemiology of yellow mosaic disease of horsegram (*Macrotyloma uniflorum*) in South India. In: *Plant Virus Epidemiology* (R.T. Plumb and J.M. Thresh, eds.). Blackwell Scientific Publications, Oxford, U.K., pp. 331–335.

Nene, Y.L. (1972). A survey of viral diseases of pulse crops in Uttar Pradesh: Final Technical Report. *Res. Bull. G.B. Pant Univ. Agric. Tech.* **4**, 191 pp.

Nitzany, F.E., Geisenberg, H. and Koch, B. (1964). Tests for the protection of cucumbers from a whitefly-borne virus. *Phytopathology* **54**: 1059–1061.

Patel, V.C., and Patel, H.K. (1966). Inter-relationship between whitefly (*Bemisia tabaci* Genn.) to *Nicotiana* species. *Gujarat Agric. Univ. Res. J.* **1** (2): 89–92.

Pruthi, H.S. and Samuel, C.K. (1942). Entomological investigations on the leaf-curl disease of tobacco in norhtern India. V. Biology and population of the whitefly vector (*Bemisia tabaci* Gen.) in relation to the incidence of the disease. *Indian J. Agric. Sci.* **12**: 35–57.

Saikia, A.K. and Muniyappa, V. (1989). Epidemiology and control of tomato leaf curl virus in southern Indian. *Trop. Agric.* (*Trinidad*) **66**: 350–354.

Shaheen, A.H. (1983). Some ecological aspects of the white fly, *Bemisa tabaci* Genn., on tomato. *Bull. Soc. Entomol. d'Egypte* **62**: 83–87.

Sharaf, N. (1986). Chemical control of *Bemisa tabaci*. *Agric. Ecosys. Environ.* **17**: 111–127.

Shivanathan, P. (1983). The epidemiology of three diseases caused by whitefly-borne pathogens. In: *Plant Virus Epidemiology* (R.T. Plumb and J.M. Thresh, eds.). Blackwell Scientific Publications, Oxford, U.K., pp. 323–330.

Thresh, J.M. (1986). Plant virus disease forecasting. In: *Plant Virus Epidemics, Monitoring, Modelling and Predicting Outbreaks* (G.D. Maclean, R.G. Garret and W.G. Ruesink, eds.). Academic Press, New York, pp. 359–386.

Valand, G.B. and Muniyappa, V. (1992). Epidemiology of tobacco leaf curl virus in India. *Ann. Appl. Biol.* **120**: 257–267.

Verma, A.K., Basu, D., Nath, P.S., Das, S., Gatak, S.S. and Mukhopadhyay, S. (1989). Relation between population of white-fly, *Bemisia tabaci* Genn. (Homoptera: Aleyrodidae) and the incidence of tomato leaf-curl virus disease. *Indian J. Mycol. Res.* **27** (1): 49–52.
Vetten, H.J. and Allen, D.J. (1983). Effects of environment and host on vector biology and incidence of two whitefly-spread diseases of legumes in Nigeria. *Ann. Appl. Biol.* **102**: 219–227.

Printed and bound by CPI Group (UK) Ltd, Croydon, CR0 4YY

23/10/2024

01778232-0001